Seymour Britchky's
New, Revised Guide to the
Restaurants of New York

SEYMOUR BRITCHKY'S
NEW, REVISED GUIDE TO THE
RESTAURANTS
OF NEW YORK

An irreverent appraisal of the best, most interesting, most famous, most underrated or worst restaurants in New York City

RANDOM HOUSE   **NEW YORK**

Library of Congress Cataloging in Publication Data

Britchky, Seymour.
Seymour Britchky's New, revised guide to the
restaurants of New York.

Edition for 1974 published under title: The
restaurants of New York.
Includes indexes.
1. New York (City)—Restaurants—Directories.
I. Title. II. Title: New, revised guide to the
restaurants of New York.
TX907.B74   1976   647'.95747'1   76–15180
ISBN 0–394–73222–7

Manufactured in the United States of America
9 8 7 6 5 4 3 2

CONTENTS

Foreword to the New, Revised Edition

The current revision of *The Restaurants of New York* is appearing a scant two years after publication of the first edition. This may seem like a hasty return to market for a New York restaurant guide (to judge by competitors' sluggish standards), but like the city itself, the restaurant scene is being constantly transformed: here the overnight disappearance of what once looked like an indestructible institution, there the evaporation of a predictably short-lived fly-by-night. Last year's glistening new eatery is soon tarnished and no longer merits so much as the space required to be literately bored with it; less frequently, restaurants mature, calling for revised words of praise or of higher praise; and, as ever, entrepreneurial optimists, with a new gimmick or a variation on an old one, throw open just-painted doors to fresh linen, new broadloom and trite hopes. On occasion your reporter is seduced, honors a Johnny-come-lately with a couple of pages, perhaps even a star or two, and lives not much longer before he regrets it (not many of those, but they *are* dismaying).

For the new edition we have made timely all information about credit cards, reservations, liquor licenses, closing days, etc. We have also revised our rating system—what used to be a three-star (★★★) restaurant is now called a four-star (★★★★) restaurant; two-star (★★) restaurants of the past are now credited with three stars (★★★); and the places that used to earn one star (★) now earn either two stars (★★) for "Good" or one star (★) for "Good, but not *as* good." The former designations for "Acceptable" (●) and "Unacceptable" (○) are un-changed. The principal purpose of these changes is to add confusion to a simple situation, so that readers will give more of their attention to the text (wherein there is much wisdom) and less to the stars and circles (there are no shortcuts to the Word).

INTRODUCTION

The restaurant reviews that make up this book appeared first in a little-known newsletter called *The Restaurant Reporter,* which I began publishing in 1971, the result of a long-time fascination with the New York restaurant scene.

One might casually judge that writing about restaurants is a repetitive business. True, restaurants do not make up as heterogeneous a universe as, say, the characters in books, or for that matter, in life, but despite the inroads of Steak & Brew, Howard Johnson's, Benihana and the other drawing-board, sit-down supermarkets of America, New York retains a healthy, individualistic restaurant tradition. The appetites of its citizens, cultivated in a jungly preserve of stubborn culinary nationalisms (each espoused in myriad ways by tribes of egomaniacal and idiosyncratic restaurant proprietors—the best restaurants have no other kind, and many of the worst do, too), are receptive to, in fact eager for, originality in their eating places. Each time the death of the restaurant business in New York is announced (with every renegotiation of the restaurant workers' contracts—when, in fact, a handful do cave in, often for reasons of pique rather than economics), the business goes right on being reborn, with new ingenuities and styles.

Even if you never meet men you don't like, you may well encounter such restaurants, and though going from one to another is sometimes dull, the rewards are often in unlikely places, which seems to double their value. There are flashes of style where you don't expect them—a scholarly preoccupation with spinach in what looks like a run-of-the-mill Italian place; service that is present, anticipatory, considerate, helpful, amounting to a spoiled child's fantasy, in a restaurant that could pass (and does) for just another midtown executive trap; a varied hoard of Burgundies in one West Side bistro, of Bordeaux in another; etc.

As neither my name nor face is household-familiar, it was possible for me to gather the impressions that led to these opinions with nearly absolute anonymity. In only a handful of the restaurants reported on am I known by profession, and the owners of these places have affirmed, unanimously, that the grand privilege of my acquaintanceship was offset, rather than rewarded, by their treatment at my hands.

If you write about restaurants, you are asked the same questions and the same kinds of questions again and again: Which is the best restaurant in New York? Which is better, Lutèce or La Caravelle? Hunam or Uncle Tai's Hunan Yuan? Which is the best steakhouse in New York? (Steak is a local as well as a national obsession.) Of course these questions are unanswerable. Just as there is unlimited variation in kind and quality along the spectrum of New York eating places, in almost every one of them there is something to please and something to offend. One man's best is another man's bust. Where you may wish to refuse to, say, stand in line in the cold, on a perilously steep flight of steps, for the privilege of suffering the rudeness of the waiters at Grotta Azzurra, your spouse or other companion may not notice any of that, content that the uncompromisingly strong, blunt food is all. Everyone's favorite restaurants are those whose faults he does not care about or is able to forgive. (There is also a class of jolly sufferers, those who quiver with pleasure when they are insulted by Elaine, of Elaine's, and swoon when they are sneered at by one of the captains at Lutèce. That, however, is a subject for a doctor.) But for the benefit of those who must have their rankings, the restaurants are scored, as follows:

★★★★	Excellent
★★★	Very Good
★★	Good
★	Good (but not *as* good)
●	Acceptable
○	Unacceptable

Most of the restaurants in this book are graded "good" or better. Someone is certain to point out that most of the restaurants in New York are, on the contrary, bad or worse. There is no discrepancy. I am correct about the restaurants in this book, and Someone is right about the restaurants in New York. This volume is not comprehensive. It deals with three categories of restaurants: the best, the best-known, the little-known but worthwhile.

Ten Sensible Rules About Going to, Eating in, Paying at and Departing from New York Restaurants

1. RESERVATIONS. Before going to a New York restaurant, telephone to make a reservation. True, reservations are often not accepted, but this is sometimes because the restaurant no longer exists. By telephoning you determine whether the place is still in business, and if so, whether you can get a table when you want one.

2. NO RESERVATIONS. If a restaurant does not accept reservations, it is probably because it is so busy that it can get away without offering the convenience. Ask if the place is likely to be crowded when you want to go. Sometimes you will get a helpful answer, sometimes an honest one, sometimes both.

3. COMPLAINTS. It's no fun to complain throughout your meal. After all, you go to a restaurant to enjoy yourself, your food and your companions. But it's a good idea to complain about *something* early on. People who complain are people who seem to know what they want and what they are about, and they get better treatment than the timid or unsure. If you are shy or diffident, or don't know what you want, that's too bad, but it need not be a guarantee that you will not enjoy eating in New York restaurants.

4. SENDING BACK. If you don't like something you ordered, tell the waiter it tastes terrible and send it back. Do the same thing if what should be hot food is cold or if there is anything else clearly wrong with what is brought to you.

5. WINE. If you like wine but don't know much about it, order an inexpensive bottle. Modestly priced wines are the most reliable ones in restaurants. They are what they are. Restaurants are not the places to give yourself a wine education; it is much too expensive and unreliable. Expensive wines in restaurants may be too young or too old, or damaged from poor storage, and if you're unsure of yourself, you may not know why you don't like what you get and whether you really ought to return it. If there is a sommelier (the man with the chain around his neck), his business is to sell you wine (after suitable discussion), pour your first glass, and generally convert the purchase and consumption of a bottle of mild booze into an important event. Few New York restaurants have sommeliers any more, but those that do generally have pretty good wine stocks. If the sommelier seems like a decent sort and if you want to spring for a fancy bottle, tell him how much you are willing to spend, and he will recommend a bottle at the price, and probably a good one.

6. EMERGENCIES. If you need service at once and are unable to catch your waiter's or captain's eye, the best system is to rise from your chair and approach the nearest responsible member of the staff. The late English conductor Sir Thomas Beecham used to brush dishes to the floor to get attention, but as most dining-room floors in New York restaurants are carpeted, this ploy might

go unnoticed. Flinging dishes against the walls or ceiling, however, is a sure-fire way to bring the help.

7. YOUR CHECK. Review it. It's wrong about one time in ten; in your favor about one time in a hundred. Ask for a menu to check the prices if you think you have been overcharged or charged for a more expensive item than the one you ordered. Check the addition. Of course you may have had a few drinks and a bottle of wine, while the waiter is probably sober, so he may be right, and you may be wrong.

8. TIPPING—HOW. Don't leave your tip under a plate. It simply is not done. If you want to give someone a tip, hand it to him. If you don't spot him, leave the money out in the open where it is easy to see. If you're tipping on a credit card voucher, write in the tip *and write in the grand total.* If you do not, an emendation may be made favoring the waiter and penalizing you. This is so common that the credit-card companies have a name for it; they call it an "override."

9. TIPPING—HOW MUCH. Par is 15 percent of the before-tax food total, plus some lesser percentage of the liquor and wine. If you are served by both a waiter and a captain, 20 percent is fair, most of it to the waiter, the exact proportion depending on whether the captain did no more than cursorily take your order or if, at the other extreme, he thoroughly explained the menu, prepared sauces and desserts, and helped with the selection of wine.

Reasons for tipping more: You ate the least expensive items on the menu and occupied the table for three hours; the service was terrific; you are feeling expansive.

Reasons for tipping less: The reverse of the above, except that waiters should not be penalized for your depression unless it is their fault.

Sommeliers should be tipped $1 per bottle, but no less than $2 in total if they have been really helpful.

Coatroom attendants should not be tipped at all. They are salaried, their "tips" go to the management, and you have just finished paying adequately for your meal.

10. DEPARTURE. Leave when you are good and ready. It is your right to eat at your own pace, including lingering over a second cup of coffee. Enjoy possession of a table that others are waiting in line for. Later they will.

A Note on Prices

The restaurants in this book have been classified as "inexpensive," "medium-priced," "expensive" or "very expensive."

When the book went to press, these categorizations were roughly defined as follows, for complete dinners for two, with wine or some other suitable beverage, tax and tip included:

Inexpensive: $25 or less
Medium-priced: $25 to $40
Expensive: $40 to $50
Very expensive: More than $50

By the time the book is printed, bound, distributed and purchased by you, these definitions, in many instances, will no longer be accurate. First, prices in all restaurants seem to go up steadily—that is inflation. Second, if an inexpensive or medium-priced restaurant is doing very well, it may shift from one category to the next—that is the profit motive. A press-time $25 dinner may run to $40 by the time you eat it.

In some few instances specific prices of dishes or drinks or wines are referred to in the text. They are meant to give an impression of the restaurant's pricing policy. The information was correct when written, and the impression is probably still correct, even if the exact price has changed.

Listings of Restaurants

BY TYPE OF FOOD

COMPARED TO MIMI SHERATON'S N.Y. TIMES GUIDE TO N.Y. RESTAURANTS

BY RATING

Il Rigoletto **97**
El Rincon de Espana **38**
Ruc **234**
Sakura Chaya **294**
San Marco **101**
San Remo East **103**
Sea Fare of the Aegean **128**
Shalimar **237**
Shun Lee Dynasty **151**
Sloppy Louie's **129**
Sushiko **238**
Swiss Pavilion **240**
Szechuan **309**
Tavola Calda da Alfredo **40**
Torremolinos **139**
Le Touret **70**
Il Valetto **104**
Vašata **241**

★ GOOD (but not *as* good)

Ararat **215**
Aunt Fish **280**
The Balkan Armenian **216**
Ballato **244**
Barbetta **78**
Berry's **45**
Billy's **108**
Bradley's **14**
Brasserie **256**
Brazilian Pavilion **132**
Brittany du Soir **160**
Cabana Carioca **133**
Casey's **15**
Charlie Brown's Ale & Chophouse **258**
Chez Vous **16**
Csarda **302**
Czechoslovak Praha **222**
DaSilvano **19**
El Faro **20**
Fleur de Lis **285**
Frankie and Johnnie's **4**
Frini **134**
La Fronde **22**
El Gaucho Segundo **23**
Genghiz Khan's Bicycle **286**
Girafe **86**
Grand Ticino **24**
Grotta Azzurra **63**

Hopper's **26**
Inagiku **226**
Jai Alai **28**
Joe Allen **270**
John's **65**
Lady Astor's **47**
Liberty Café **289**
Ma Bells **261**
Mama Laura **88**
Maxwell's Plum **271**
Minetta Tavern **30**
Mr. Mike's **114**
Nippon **230**
O Lar **305**
One if by Land, Two if by Sea **34**
162 Spring Street Restaurant **51**
Oscar's Salt of the Sea **125**
Parioli, Romanissimo **306**
Parkway **231**
Paul & Jimmy's Place **69**
Pearl's **273**
Promenade Café **262**
Raoul's **53**
Red Tulip **233**
Romeo Salta **99**
Saito East **236**
Szechuan Taste **154**
Tito's **42**
La Toque Blanche **192**
Vincent's Clam Bar **72**
Wo Ping **157**

●ACCEPTABLE

Adam's Rib **297**
Algonquin Hotel **266**
Bo-Bo **315**
Brussels **172**
The Coach House **17**
The Duck Joint **250**
Elaine's **268**
Fiorello's **284**
Gallagher's **111**
The Ginger Man **288**
La Goulue **269**
Katja **179**
Keen's English Chop House **7**
Laurent **180**
Mamma Leone's **317**

BY LOCATION

WEST SIDE, 42ND STREET TO 50TH STREET

WEST SIDE, 51ST STREET TO 59TH STREET

WEST SIDE, ABOVE 59TH STREET

BROOKLYN

OPEN ON SUNDAY

SUITABLE (by reason of economy/menu/accommodations) FOR LARGE FAMILY GROUPS

OUTDOOR DINING

ENCLOSED SIDEWALK CAFÉS

BRING YOUR OWN WINE (or whatever)

OPEN LATE (until midnight, or later, each night that the restaurant is open for business)

Algonquin Hotel **266**
Asti **313**
Barbetta **78**
Benito's **58**
Bo-Bo **315**
Bradley's **14**
Brasserie **256**
Broadway Joe Steak House **109**
Casey's **15**
Chi Mer **144**
Elaine's **268**
El Faro **20**
Fiorello's **284**
Fleur de Lis **285**
Forlini's **62**
Frankie and Johnnie's **4**
Frini **134**
La Fronde **22**
Gallagher's **111**
El Gaucho Segundo **23**
Genghiz Khan's Bicycle **286**
The Ginger Man **288**
Granados **136**
Grotta Azzurra **63**
Hopper's **26**
Jacques' Tik Tak **227**
Jai Alai **28**
Joe Allen **270**

Joe's Pier 52 **316**
Lady Astor's **47**
Liberty Café **289**
Maxwell's Plum **271**
Minetta Tavern **30**
Monk's Inn **290**
Mykonos **229**
Nickels **303**
O. Henry's Steak House **32**
Oh-Ho-So **49**
O'Neals' Baloon **292**
162 Spring Street Restaurant **51**
Orsini's **96**
Patrissy's **68**
P. J. Clarke's **274**
Le Poulailler **293**
Les Pyrénées **166**
Raoul's **53**
El Rincon de Espana **38**
Russian Tea Room **275**
Shalimar **237**
The Sign of the Dove **320**
Sushiko **238**
"21" Club **276**
Il Valetto **104**
Victor's Café **310**
Vincent's Clam Bar **72**
Wo Ping **157**

Seymour Britchky's
New, Revised Guide to the
Restaurants of New York

Old New York

Despite the intrepidness with which New York perpetually destroys and re-builds itself, there are restaurants in the city that are today very much what they were forty years ago or more. Some cater to stubborn cultural enclaves that retain their customs (including culinary ones) despite the spread of culinary regimentation. These places preserve the past, and they are preparing food in ways that seem fresh because they are largely forgotten.

When a circle of Brooklyn politicians hunches over a circle of plates at Gage & Tollner, they are not only unwittingly reenacting the distribution of Brooklyn school-construction contracts eighty years ago, they are doing it under the same gaslights and over a huge variety of seafood dishes evolved in the city's early days.

Some of these old establishments vulgarize the past and, thereby, themselves. Keen's, for one, sells its authenticity and age in such gross, contemporary terms (the collection of c. 1900 playbills is referred to as "memory-stirring" on the menu) that the past is all but obliterated in the process.

But Keen's is only one, and there are places that preserve without peddling the fact. At Frankie and Johnny's, for example, you can get some notion of what speak-easies must have been like—with the advent of Repeal the only change this place made was to get a license, and the upstairs hideaway still has shuttered windows and a nervous host.

★ FRANKIE AND JOHNNIE'S

269 West 45th Street
DINNER.
Closed Sunday.
Reservations, Cl 5-9717.
Credit cards: AE, DC, MC.
Expensive.

This is an upstairs restaurant, once a speak-easy, and it is still like a lair. The windows are shuttered; the limited space is allocated stingily—a tiny bar (framed *Playbill* covers, photographs of ball players, actresses and archbishops) directly across a narrow aisle from a minuscule kitchen (multilingually boisterous, though the noise cannot compete with the customers), and more tables than there is room for (including one so close to the gas-heated coffee station that it is accepted only by novices, and usually abandoned for something better after a couple of minutes of perspiration).

The tuxedoed, middle-aged waiters are selected for reasons of nostalgia: there are Edward G. Robinson, Clifton Fadiman, George Jessel, Boris Karloff and Dick Tracy—at least good stand-ins for them. Many of the customers they serve are appropriately theatrical. They are noisy and sexy: enter a couple of disparate age—his cauliflower face goes unnoticed as the entire room easily estimates the dimensions under her casual scarf top; other customers give their names to the host and tell him they are expecting calls from their producers; lots of kisses are blown. And the younger people here eat like actors too—ravenously, as if each meal is a miracle, perhaps never to be repeated.

It's not a miracle, but it's not bad. Most New York steak restaurants augment their steakhouse menus with a handful of Italian dishes, but here the exotic items are mostly Jewish, so you can start your dinner with a homey dish of chopped chicken liver—the stuff is spread on the bottom of a plate, like jam on a cracker. It is rather bland, but that's OK because it is covered with oil, and garnished with minced raw onions and a chopped hard-boiled egg, and you eat it with the thick slices of fresh rye bread that are part of the complement of motley items in the bread basket (Melba toast, salt sticks, seeded rolls and the rye). There is also matzo-ball soup, but most of the first courses are what you expect: clams and oysters, in good condition; a shrimp cocktail which, as in many New York restaurants, has been attenuated to five (5) shrimp, and they are overcooked and mealy, anyway; melon (a gigantic slice—a smaller, riper one would suit); and a decent pickled herring.

But broilings and potatoes are the main events here, and they can be pretty good. The steaks are not the thickest in New York, but they are not the most expensive either —a little cheaper than at Broadway Joe's, a couple of blocks away, cheaper still than at the places across town on Steak Row. There is a steak ritual: the waiter shows you your steak, you nod or murmur; from his inside coat pocket he withdraws a small scabbard, from that a small knife; he grabs a fork from somewhere and carves the meat off the bone. In like manner he separates the eye from the rib of the thick, delicious, juicy lamb chop (best item here), and the breast from the wing of the chicken (blackened skin, moist meat, made to order). Even the liver is pretty nice here—it is, as stated, calf's liver; it is fresh and bloody, and it is garnished with bacon (not dried out) or sautéed onions. Chicken in the pot, with matzo balls; chicken à la king.

Everything is à la carte. Lyonnaise potatoes (home fries with onions), home fries (lyonnaise without onions), cottage fries (re-fries, really, and hardened, like wooden nickels), French fries, potato pancakes. Skip them all and have the broiled mushrooms —almost everyone does. They are certainly the best vegetable—how can you go wrong if you butter fresh mushroom caps and broil them? The French fried onions are lightly battered, thin and crinkly—pretty good stuff. Everyone also seems to have the Frankie and Johnnie Special Salad—it is huge, made up of crisp lettuce, strong raw onions, tomatoes that are pretty good for these days, green peppers and anchovies, all in a forthright red-vinegar dressing.

The blueberry pie with whipped cream is not what those simple words suggest, but rather a thick slab of fresh cake under half a pint of stewed berries that are covered with half a pint of whipped cream, which, in turn, is embellished with a great dollop of blueberry sauce—a child's blueberry fantasy, for adults. The strawberries are OK, and the cheese cake is steakhouse cheese cake. Better to share one of the blueberry extravanganzas with a friend.

Frankie and Johnnie's is an erratically busy place, and sometimes your table will not be available at the appointed hour. The beverage of choice with dinner seems to be the martini; tourists who do find the place (it is in the theater district, and it is in the guidebooks) prefer coffee; the wine is overpriced; there is beer.

After you've been here a few times you hardly notice the constantly ringing bell that summons the waiters to the serving counter. It contributes to a cheerful din that assures conversational privacy. This is far from a great restaurant, but it has a distinct New York Broadway flavor that can't be found anywhere else in so well-preserved a state. The clear-skinned ingénues, heavily made up former ingénues and their bluff escorts, but for their clothing, seem like museum pieces.

★★GAGE & TOLLNER

372 Fulton Street, Brooklyn (near Borough Hall)
LUNCH, MONDAY TO FRIDAY; DINNER, MONDAY TO SATURDAY.
Closed Sunday.
Reservations, TR 5-5181.
Credit cards: AE, DC, MC.
Medium-priced.

During the famous power blackout, Gage & Tollner was one of the few places in New York with illumination. The gaslights, still in place in their nineteenth-century chandeliers and regularly turned on on Mondays, Tuesdays and Saturdays during winter months, were on that famous occasion pressed into emergency service. Unaided by electric bulbs, they cast a rather dim glow, but adequate. The customers felt lucky, privileged, even wise to be in that place on that night.

On Friday nights the remnants of Brooklyn's upper classes emerge from their door-man-protected enclaves in Brooklyn Heights with their families for Gage & Tollner dinners, as do those Brooklyn boys who made it big in Manhattan but still cross the river to sleep, and as do the powers in Brooklyn politics, looking very bored out of the arena, e.g., Mr. Cuite, seated glumly across the table from their wives. These types make it to Manhattan on Saturdays, or to their country retreats, and they are replaced by the up-and-comings from the so-called brownstone revival communities in Boerum Hill, Cobble Hill and Clinton Hill—stockbrokers, assistant curators and twenty-minute-movie makers. Brooklyn isn't what it was, but all of the patrons are trying to clarify a memory or to experience a first taste of it in this well-preserved relic—huge arched mirrors from front to back, well-worn mahogany tables, cane-seated chairs, carpeted floors (rubber runners in the main aisles, rain or shine), which dim even further the restrained sounds of these eaters.

The eight-page menu, famed for its length, is slightly promotional, but only on the cover, and so awkward and amateurish that it is a point of charm. On the cover we find an illustration of a black waiter, tray in hand, leaning forward, and the only thing missing is the caption "At your humble suhvice." A homily signed by the proprietor is innocently redundant: ". . . We intend to preserve the nostalgic atmosphere that serves to bring back fond recollections . . ." etc. And, further down: "Our waiters wear service emblems: Gold Eagle—25 years; Gold Star—5 years; Gold Bar—1 year." And, they might add, no Afros.

On the inner pages, however, things are quite honest, and among the appetizers and soups are a few items unique in New York. Soft Clam Belly Broil Appetizer consists of the contents (sans necks) of a dozen soft-shell clams, lightly breaded in corn meal, briefly broiled over anthracite coal, and served on toast, with half a lemon. Tender, elemental, superb. Shell roast clams and oysters (littlenecks or cherrystone clams; bluepoint or larger oysters) are baked in their shells (until they open) and served in the halves with melted butter. They are delicate, oceanic, sweet, soothing, pure—a wonderful preparation for clams or oysters. It's difficult to choose among the shellfish appetizers here—oysters and soft- and hard-shell clams are also available broiled with celery or in milk, or both, broiled plain, stewed in cream, fried, and on and on. They can also be had fricasseed (sautéed in butter, stewed in milk), but this double preparation usually toughens the meat and is the least successful of the many clam and oyster dishes.

The bisques—basically white sauces of shellfish stock combined with minced cooked oysters or clams or lobster, further enriched with cream and eggs—are extremely thick and strongly flavored. Have only a cup. If you eat a bowl, your meal will be over.

You might consider making a meal of items on the appetizer, soup and shellfish lists only, because the fish is OK, but nothing you can't get elsewhere. A dozen varieties of fish are listed, and four or five are usually available, served broiled only; there is bluefish, snapper, lemon sole, sea bass. The lobsters are good, but often not available if market conditions are bad and prices up. Scallops (the real thing—little bay scallops) are served in all the ways that the oysters and clams are, and not as Coquille St. Jacques.

Gage & Tollner is not exclusively a seafood restaurant, but that is the bulk of its menu and reputation. There are good steaks; there are mutton chops that are, like those at Keen's, mild for mutton, though here they are at least broiled to order and therefore tender and juicy. The fried chicken is crisped without breading and served with good corn fritters which are made brilliantly successful by the addition of the dark, clear maple syrup that arrives in a little pitcher with them.

Shredded cabbage here is shredded cabbage, not cole slaw. It is covered with a sparkling red-pepper dressing. The hashed brown and lyonnaise potatoes are very good, and the French fries are not. There is something called Spaghetti au Gratin.

For dessert: moist applesauce spice cake; blueberry pie with huge berries, a lattice crust and a five-inch arc; and sweet-potato pie that is superior to pumpkin pie in exactly the way sweet potatoes are superior to pumpkins.

In the evening, downtown Brooklyn is like downtown Main Street. There are lights

—the movie marquee, store windows and a few passing cars, but the only people in sight are patrolmen and the fast-disappearing crowd when the movie lets out. It is an uninviting neighborhood to travel to, but Gage & Tollner is worth an occasional trip.

The waiters are kind and they know their stuff, but some of them keep it a secret:

"What are Shell Roast Clams?"

"I'll get you some nice casinos." (He's writing already.)

"What are Baltimore Broiled Scallops?"

"You'll like them."

"What's the difference in the four kinds of Welsh rabbit?"

"Which one do you want to know about?"

But they are not all like that.

Miscellaneous items: scrambled eggs, milk toast, chicken sandwich, hot chocolate. No marshmallows.

Half portions of most items are available at a small premium.

• KEEN'S ENGLISH CHOP HOUSE

72 West 36th Street
LUNCH, MONDAY TO FRIDAY; DINNER, DAILY.
Reservations, WI 7–3636.
Credit cards: AE, BA, CB, DC, MC.
Expensive.

Survey: How often have you heard it said, at mention of Keen's English Chop House, that Keen's serves excellent mutton chops? And of the people you have heard say it, how many have had mutton chops any place but at Keen's? Which explains this establishment's reputation—mutton is hard to find in New York restaurants.

Actually, the mutton chops at Keen's are pretty bad. The mutton is selected for the timid palate and is milder than good lamb. The chops are partially cooked in advance, then placed under the broiler before serving, so that the outside of the chop is dry and tough, though the meat is apparently well aged—the inside, while rather tasteless for mutton, is moist and tender.

If Keen's was ever a good restaurant, it is now so busy merchandising its gimmicks that it has forgotten what restaurant management is all about. Some of the menu's puffery is worth considering: "Welcome to one of New York's oldest and most celebrated eating places . . . [dots theirs] counterpart of those early English taverns immortalized by the patronage of such men as Shakespeare and Hogarth, Isaak Walton, Dr. Johnson, Pepys and Garrick, Thackery and Dickens!" [exclamation point theirs]. "KEEN'S CHOP HOUSE started here at the turn of the century, in the old Lamb's Club, that respected society of actors, playwrights, producers and others identified with the theatre. George M. Cohan, John Drew, David Belasco, Lester Walleck, Lew Fields, the Barrymore's [sic] . . . these and many others were KEEN'S earliest patrons. As time went on they were joined by notables in other professions: Theodore Roosevelt, Enrico Caruso, 'Buffalo Bill' Cody, Howard Chandler Christy, Irvin Cobb, Leo Fiest, Rube Goldberg. It was their sentimental interest in early tavern customs that revived the ancient practice of having a long clay 'churchwarden pipe' in the custody of 'ye innkeeper.' Today, KEEN'S PIPE CLUB has more than 93,000 members. In the Pipe

Register, you come across the names of Raymond Massey, Sir Cedric Hardwicke, Orson . . ." blah, blah, blah. It is significant that in all of the irrelevant bunk printed on the menu, no claims of any kind are made as to the quality of the food or service. To the management of this kind of restaurant, the food and service are beside the point.

A meal at Keen's may begin with murky wineglasses, toasted rolls that taste like toasted Wonder bread, and a dish of celery, olives and radishes in mint condition.

There is a dull list of appetizers, none of which requires any kitchen preparation beyond the overboiling of shrimp and lobster for the shrimp and lobster cocktails. You may have half a grapefruit for $1. Like many restaurants in New York, Keen's lists Cape Cod oysters as well as bluepoints, but the Cape Cods are almost never available. Of the soups one is led to expect great things from the oyster stew, which is, in fact, quite remarkable: the oysters have lost their flavor in the cooking, but the buttery broth in which they were cooked failed to capture it—quite a trick. Where did it go?

If you must try the mutton at Keen's, have it as part of the Mutton Chop Combination. The grilled kidney, sausage and bacon are all better than the chop—the kidney is thoroughly boiled before grilling, the sausage is strong and not overly greasy, and the bacon is not done to a brittle crisp. The roast beef is more tender than tasty, and the serving is large. Unfortunately, the so-called Yorkshire Popover that comes with it is more popover than Yorkshire. It is not made in beef drippings but in a tasteless shortening—it resembles a breakfast popover at a salesmen's hotel. The steaks are reliable, but the fish dishes are not. The baked potatoes that accompany most of the main courses are, thank goodness, baked without aluminum clothing—the skin is crisp and the potato is thoroughly cooked, yet still firm.

In a place like this, one is entitled to expect that at least the mince pie and plum pudding would be safe. They are unsafe. The mince pie is in a good lard crust, but the filling is not nearly as good as Horn & Hardart's; it is low on suet, nutmeg and liquor, and high on sugar, apples and candied rind—insipid. The plum pudding (also bland) is served with a really third-rate hard sauce—sickeningly sweet, virtually devoid of brandy and tainted with artificial rum flavoring.

To make you feel right at home, at around ten o'clock a busboy noisily clears the unoccupied tables of salt and pepper and ashtrays. And if that doesn't get the message across, a gentleman strolls through the dining room announcing last call for drinks from the bar.

Keen's has one of those insulting wine lists on which wine is overpriced and underdescribed.

Some joiner types with nothing to join come here and overspend at dinner for the privilege of displaying themselves smoking Keen's silly pipes. The pipes are all over the ceiling, and old theater bills are all over the walls.

○ LÜCHOW'S

110 East 14th Street
LUNCH AND DINNER.
Reservations, GR 7–4860.
Credit cards: AE, BA, CB, DC, MC.
Medium-priced.

High up on one of the muraled two-story walls, prehistoric man, lean and muscular, is competing with wild beasts for his daily meat, and across the room, blond, red-cheeked Valkyries aboard their steeds are escorting the souls of the heroic dead to Valhalla. Down below, the rotund customers drink a lot of beer, don the management-supplied red Tyrolean hats (green feather) and wax moody with the music—sometimes a squad of flushed tootlers and blarers, in short pants that reveal knobby knees, instills martial feelings; at other times a chamber trio spins out violinistic medleys of Franz Lehár operetta tunes while, at the tables, stubby fingers clutch at plump knees in a romantic, aromatic haze of weinkraut and cigar smoke. Stuffed moose look down, impassive.

It has been said that all of the food at Lüchow's is terrible. Of course, nobody knows. There are close to 200 items on the menu, and many of them engender so little curiosity that only some kind of crazy, obsessive investigator/cataloguer would ever look into them all. Are you, for instance, interested in getting the scoop on the Vegetable Plate of Green Beans, Baby Carrots, Asparagus Tips, Creamed Spinach, New Peas and Boiled Potato? Or are your awe and wonder aroused, rather, by Berliner Eisbein (Boiled Corned Pig's Knuckle) with Sauerkraut and Mashed Potatoes? Perhaps you would be more interested in getting the low-down on Home Made Bratwurst, Sauerkraut, Mashed Potatoes. Well, don't bother. It has been established that a blindfolded man, sober, admittedly without the aid of mind-expanding drugs, could not differentiate between the sausage and the mashed.

But some of the food here is good. The Schwarzwälder Pfifferlinge are little pointed-cap mushrooms, imported in perfect condition from Germany, sautéed in butter and served in a lovely warm dill sauce. You can have a good bit of it as a main course, or considerably less as an appetizer. It is one of the few dishes here that would do credit to a first-rate restaurant. There are excellent herrings, including a really sour but not acidic Bismarck, and soft, sweet maatjes. The so-called chopped chicken liver is just a tasteless mousse, and the headcheese a dismal amalgam of variety meats. There is a hot, peppery, thick lentil soup, which is satisfying despite the peregrinations of homeless frankfurter discs therein.

The main courses are the real comedown. The boiled baked beef is a satisfactory pot roast, and the knackwurst is spicy and properly fatty, but such items as Kassler Rippchen and the braised veal knuckle really test your control of the gag reflex. One bite, and you know what it feels like to be in the last stages of an eating contest.

The desserts are mostly stewed fruits in cloth pancakes or leaden pastry, plus such heavy weights as cheese cake and marzipan torte.

But, with all that, this place is really something to see. Had Wagner written a comic opera, this would be the set. The waiters bungle on a grand scale, and the customers eat on a cosmic one. The servings here will hold you through the Ring cycle. During the Sommerfest a well-advertised dessert for two consists of "one and one half feet of Apfel Kuchen."

There is an amazing selection of wines, with about thirty-five German ones and as many from France listed on the menu, and many others available. But the wines are overpriced, and anyway, the proper drink with the food here is Alka-Seltzer.

★★ LUNDY'S

Ocean and Emmons Avenues, Sheepshead Bay, Brooklyn
  Emmons Avenue exit on the Belt Parkway
LUNCH AND DINNER.
No reservations (646–9879).
No credit cards.
Inexpensive.

Lundy's is probably the largest restaurant in New York. A block long by a block wide, and two stories high (the upper floor hasn't been used in a number of years), Brooklyn Moorish by design (sand-colored columns and lofty arches) but Fulton Fish in spirit, this unbelievable relic (in good repair) looks like a movie set converted into an officers' mess. The crowd scene stretches to a dim horizon, but the backdrop is real, not painted scenery.

The menu is basic seafood—always fresh—augmented by the usual steaks and chops, plus broiled chicken. (To hold you while the casual service catches up with your needs, an oversupply of hot biscuits, pilot crackers and Oysterettes is planted before you, with enough butter to fossilize an elephant's aorta.) Only simple preparations are available, and the prices are positively nostalgic. Where else in New York can you sit down at a large table with comfortable chairs, and be brought a dozen littlenecks, six oysters, good chowders, strong clam broth, a giant plate of steamers, at prices from 50 cents to $2?

Lobsters are alive until cooked (never over), and the fish, broiled or fried, are firm and flaky—bluefish (the whole animal), sea bass and smelts are available. Not on the menu, and, therefore, long favored by cognoscenti, is a lobster stuffed with crabmeat, but now, with crabmeat very dear, it is overly breaded, and to be avoided. The steaks and chops are rather heavily charcoaled, but the meat is good and cooked as ordered. If you are really hungry, there are complete dinners at discounts—Shore Dinner, Cold Lobster Dinner, Fish Dinner, Chicken Dinner, Chops and Steak Dinner (their nomenclature).

The sleepers here are the à la carte vegetables. Skip the green ones, and try hashed brown potatoes—perfectly seasoned, artfully browned, firm and copious; or lyonnaise —the same partly cooked potatoes fried in good grease, made even more irresistible by an intermixture of lightly fried onions. Not better, but more surprising, are the French fried onions—lightly breaded, crisp on the outside, the onions still crunchy within; and julienne potatoes—the matchstick French fries which, in most places, are either hard from overcooking, or limp from under-, but here are usually crisp, soft inside. Another item not listed is potatoes au gratin—not as good as those mentioned, but if you order them, you look like an old-timer. The desserts are OK, the blueberry pie actually quite good, but the best food appears higher up on the menu.

In summer the beach bugs by the thousands, enervated but happy, trudge from the hot sand to their apartments, hotels, rooming houses and summer sublets to shower away the salt and then sprint to Lundy's, where they wait interminably, but happily, for a table—perhaps, God willing, in a nook beside a window. (Even an amphitheater can have a nook.)

This stable's colors are orange and green, and chair slats, washroom tiles and the waiters' uniforms carry out the scheme. There is a long clam and oyster bar, where people too restless to wait can get quick service. A surviving Lundy lives upstairs, and each morning, it is said, he loads a score of dogs into his miniature bus and drives them out to Long Island for a romp.

For most New Yorkers, there is not a more foreign, or more genuine, cultural encounter, *au restaurant,* than an evening at this bustling mausoleum. The archaism of an all-black serving staff is irksome, but the clientele is like a memory of Brooklyn's forgotten working classes. Italians find no pasta here, blacks no soul food, Jews no chicken soup, but they all come, and at Lundy's even a lobster is kosher.

• SWEETS

2 Fulton Street (near South Street)
LUNCH AND DINNER.
Closed Saturday and Sunday.
No reservations (825–9786).
No credit cards.
Medium-priced.

The food is not bad, the service is not good. The waiters are the worst brand of sufferers. They wake up exasperated and become more and more impatient as the day wears on. Customers find themselves giving orders to elbows or trousers because these food handlers find it a bit beneath them to face a customer directly or attentively, though they appear eager enough when you sit down—they ask for your order before the menu is so much as unfolded, and they exchange significant glances with their counterparts at adjacent stations when you presume to read the thing before selecting from it.

This is the famous Sweets, where reservations are unheard of, and where the line extends down the stairs and into the street at the busiest part of the lunch hour. When you mount the last of the steps, you find yourself in a room that makes the Palm Restaurant look like the palace at Versailles. The floor slopes down toward the center of the restaurant from each end of the building at an angle of at least five degrees. There are oil paintings on the dingy walls which are not only hideous but for sale. The back dining room has a special air of excitement about it because it leads directly to the kitchen. The waiters open the swinging doors with solid kicks to the steel plates nailed thereon for the purpose, and while the doors are ajar, one is entertained by momentary amplification of the otherwise merely intense kitchen noises—a dishwashing machine powered by a prehistoric locomotive, and a constant exchange of pleasantries between the dining-room and kitchen staffs at sufficient volume never to require repetition: "Where's my herring?" "Look in ya pocket."

But as noted, there is the food. The deep-fried oysters have been lightly breaded and fried rapidly. They taste good and are tender, but somehow the oyster has been lost. The clam stew consists of milk, butter, clams and clam broth, artlessly compounded and innocuous. It is called Little Neck Stew and is made with huge, tough cherrystones, almost chowders, sometimes. It's best to begin a meal with raw clams here. (In this venerated seafood joint, raw oysters are not even on the menu.)

The broiled fish is pan-broiled, which is OK, and it is lightly breaded first, which is also OK, though corn meal would make a better breading than ordinary flour. A dozen varieties are listed, and most of them are usually available, including grey sole, flounder, haddock, pompano, shad, and so on. The broiling is expert, and you will get a very fresh, perfectly broiled fish here nine times out of ten. Avoid with great enthusiasm the Newburgs, au gratins, sautées and Creoles. They are, here, methods of defiling good food. But do try the finnan haddie, in the preparation pretentiously called "à la Sweets." The fish is extremely smoky, rather salty, baked in milk (manna to the English), and a singular dish. It is made perfectly here.

A good vegetable: deep-fried eggplant—the moisture sealed inside by breading and by the use of very hot fat. The potatoes, other than the French fries, are OK.

One is rushed through one's dinner here (the used dishes are dropped loudly onto metal trays), and it is soon time for dessert. Don't have it. The Nesselrode pie is sickening and overwhelming—tutti-frutti within, shreds of bad chocolate atop. Ice cream, stewed prunes and orange juice are also listed.

In the old joke, you can lead a horse to water but if you can get him to float on his back, then you really have something. The horses who come here do a water ballet and pay for the privilege, then go forth to talk the place up.

A bad restaurant for a relaxed dinner, but a tolerable one for a fast lunch—the pace and noise seem appropriate to the noontime clientele, busy Wall Streeters.

The menu says: "The Management will Appreciate your reporting of any Discourtesy on the part of our Employees. Thank You." You're welcome.

Greenwich Village

Part of the appeal of the restaurants in this legendary and quite real section of New York is the heterogeneity of the clientele. The Village is the most diversely populated of any section of Manhattan. The radicals and the rich eat side by side, and if you dichotomize the human race any other way—by cultural endowment, sexual conformity, racial majority/minority, the color of the workshirt collar—you will find representatives or proponents of the full lengths of these continuums joined together in the community of the public table. That is the *old* diversity of Village restaurants, undiminished to this day.

There is a *new* diversity—of the restaurants themselves. The old Village had plenty of places to eat, but with a handful of exceptions they were one like another, pizza parlors and spaghetti joints. A few of the old places that survive, in name if not in proprietorship, are superior to what they once were—Minetta Tavern, Grand Ticino; and most of the new places are at utter variance from the meatball/meat-sauce/marinara tradition, serving such rare (for the Village) stuff as French, Rumanian, Armenian and soul food.

★ BRADLEY'S

70 University Place (near 11th Street)
LUNCH, MONDAY TO FRIDAY; DINNER, DAILY.
No reservations (CA 8-6440).
Credit cards: AE.
Medium-priced.

Bradley's is presided over by a fellow named Bradley and his partner, McGruddy. Bradley is a cartoon dinosaur, tall, ample, sage and weathered. His clothes hang on him like an old, softened shell. When he smiles, an arc of a hundred gleaming teeth bisects his leathery visage. To cope with the occasional difficulty, he puts on the look of the sleepy killer who will, if necessary, tiresome as it all is, dispatch with dispatch. He has it all down pat.

Someone should write material for Bradley and McGruddy. They are a team in search of an act, as disparate in look and manner as Laurel and Hardy or Shirley Temple and Babe Ruth. McGruddy is slight, neatly pressed, trimly tonsured and mustached. His open shirt is the concession made by British officers to tropical heat.

There is insistent jazz from musicians in a corner between the barroom and the back room. Up front there is the long bar under dim, low-hanging lights—you can study the back of your hand. (Here Bradley man-talks with the customers who have made it and has a hamburger when he is hungry.) In back are most of the dining tables. (Here McGruddy coolly dinners at the dinner hour.) Throughout stride the busy waitresses (various degrees of stunning). Dark walls, wood-grained, glazed, hung with sriking art, spotlighted.

A singular fixture behind the bar: above the bottles an artfully placed tilted mirror, the length of the bar—you can scan the place and the people without turning your back on your drink. You consider the Village spectrum as it is currently composed, from the aging individualists (wry, cynical, taciturn), who drank in Village bars in the forties, to the communal young (optimistic, flagrantly sentimental, joyous). The generation gap is not a no man's land between embattled camps. The Village preserves its reputation as a haven for all kinds of nuts and sanes.

Bradley's is a good place to visit if you like hamburgers and steaks. The hamburgers are plump (at $2.50, could they be svelte?) and juicy, and the flavor of the good beef is unsullied by bread crumbs or seasonings. The steaks are tender and accurately cooked. There is a big steak and a small steak, the latter much like the former, but smaller. Nice onion rings with the steaks—crisp, and the onions still taste like onions. The cottage fries are well-browned discs. And those are the high points, except for the bread. The bread should be your appetizer—it is delicious bread, from one of those Italian bread houses in the Village, and surpasses the underseasoned snails, frozen shrimp with bland cocktail sauce (horseradish should be brought), and the avocado stuffed with the kind of crabmeat salad that is acceptable as a sandwich filling at a drugstore—in a small town in Nebraska. If you really can't go for straight bread as your first course, the clams are your best bet. It is suggested that the Italian-bread supplier be approached and asked for the name of a good Italian cheese-cake supplier. There is ice cream. If you are into Gleam II, you will like the Mint Parfait.

The music starts at around nine-thirty. Sometimes there are such commonplace instruments as piano and bass, sometimes instruments of the future. Have you heard of a Fender-Rhoades piano? It is an electric piano. It's quite possible for the uninitiated to stare at a cluster of playing musicians here and not know what sounds are coming from which device. You don't have to look to know they are high-class sounds.

★ CASEY'S

142 West 10th Street
LUNCH AND DINNER.
Reservations, 255–5382.
Credit cards: AE, DC, MC.
Expensive.

An overpriced restaurant from shortly after its founding, Casey's is now ludicrously expensive, which accounts for the fact that tables are not as hard to come by as they once were and for the condition that this Greenwich Village restaurant does not sport the standard Greenwich Village clientele, except at the bar—rampant prosperity and propriety are evident at every table, also baldness and stoutness and neatness and cleanness. But for the slightly offbeat look of the place—brick walls hung with ancient sculpture, candlelight, huge mirrors—you might as well be uptown. The waiters are now uniformed in formal black and white; the tables near the bar at the front, which were once given over to cocktailing even during the dinner hour, are now linened. But the busboy is the giveaway—long hair and clutching three water glasses to his printed T-shirt; later he empties your ashtray into an oyster shell; you are not on East 55th Street.

Always justifiably known for the freshness of its seafood, Casey's still serves up excellent oysters, about as newly fished out of the sea as any in New York. At one time they were served with a dreadful version of sauce Mignonette, and rather than improve this sauce, they have dropped it—you get a pitcher of cocktail sauce instead, which you should eschew for the lemon that is provided and for the gratings of the pepper mill that can be had on request. Good snails, poorly sauced—the little mollusks are plump and tender and tasty, cooked in good stock, but the sauce is insipid in its barely seasoned butteriness. If you arrive famished, get the pâté—two mammoth slabs of heavily salted ground duck, liver and seasonings—it is billed as Pâté de Canard, and though the quality of the duck is lost in this strong treatment, the result is fine.

Something called Agneau en Brochette, and further elucidated as Skewered Lamb Provençale, turns out to be a lame entry in the city-wide non–Near Eastern shish kebab contest, the one in which no one is the winner. It comes with a side of reddened rice, overcooked carrots, and a red sauce the like of which is no more Provençale than your brother-in-law's Bar-B-Q concoction.

On occasion there is offered a Lobster à l'Américaine. The crustacean is minuscule (your companion is loath to part with a sample, though you are starving on bad lamb) and it is served in a sauce that is more thermidor than the thick, red, spicy kind of thing that characterizes good versions of this dish. But the lobster tastes as though it were live until just before it was cooked, and the cooking is to the perfect point, so that what little you get is, if you scrape away the sauce, delicious. You are better off ordering your lobster straight—Homard du Maine Grillé.

The listed steaks are prepared Marchand de Vin and Maître d'Hôtel, but once in a while they make a Béarnaise, and it is a superbly rich sauce, redolent of tarragon, thick without being cloying, and the meat they serve here is aged, tender, tasty and cooked accurately. The green vegetables that are available at substantial à la carte prices do not seem to be cooked to order, nor, on the other hand, do they seem like the steam-table kind of thing—they are just a little overdone. The calf's liver with shallots is still excellent, and the snapper and salmon are fresh and carefully prepared.

The chocolate mousse is thick, airy and pungently chocolate-flavored; the Orange à l'Arabe, sliced oranges in Grand Marnier, is a simple, sweet and delicious dessert; the strawberries in wine are heavily sugared, which makes them taste very good, though the berries themselves are not all perfect.

★ CHEZ VOUS

78 Carmine Street (near Seventh Avenue)
LUNCH, MONDAY TO FRIDAY; DINNER, MONDAY TO SATURDAY.
Closed Sunday.
Reservations, CH 2–2676.
Credit cards: BA, DC, MC.
Medium-priced.

It must be stated first that despite the name, Chez Vous is an Italian restaurant, not a French one. It has a miraculous interior, in that a surrealistic hodgepodge of hideous elements is combined into a comfortable, even attractive restaurant. If you can fix in your mind a room in which the walls are camouflage green, hold it; and now superimpose on said ghastly enameled walls a pattern (for want of a better word) of ivory stains achieved by random application of a paint brush, here a stroke, there a dab, there a poke; on these walls you then hang Washington Square Art Show paintings, hundreds of wine bottles in their baskets, and bunches of purplish-green plastic grapes, being careful not to obscure the fuse box or the conduit leading thereto; at the front window, place a curtain of garish gauze (luminescent blue), and on the white ceiling beams inscribe witless testimonials to the glories of wine, in several languages. This is Chez Vous, to which repair such celebrities as the Bishop of Brooklyn (Roman), and from which departed, a number of years ago, the original owners, to open Aperitivo on West 56th Street. The present owner, Mr. Savarese, does what he can to perpetuate the notion that Chez Vous has always been his, and he asserts for all to hear that Aperitivo was opened by a couple of his former dishwashers when they got the absurd notion into their heads that they could cook.

In fact, there has been a little slippage here since the present proprietor took over, and though you can often get splendid food at Chez Vous, it is a good idea to know your way around the menu rather than accept the suggestions of your host, because the meat dishes in particular are second-rate.

Of the appetizers, one of the best is the Crostini alla Romana. This is a sandwich of mozzarella cheese and American bread, battered and deep-fried, and served in a sturdy sauce of anchovies, capers, lemon juice and butter. The sauce is salty and tart, of course, but the sandwich is gooey and mild, and the combination is perfect. Or you can begin with the Shrimp alla Rino, firm and tasty shrimp in a winy sauce that is thick with butter and heavily flavored with garlic and fresh parsley, and a subtle but distinct smoky taste, as if the dish had been exposed to a charcoal broiler. The most popular first course is the Shrimp Chez Vous, which is a substantial bowl of good, cold shrimp, in a thick, well-seasoned Russian dressing. The regulars here have one order for two, half in the bowl for her, half on the plate for him.

There are good soups, including a sound lentil soup which becomes even sturdier when a few tablespoons of Parmesan cheese are added.

The Spaghetti Carbonara is made with ham instead of the usual bacon, and there must be half a cup of the little red slivers of meat per portion. There are also sautéed onions in the thick egg-and-cheese sauce. When fresh pepper is ground over the firm noodles, the whole thing develops a flavor something like that of an omelette, because in this version of the dish the eggs are permitted to cook a little (usually considered a sin), which makes for a stronger, less creamy dish than the usual Carbonara. The gnocchi (the menu calls them homemade) are a little leaden, and the sauce Bolognese is rather harsh.

It may be wise to make your meal from among the appetizers, soups and pastas. The Rollatino di Vitello, for example, is of tender veal stuffed with cheese, ham and pine nuts, but it is served in a sour tomato sauce that obliterates whatever flavors may be built into the dish. The Calf's Liver alla Veneziana is of thick chunks of liver that have to be cooked to toughness to cook them at all—the not-so-secret secret of liver is to cut it thin and cook it fast. A recent Sliced Filet Mignon with Wine and Mushrooms was cooked accurately, but the mushrooms were 30 percent fresh and 70 percent canned, which ruined the otherwise well-made dish. The Chicken Casalinga (which translates to homemade chicken), on the other hand, is a well-browned serving of chicken with sautéed fresh mushrooms and onions, in a sauce that is only mildly tomatoed and well flavored with rosemary and bay—a very good dish.

The Key Lime Pie for which Chez Vous was always famous has not changed under the new management. It is made up of a flaky brown crust, a strong, slightly tart lime chiffon, and a couple of inches of whipped cream. There is also an excellent Zuppa Inglese here, consisting of layers of cake, custard, soft chocolate and whipped cream, all soaked in liquor.

Chez Vous sports a very classy wine list, including a number of fancy Bordeaux. Since this is an Italian restaurant, you may prefer to stick to Chianti Classico or to the Gattinara, a soft red wine from Piedmont.

• THE COACH HOUSE

110 Waverly Place (near Sixth Avenue)
LUNCH, TUESDAY TO FRIDAY; DINNER, TUESDAY TO SUNDAY.
Closed Monday.
Reservations required, SP 7–0303.
Credit cards: AE, CB, DC, MC.
Expensive.

This restaurant's insistent conservativism creates undue confidence. The Coach House has been variously described as "a safe place to take your mother," "the right place to bring foreigners who want to sample American cooking" and "the best solution to the problem of feeding a friend who has an ulcer."

Your mother deserves better; most of the dishes are foreign, and the remainder are plain rather than American; and your friend's ulcer, though it may be soothed by some of the bland food, may also be inflamed when a hapless waiter delivers a Quiche Lorraine which is quiche, but not Lorraine (no bacon or ham), or one of the many versions of overcooked meat, or a colorful salad of brown as well as green lettuce.

The Coach House knows how to do, but not always what to do. They have been cooking many foods correctly for the last twenty years or so, and many incorrectly. A couple of decades ago, well-done meant done well, so the chicken livers are brown through and through, and the shish kebab is dry. Rare steaks and roast beef are available, but the meat is bloodless.

Yet, as in many places, one can have an excellent meal here if the ordering is careful. Of the appetizers the Mushrooms à la Grecque are better than average—actually made with fresh mushrooms, marinated in French dressing, garlic, chives and parsley; the mislabeled quiche is very well prepared, in a partially pre-baked crust, which ensures a crisp base without overcooking the filling; the clams and oysters are always fresh; the pickled herring (which does not come from a jar) is served with plenty of sour cream, and onions that are not wilted; and the black-bean soup deserves its reputation—it is solid and hearty, well flavored with madeira.

Though avoiding the meats, in favor of the seafood, is a sound rule here, the Veal Chop à la Campagne is an exception. The chop is grilled, and chestnuts, hearts of artichoke and mushrooms are combined in a sauce made in the pan before serving. The excellent vegetables make the dish.

Oysters Ambassadore are perhaps the best main course on the menu. The oysters are stuffed with crabmeat, covered with the lightly cheesed white sauce called Mornay, and broiled briefly. The oysters do not toughen in the quick process—they retain the taste and texture of raw oysters, even though they are warm—the flavor of the Mornay is heightened by the light browning, and the crabmeat adds the perfect, somewhat sharper accent.

Vegetables at The Coach House are usually pretty good—fresh and slightly more imaginative than at most so-called American-style eating places. Have the sautéed potatoes if they are du jour; they are like Pommes Anna but done in fat instead of butter, with crisp slices on the outside, soft slices within.

The Coach House is very proud of its dacquoise (the dessert has a little place all to itself in the dessert listings), and, to some, The Coach House is *known* for its dacquoise. This must be because no one else around serves dacquoise. It is supposed to be a delicate almond-and-egg-white pastry filled with a flavored butter. Here the pastry is papery rather than flaky, and the filling, though well flavored, is cloying, because there is too much of it in relation to the crust. Nevertheless, it is an interesting dessert to try, as it is rarely found hereabouts. The Hazelnut Torte is a nice nut cake, with a thin layer of orange preserve; and the Mocha Bavarian Cream is cool, light and fresh. The listing of "Imported Cheeses" refers to American and Swiss.

The wine list shames the food, though, whimsically, only three of the wines are identified by year, out of a total of seventy. The less expensive French wines are from good shippers, and at the higher prices there are many excellent Burgundies and Bordeaux, though you will have to look at the bottle to determine its vintage.

A waiter who neither speaks nor understands English very well can be an inconvenience. When he becomes irritated and raises his voice sharply because he doesn't catch the drift of a request, he becomes an unfunny joke. Attach yourself to one of the captains, who are very competent.

The proprietor greets you with a lugubrious air, and the dead seriousness of the sacred Colonial surroundings adds to the effect of managerial self-importance.

★ DaSILVANO

260 Sixth Avenue (near Bleecker Street)
LUNCH AND DINNER.
Closed Monday.
Reservations, 982–0090.
No credit cards.
Medium-priced.

Yet another atypical Greenwich Village Italian restaurant, this one subtitling itself "Florentine Cuisine." (Eventually the atypical will be typical?) About a dozen crisply linened tables in a neat-of-newness little room, ivory walls plus (almost a requirement) one of bare brick, greenery at the front window, a tiny espresso station in a rear corner, with a gleaming new coffee machine on the counter, a bowl of fruit beside it, bottles of liquor on the shelves behind. From certain tables in the dining room the small gleaming white-tiled kitchen is visible. All is orderly.

In the dining room one is greeted by a pretty and efficient young woman who will very patiently explain to you the nature of the dishes listed on the small blackboard menu. Later in the evening, when things are slowing down, the chef/proprietor himself, a handsome gent in his thirties, emerges from the kitchen to wander from table to table to demonstrate Italian conversational savoir-faire.

Somehow one does not get the impression that the first purpose of this proprietor is to run a good restaurant (though he does run one), but, rather, to run a profitable one, and the suspicion is that once the place has made it, as it is well on the road to doing, the standards will be forgotten. An incident seems to suggest this: one orders a cold seafood salad, one receives and tastes it, one complains to the hostess that it is gone bad. The hostess repairs to the kitchen with this intelligence and returns with the announcement that it couldn't have gone bad because it was "made fresh yesterday." This is not to suggest that you will often get bad food here (in fact, you rarely will), but that the gentleman of Florence lacks a certain passion for excellence, that he has, in its place, a certain tolerance of compromise, a notion that excellence may be the right road to success, but that if there is another road he is willing to try that one, too.

That seafood salad (when it is fresh) is a perfectly respectable mixture of squid and mussels, flavored with fresh parsley and moistened with an unimpeachable, if uninspired, vinaigrette. You are better off with the dishes that are peculiar to the place, which includes panzanella, or bread salad. Relax, it is not a salad of bread. It is, rather, a salad of cucumbers, green peppers, raw onions, lightly cooked string beans that are cool and crisp, chunks of tomato and herbs, dressed with morsels of bread and bread crumbs that have been soaked in a strongly vinegared dressing. The bread serves to hold large quantities of the dressing, so that each forkful of salad is heavily dressed; the bread also adds a pleasantly grainy texture to the crisp salad.

An item which seems to be borrowed from French and Jewish cuisines is called

Crostini. It consists of slices of Italian bread spread with a thick, heavy paste of abundantly oiled and strongly seasoned ground liver. It is the use of olive oil instead of butter that gives this simple dish its unmistakable Italian quality.

Among the few pasta dishes is one called Puttanesco, which is spaghetti, perfectly cooked, served in a pungent dressing of black olives, strands of sautéed anchovies, and small chunks of tomato. This is an exceptional spaghetti dish, the sauce positively profound of these strong dark flavors. DaSilvano also serves a Tortellini alla Panna that is at distinct variance from the usual thing. The tortellini themselves are standard, little circlets of pasta wrapped around a filling of chicken and cheese and served in a sauce of cream and cheese; but this sauce is heavily seasoned with nutmeg, which gives the dish that spice's distinctly fragrant quality.

Pollo Umbriago is something akin to chicken in the pot, except that the broth has been enriched to a sauce made slightly bitter by an admixture of beer. Understand, this is not a fricassee, for the chicken is not browned before it is poached in the beer; you must be a fan of plain boiled chicken if you are to accept this Italian variant.

Listed on the blackboard is a veal dish of the day, sometimes a veal stew, which is a nice enough dish, the veal well-browned before it is slowly stewed for at least a couple of hours—the meat retains its shape, and it is tender and has taken on some of the flavors of white wine, carrots and butter.

There is also a fish of the day, sometimes codfish, fresh and moist, served in a simple and herby tomato sauce—a dish of perfect simplicity.

The vegetable garnishes are a step above the usual—nicely browned chunks of roasted potatoes, for example, or sautéed zucchini, sometimes sprinkled with rosemary. And there are cool salads if you wish, including white beans and raw onions, heavily parsleyed and served in a good vinaigrette. The dish suffers a bit from the onions being chopped long before the salad is served, which robs them of much of their strength.

Your chef, who takes all the credit he can get, informs you that the apricot tart is not, it is true, made on the premises, but, he assures you, it is made according to his rigid specifications. It is a good tart, but canned apricots were specified, and the custard and sweet crust are fine. The other desserts are fruit, cheese, fruit and cheese, and anything else you can make from those ingredients.

★ EL FARO

823 Greenwich Street (at Horatio Street)
LUNCH AND DINNER.
No reservations (WA 9–8210).
No credit cards.
Medium-priced.

El Faro means "the lighthouse," which is probably the least appropriate name this place could have. El Faro is situated in a section of the West Village that is virtually dead after sundown, and the place does not call attention to itself. To find it you must know where it is, with confidence; for years more people have been finding it than the place knows what to do with. This is one of the oldest and most popular restaurants in Greenwich Village, and it is an astonishment to approach it down dim, deserted streets to discover, when you go in, that the place is clamorous. You enter into a small, low-ceilinged barroom, complete with beer-sign clocks, juke box, coatrack, cigarette machine, air-conditioning machine, and customers at various points of alcoholic contentment, depending on how long they have been waiting for their turn for the next available table.

The dining room is small, efficiently filled with Formica-topped tables, and somberly, anciently muraled with grimed-over flamenco dancers. Between the tightly packed tables skip the red-vested waiters—more of them than you will find in other restaurants this size, but they are busy all the time.

It is the way of these busy places—to keep you quiet they bring your salad right away; but in a way that is *not* the way of these places, it is made of fresh lettuce and crisp red cabbage, in a thick, red, peppery Spanish dressing. ("Our Salad Dressing is available to Our Customers," it says on the menu.)

The food here is usually good; the first courses always best. The Broiled Chorizos are discs of spicy Spanish sausage, crisped and browned on the outside, served in warm, peppery oil—they make you thirsty. Ham and olives is referred to as Ham and Olives Spanish Style. Well, they look like ham and olives, and they taste, respectively, smoky and salty—they make you thirsty. Salpicon is crabmeat salad, a piquant and peppery mélange of crabmeat, minced eggs, green peppers, raw onions and parsley in a lemony dressing. It will *not* make you particularly thirsty, though the Galician Soup may— this is the familiar Caldo Gallego, the thick bean soup made with meats or sausages and turnip greens. The version served here is thick and loud.

Your waiter refers to the Cornish hen as *perdiz*. It is the only word you know in Spanish, but you leap at the opportunity to insist that he not misrepresent a domestic hen as a partridge. He's impressed with your knowledge of the Romance languages and waffles uncomfortably for a bit. The minor misrepresentation notwithstanding, this is a splendid dish—you get a big enameled iron pot in which there are several moist, plump parts of a moist, plump bird, in two inches of an oily gravy that is powerfully and fragrantly flavored with clove, onions and bay. If you're going to come here once, the hen is the dish to have. There is, of course, pork with almonds. It is pretty good, the thick slices tender and moist and all that, but the almond sauce lacks an edge, so the dish is satisfying without being exciting. There are shrimp dishes and there are lobster dishes. If you want seafood, eschew the latter in favor of the former. Lobsters do not suffer well the perils of freezing and casual cooking. To overcook a frozen lobster is to add toughness to fibrousness. The green sauce you can have it in is thick and winy, but it does not rescue the lobster. The Shrimp al Ajillo, however, is something else— the shrimps themselves are just OK, but the sauce has character: it is fiery and spicy, redolent of garlic, and uncompromisingly oily.

Spanish desserts are, admit it, dull. Perhaps not to Spaniards. Anyway, the ones you get here are about as good as they ever get: firm, red, crunchy guava shells with a chunk of cream cheese and crisp saltine crackers, for example, can be simple and delicious if all the elements are fresh; the flan is cool, firm and nicely flavored with the lightly burnt sugar; and there is natilla, the *other* custard, gooey and vanilla-flavored and very sugary.

★ LA FRONDE

605 Hudson Street (near West 12th Street)
DINNER.
Reservations, 675–9839.
No credit cards.
Beer and wine.
Medium-priced.

"International Cuisine" is the way this place bills itself, which gives it a lot of leeway. "International cuisine" can usually be read as "nothing in particular." There is, however, a distinct emphasis on Scandinavian food in the appetizer portion of the menu, and these dishes alone make the place worth a visit. La Fronde serves Gravlax and Janson's Temptation in versions which may not match what you get in Copenhagen or Stockholm, but then again, you are not *in* Copenhagen or Stockholm, you are in New York, and there is a scarcity of Scandinavian food in this town.

Gravlax is salmon that has been marinated with salt, pepper, sugar and dill. The marination "cooks" the salmon and makes it very firm, almost chewy, and slices of the dark-red fish are served in a mustard sauce that is sweetened with brown sugar, fortified with vinegar, and accented with plenty of fresh dill. This is strong food with finesse.

Janson's Temptation is quite another matter. This is a simple but extremely tasty hot potato dish. The potatoes are baked with onions, anchovies, cream and butter until they are quite brown and oily, the onions sweet, and the anchovies very fragrant—it is like a hot potato salad in a strong creamy sauce.

La Fronde is one of many Greenwich Village restaurants that are based on the theory that if you can make good food at home, you can make it in a restaurant. These enterprises, usually the effort of two or three young people with one dream, work out well if they stay within the parameters of their talents and maintain their standards in the kitchen and dining room after the business has been built up.

The look of this place is fairly typical of what you can expect in these restaurants. It is a small high-ceilinged place, with the front window full of plants, which is standard, an attractive wall of glazed brick, the others of stark white plaster, numerous paintings and prints, tastefully hung. The floor is of plain wood. The orange linen on the tables adds a warm, colorful note. There is women's liberation in the air. La Fronde is run by women, you are served by women, and many of the customers are women in groups. But the place is being discovered by intrepid Villagers.

You are presented, to begin, with a quite nice salad of crisp fresh spinach and grated carrots in a dressing that is principally oil. And you are also presented with excellent bread. In addition to the aforementioned Scandinavian first courses there are (to remain in Scandinavia) herring salad and a quite buttery liver pâté that is flavored with herbs and a bit of cognac—it would be much better if it were not cold. The Caldo Verde, the Spanish soup made with sausages and collard greens is unfortunately sweet—there is a nice sharp taste of the greens, and the sausages are good, but the very presence of sweetness is all wrong.

These places can surprise you. The couscous is good—the grains of wheat, steamed over broth, are firm and oily, the stuff is mixed with sweet, dark raisins and chickpeas, and served with the moist and spicy chicken that is the meat of this African stew, and big chunks of turnip. There is also a dish of noodles with pesto sauce, the green Italian sauce made with basil, cheese, garlic and pine nuts. With this dish it is every man to his own taste, and the taste here is toward perfectly fresh basil, not much garlic, and pine nuts that are whole, for a textural note. The sweetbreads in orange sauce are precisely the kind of thing a place like this should not undertake, because it is too complicated. The sweetbreads should be carefully browned, and the sauce should be made with a very solid meat stock. Instead we have sweetbreads that are cloyingly rich without the relief of crispness that browning gives them, and a shortcut sauce that lacks foundation and is merely sweet. The vegetable garnishes are carefully made—crisp red peppers and zucchini, warmed in oil, are nice with almost anything.

The banana pudding is a pure and simple combination of ripe bananas, airy whipped cream, sugar and cinnamon. Such a thing cannot be bad. But cheese cake can and in this instance is—cakey, heavy, excessively lemoned and sweetened. There is a wondrous chocolate cake.

A cheerful place. If you order lots of dishes, it is reported to the cook, and she comes out of the kitchen, wiping her hands on her apron, to stare at you in contented wonder.

★ EL GAUCHO SEGUNDO

93 MacDougal Street (near Bleecker Street)
DINNER.
Reservations, 260–5350.
Credit cards: BA.
Beer and wine.
Medium-priced.

Pale-green walls, a color once known as office green, or civil service green. The ancient, stamped-tin ceiling is painted black and white, in a checkerboard pattern, following, but only roughly, the pattern of the stamped tin. Juke box, cigarette machine, open kitchen in the rear. All this is perceived through a haze of smoke, not because the place is particularly crowded with smokers, but because almost everyone orders the mixed grill (read on), and the mixed grill is planted on your table on a little hibachi, glowing, smoking coals within. True, there is white linen on the tables (red napkins forming diamonds thereon), but there the elegance ends. El Gaucho is a primitive place.

What little there is of a South American population in Greenwich Village keeps El Gaucho busy, with a little help from some of the old-family locals who have discovered that, though Argentine food bears little resemblance to the food of southern Italy, it is just as sturdy. The customers come late, casually dressed, including whole families, complete with kiddies—it seems that our Spanish-speaking neighbors have never learned that children should be in bed by eight if they want to grow up to be big and strong.

Your waiter did not attend a Swiss hospitality school, so it is a good idea to find some excuse for an altercation with him before your dinner is well under way. This will not accomplish anything in the way of the progress of your meal, but it will establish that you are someone to be reckoned with, respected, and on subsequent visits you will be shown an esteem usually reserved for the town mayor, which does not necessarily include pronto service.

In deference to the neighborhood, the platter of assorted appetizers is called Antipasto El Gaucho, and it includes discs of various potent sausages, slices of tender, oily ham, and substantial slabs of marinated eggplant. It also includes one slice of Matambre (also available in a four-slice platter of its own). This is the famous Argentine dish of marinated beef, stuffed with garlic, herbs, vegetables, hard-cooked eggs and spices, poached in stock and (usually) served cold. It is stimulating, but also satisfying, and the satisfaction will soon overtake the stimulation—consume one order and you may want nothing more. Something exaggerated as Perdiz en Escabeche on the Spanish side of the menu is more modestly and more accurately referred to as Cornish Hen Special Sauce on the English side. This is a dish of cold Cornish hen, a bird that is usually too dry to bother with. But this preparation is just the thing—the hen is cooked in stock, with vegetables, herbs, garlic and lots of black pepper, and permitted to cool. The liquid is thickened in the process, the bird moistened and flavored—the bits of garlic, green pepper and onions are delicious against the oily sauce and the fibrous meat.

That mixed grill is an impressive affair. The little smoking grill is piled high with assorted meats and sausages. You spear what you like before your companions know what hit them, and leave the liver and sweetbreads to them, or the kidney, or the blood sausage, or the meat sausage, or the "butcher's tenderloin" steak. That blood sausage is bloody, black, bready and rich, in a crackling casing (don't fight, you can order extra blood sausages). The kidney is cartilaginous, gamy, a little tough, and much aided by the charcoal flavor imparted by the smoking coals. There are chunks of red pepper in among the pieces of meat, and they are very good with the sweetbreads and liver. And there is a little pot of an extremely fiery onion-and-hot-pepper relish on every table, and that is a particularly well chosen additive for the fibrous, charred steak.

Naturally, in an Argentine restaurant you can order a straight sirloin steak, described as "The Most Famous Steak in Town." Notice how cleverly the name of the town is not given. The steak is huge, of good meat, though not prime, aged and tender. It comes with terrible French fries. Strenuously avoid the Milanesas, the Completa, and the Napolitana. These are breaded beef cutlets, variously treated, and there is very little you can do in the service of breaded beef.

No desserts worth bothering about, and after two courses of solid food at this place, dessert would be unthinkable anyway.

★ GRAND TICINO

228 Thompson Street (near Bleecker Street)
LUNCH AND DINNER.
Closed Sunday.
Reservations, 575–0642.
No credit cards.
Medium-priced.

Grand Ticino is green, always has been, always will be. A green boxlike restaurant, with rows of tables, a bar to one side. The wood grain shows through the well-worn black paint on the floor. The principal adornments appear only in winter, when the walls are hung with the coats of the diners.

The menu is lengthy, has hardly changed over the years except to be made even lengthier, and includes such oddities for Village Italian restaurants as omelettes; half a dozen different vegetables "alla Parmigiana"; queer vegetable garnishes, on occasion, such as "mashed potatoes and cauliflower au gratin"; and a 15-cent upcharge if you want your spaghetti *al dente*. One has the impression that Grand Ticino has always been written about by inquirers who strolled down Thompson Street, paused, glanced in the window, and continued on their ways. It is said always to have a conventional Italian menu, with no surprises. The look of the place surely suggests that. In fact, though much of what is served is familiar, there are any number of not-so-common items on the list, some of them among the best dishes in the place. But not the first courses, it is true, among which are a plate of decent salami, six great discs of the strong, fatty stuff obscuring the large plate it is served on; pretty good steamed clams and pretty ordinary stuffed ones; and a number of canned combinations and assortments.

Better to begin with soup, Fidellini in Brodo con Uove, for example, a strong chicken broth filled with strands of firm noodles, thickened with an egg and made fragrant with a lavish sprinkling of freshly chopped parsley, a superb steaming plate for the beginning of a winter dinner.

Better still to begin with pasta, particularly the Green Noodles al Pesto. Green noodles are made with spinach, but usually the flavor of the vegetable is lost in their manufacture and subsequent cooking. Happily, this is avoided at Grand Ticino, where the fragrance of the green ingredient is so strong that it cannot be obscured even by the heady redolence of the pesto sauce, an earthy amalgam of fresh basil, nuts, garlic and strong cheese. Alternatively, you may begin with spaghetti with anchovy sauce (if you ask for the premium spaghetti, it is 15 cents extra for noodles cooked to order and *al dente*). It is possible they will arrive a bit undercooked, but in this dish little of the texture can be noticed in the face of the potent sauce—crushed anchovies that are sautéed in oil until the paste is crusty, lots of salt and garlic, all these, with the sautéeing oil, poured over the noodles. Considerably less successful are the Agnolotti in Meat Sauce. These are little pasta dumplings filled with meat and served in a good sauce Bolognese—the sauce is fine, meaty and thick and oily, but the dumplings are tasteless, the green ones indistinguishable from the white ones, all of them very much like nothing in particular.

Naturally, there is available the entire spectrum of veal scaloppine dishes, but hidden in that long listing are a couple of the relative rarities that give this place its special interest. Trippa Parmigiana, for one, which is tripe (fair warning)—strands of the glutinous, slightly rubbery stuff in a strong red sauce that is pungently flavored with bay, a platter of the thick stew, sprinkled with Parmesan cheese and served lightly browned—is satisfying and cheap at $3. For another, there is Calf Brains al Burro— soft, rich brains, lightly breaded, browned until they are a deep mahogany and served quite glistening in the sautéeing butter, sprinkled, prettily, with brilliantly green fresh parsley. In this line of innards, Grand Ticino also does liver pretty well, but if organs turn you off, the standard scaloppines are fine, including a Veal Scaloppine Pizzaiola that is made with carefully sautéed slices of pale veal in a sauce that is red, thick, sour and spicy. The vegetables that accompany these items are many levels above the monkey dishes of canned vegetables that pointlessly accompany even decent main courses in many low-price (and high-price) places—chunks of potato (a day or two old when they were fried, which gives them a stout flavor), soaked in grease, blackened at the edges; the aforementioned mashed potatoes and cauliflower au gratin, a homey little item, soft, bland but for the slightly sharp accent of the cheese against the simple vegetables; escarole that has been sautéed in oil and garlic, the coarse, fibrous leaves made limp and loud by the treatment. The à la carte vegetables are, by and large, less interesting than the free ones—the Spinach Parmigiana is perfectly good spinach and perfectly good cheese adding up to very little; the String Beans al Oglio e Aglio are better—barely cooked beans, crunchy, in oil and garlic, heavily seasoned with salt and pepper.

You must inquire about the cheeses if you want one for dessert—the Parmesan is usually domestic and uninteresting, but sometimes there is soft, ripe Gorgonzola available, from Italy, and that with a salad of crisp escarole and tomatoes is a better dessert than the standard ice cream items or cheese cake.

★ HOPPER'S

452 Sixth Avenue (near West 11th Street)
LUNCH AND DINNER.
Reservations, 260–0250.
Credit cards: AE, BA, CB, DC, MC.
Expensive.

Since the demise of the once-respected Charles French Restaurant, there have been a number of short-lived attempts at restaurant revival on the old premises, all failures. This latest essay is a complete departure from what has gone before, and though it is unlikely the vast spaces that make up this place will ever fill the way Charles did in its heyday, Hopper's will probably make it.

It is that very problem (or opportunity, depending on how you look at it) of spaciousness which explains one of Hopper's queernesses: Hopper's is billed as "restaurant, café, market," and they could have added eighteen holes of miniature golf and bleachers, for Hopper's is room upon room—a bit farther and it would open onto Fifth Avenue at the back. Figuring, probably correctly, that they are stuck with more space than they can use, a little plot of store just to the right of the front entrance has been given over to retail sale of meat and fish.

Nothing of the olden days remains but the low-hanging crystal chandeliers. They no longer illuminate Charles's overstuffed elegance—Hopper's is sleek, angled and gleaming. Functional as a guillotine and cozy as a hospital corridor, the place is wrapped in smooth dark-brown walls, relieved here and there by short stretches of varnished wood. The bar at the front is massive and glinting, the linened tables in the room beyond it lined up on a raised platform that is like an oblong boxing ring, polished brass guard rails in place of ropes, black and white asphalt tiles on the floor, instead of canvas. The treatment works—once you are the two steps up and seated you are truly on a tableland, the reaches around fallen away, your shared plateau a dining room of human proportions. Separated from these semiformal quarters by a wall of window panes in dark wooden frames is the café—red-and-white checkered tablecloths, a wall of rosy brick, and a baby grand identify this as the intended Hair-Down Room.

You want some wine while you consider the menu, and yes, Hopper's has the latest gimmick in wine lists: picture a deck of cards, about twice the normal size, a hole in the upper left-hand corner of each card, the cards held together by a chain through the holes; on each card (they are of white plastic) there is affixed the label off a wine bottle. Presumably when an item runs out, the card is removed from the deck; when new wines come in, cards are added. All very cute, but at these prices a sheepskin menu with lettering of gold leaf would be more appropriate.

As the premises are extensive, so is the menu, offering more than two dozen items with which one may begin one's dinner. Among these mostly commonplace items are a few that look as if they may be mavericks, including something called Black Forest Ham. But you discover soon enough that only the name is odd, the dish itself simply good smoked ham, pink, salty, and tender. Then there is a section of the menu headed "Special Salads." These are not the things you eat before dessert, being composed mostly of nonleafy vegetables in the kind of dressing your waiter refers to as "vinegarette." Cold String Beans and Bermuda Onions, for example, get this treatment. The beans are barely cooked and, therefore, they are crisp and tasty, but the red onions, minced long before they are served, are devoid of bite. The dressing is augmented with a sprinkling of oregano, which is a well-chosen herb for these vegetables.

From the title Fresh Artichoke stuffed with Capers and Black Olives, you will probably conclude that this hot appetizer consists of an artichoke stuffed with capers and black olives. Guess again. Perhaps they are working on it, but at one sampling the stuffing consisted only of seasoned bread crumbs and cheese, nicely browned and moistened with consommé and oil—all quite nice, the artichoke only slightly overcooked, but it would be well if a copy of the menu were posted in the kitchen so that the kitchen help might prepare what the waiters sell. Scampi are offered, and these shrimps are fresh-tasting, crunchy, and awash in butter that is lightly seasoned and flavored with garlic.

The busboy stacks your appetizer plates on the table, right before your very eyes (presumably he would empty the ashtray on the top one if you smoked), and you proceed to your modified-steakhouse main courses, beginning with those modified steaks known as your Double Thick Loin Lamb Chops, which are bigger and a little less expensive than your Double Thick Rib Lamb Chops. Of course they are not the tender nuggets of lamb that come on those tiny ribs, but that was your choice, and this is very acceptable meat, accurately grilled, and served with a baked potato that is neither baked in aluminum foil nor overbaked—the jacket is crisp, the interior firm and moist.

For those of you who are determined to gain at least a little weight every day, Hopper's munificence in its serving of Country Chicken and Sausages will take care of an entire weekend's goal. You are presented with a mound of food the size and shape of an NFL football bifurcated longitudinally. Chunks of chicken, the skin well browned and crisped; inch-long discs of spicy and oily sausage; and slices of sautéed fresh mushroom are the principal ingredients in this solid dish. They are bound together in a consommé-based gravy and adorned with an ample dusting of fresh chopped parsley. Skip lunch.

Hopper's makes much of its fish. "Because of our 'daily fresh' policy," the menu reads, "some items are not always available." So far, none of the fish or shellfish sampled has been frozen, though one wonders whether the Dover sole or Channel turbot can be legitimately listed under "daily fresh." Moreover, some of the local stuff, specifically a striped bass, did seem something more than half a day from the Atlantic. The fish was perfectly prepared, moist and flaky, superfluously reddened with very mild paprika, but it lacked the pristine sweetness of the just-caught article. Perhaps scallops are easier to hold, for the sea scallops served here are not only impeccable, but as copious in the serving as the aforementioned chicken-and-sausage extravaganza. Moreover, the little white nuggets are very delicately sautéed and browned, after being lightly battered, and the insides are tender, moist and sweet—a simple, lovely dish. If you prefer, you can have them broiled.

There is less ambition and variety in the dessert portion of the menu than in the other sections, but most of what is offered is nice enough, including a superior cheese cake of the domestic (cream cheese) variety—extremely light and airy, delicately lemoned, and with a crisp graham-cracker crust. The Fresh Fruit Cup is indeed of fresh fruit. The Fresh Strawberries are, 90 percent of them, ripe-red and sweet, though the so-called Cannoli Cream you can have with them for a premium of 55 cents is actually denatured Styrofoam.

The Village has acquired a minor new asset of the come-one-come-all style, good for lovers, families, and bachelors keeping company with the Racing Form.

★ JAI ALAI

82 Bank Street (near Bleecker Street)
LUNCH AND DINNER.
Reservations, YU 9–5826.
Credit cards: AE, BA, CB, DC, MC.
Medium-priced.

There has been an L-shaped Spanish restaurant at this address, with an associated corner travel agency snuggled in, for more than forty years. There have been long stretches when passing Villagers wondered what kept the places going. The drowsy travel bureau (the ancient sign pushes steamship passages) was often assumed to be a front for something other than the restaurant in the back, and the dim restaurant, it was assumed, subsisted, but just barely, on the fairly steady flow of booze that passed over the huge U-shaped bar just to the left of the Bank Street entrance. Now the place seems to be enjoying a deserved revival—the restaurant, not the travel agency—and if you have been avoiding this somber landmark because it is often somber, be informed that the current level of business keeps the old place pleasantly noisy, that the food is sturdy and good to eat, and that the cost is within reason.

For some of the food you may have to acquire a taste. The Spanish ham is coarse, loud, fatty, sliced thick, fibrous and even a little tough, but it has a sturdy country quality rarely encountered in city restaurants. There is also something called pickled fish—bony mackerel, lots of it, sour and oily, served in a thin, heavily peppered tomato sauce, with strong green olives. Or you can begin with Clams Marinera—clams steamed in a garlicky potato soup that is flavored with fresh parsley; when you have finished with the clams, your next course is the soup.

If you want a proper soup, the undoubted best is the Garlic Soup with Eggs—a great plate of oily garlic broth, salty and spicy, in which there is an abundance of heavy, soaked bread and a couple of eggs poached in the broth. The gazpacho is good, but not to everyone's taste—the shock of finding white grapes and bits of melon in the sour tomato liquid may just stop you.

As in many places, the main courses are something of a letdown. The partridge is nice—it is braised in a thick vegetable sauce, with green peppers; it is broiled briefly at the end, so that the sections of the bird are lightly blackened; and it is served with two substantial slices of orange, which you squeeze on to add a lively citrus tang to the delicate, moist meat and the oily red sauce. There are various forms of seafood assortments—Mariscada a la Bilbaina, Zarzuela de Mariscos, and the usual paellas. The trouble is that these are overcooked, that the shrimp are not fresh-tasting, that the clams are not added just at the end, to keep them tender. You are better off with Bacalao en Salsa Verde—salted cod in a thick green sauce, served over slices of firm, oily boiled potatoes. Whatever you eat, your dinner is augmented with a large platter of rice in which you will find discs of firm Spanish sausage.

For dessert there are the usual flan, guava shells with cream cheese, and so on.

Jai Alai is a cavernous place—low ceilings and dark, muraled walls. In summer when the singing Spanish students make their rounds, with their guitars, mandolins and robust baritone voices, the place is filled during their brief visits, with a few minutes of joyous sound.

★★ JOE'S

79 MacDougal Street (near Bleecker Street)
LUNCH AND DINNER.
Closed Tuesday.
Reservations, 764–1838.
No credit cards.
Medium-priced.

Joe's had always been one of the best of the old-style Italian restaurants in Greenwich Village: a little out of the way; a little more expensive and more elegantly appointed than most of its competitors; not frequented by the Bohemian side of Village society, rather by the stolid types whose supposed affiliations were whispered about; and serving food that went well beyond the narrow range of red sauces over noodles and veal that made up the bulk of what was served in the places with the checkered tablecloths and candles in Chianti bottles.

In the old days the riffraff stayed away; perhaps they still do; but now it is difficult to tell—it is fashionable to dress like riffraff no matter what your status, and these T-shirted and dungareed neighbors may pay their checks and pull away in a chauffeured limousine that is just like the one waiting for those obviously moneyed advertising types making all the noise. There are still a few seeming-underground potentates around—they are very stiff, apparently offended by the relaxation of standards.

You ask for the fried zucchini as soon as you sit down. This establishes you as one who knows his way around the customs and secrets of this place and, in addition, provides you with some excellent fried zucchini! It is traditionally munched, in this reataurant, during perusal of the menu, on which, by the way, you will not find said fried zucchini. (Think of the insular types—there must be such—who have been eating here for decades and have never had the famous zucchini.) The stuff comes wrapped in a napkin—the thin strands of the vegetable have been lightly breaded and deep-fried in extremely hot oil, so that the breading is extremely crisp, the strong-tasting squash barely cooked. You eat it with your fingers.

Meanwhile you have ordered your dinner, beginning, probably, with the quite remarkable stuffed mushrooms. These stuffed mushrooms are unlike any other stuffed mushrooms in town—no oiled, herbed breading; no minced mushroom stems; just cheese—ricotta and something much louder on top, the mushrooms themselves sautéed until dark, the cheese lightly browned. One order consists of four such mushrooms, which seems paltry, but they are worth more than the price. There are excellent baked clams, juicy, tender, the breading delicately browned. And you can have one of the clams and one of the mushrooms as part of the pretty good hot antipasto, which also includes some thoroughly sautéed eggplant and a huge shrimp. What distinguishes this hot antipasto from all others is its red sauce—it is studded with huge capers and loud olives.

Nowadays when you order the Home Made Egg Noodles, Carbonara Sauce, you are getting green noodles. True, green noodles are made with eggs, but one does not think of something called an egg noodle as being green. Hues aside, the food is delicious. The noodles clearly *are* made on the premises; they retain the flavor of spinach, and they are served in a thick, creamy egg-and-cheese sauce that has been mixed with slivers of smoky ham. The same noodles can be had in a very meaty meat sauce—spicy and oily —to which fresh mushrooms have been added. For something more primitively red, there is a sharp and acidic tomato sauce on the manicotti—the pasta is thin, tender and firm, and the filling is a simple one of steaming ricotta cheese.

Chicken Livers Cacciatore: soft, succulent livers; crisp mushrooms; a bright tomato sauce; a garnish of one potato croquette, fluffy, spicy and perfectly browned. Chicken Scarpariello: chunks of chicken on short lengths of bone, sautéed until browned, with chunks of garlic, big slices of mushroom and herbs. Veal Francese: good veal, if not the best, in a smooth and lemony sauce with slices of ham in the sauce, a nice variant; all in all, one of the best versions of this dish around. The stuffed veal cutlet, a sometime daily special, is good, but basically no more than a run-of-New York veal Parmigiana.

Good vegetables, including sautéed escarole that is dry, fibrous, salty, and mingled with the chunks of sautéed garlic that contribute to its potent flavor. Good salads, including, when available, very fresh and crisp arugula, in a clear, strong and salty vinegar dressing.

Joe's serves one of the best cheese cakes in New York. It is wildly excessive, very wet, intensely sweet, heavy and thickly studded with candied fruit. And an excellent zabaglione, hot and thick, and strongly flavored with good Marsala wine.

Joe's is a brightly lit, clean, comfortable place. The immaculate kitchen is visible through a portal at the rear of the front room. The waiters are at once casual and quick. A good place to know about.

★ MINETTA TAVERN

113 MacDougal Street (at Minetta Lane)
LUNCH AND DINNER.
Reservations, 575–0845.
Credit cards: AE, BA, CB, DC, MC.
Medium-priced.

Amid the devastation that has befallen MacDougal Street, Minetta Tavern has been preserved. The restaurant changed hands in the spring of 1972, and the new owners have had the good sense to alter hardly a stick of the barroom or dining room, and the even better sense to improve the kitchen.

The type has almost passed—the Village saloon, to which, in the days when the Village was the Village, aspiring admen and editors repaired (having made the quick change from young exec to Bohemian by loosening their four-in-hands on the southbound Fifth Avenue bus) to booze up in the front room and then sober up on strong food at a table in the back. Invariably these establishments were decorated with caricatures of those regular customers who were also pals of the boss, and dozens of the old drawings, framed and behind glass, cover a couple of the walls of the front room; there is a painting of Joe Gould, the quintessential Greenwich Village nonconformist; and throughout the place, framed photographs of the former long-time proprietor, slim, trim, dapper Eddie "Minetta" Sieveri, as he is referred to in all the captions, with the likes of Tami Mauriello or Linda Darnell or Willie Pep, even the famous self-conscious in their poses.

The front room has a long, shiny bar, red lights, cut glass, a handful of bare, polished tables with bowls of pretzels. The dining room is vaguely Moorish, with a couple of plaster arches decending to pillars of simulated brick, and along one wall, red drapes hanging from the ceiling to the floor, tied back to facilitate the waiters' access to the kitchen and yours to the facilities. There are wooden booths, and the tables are covered with white linen. But if you lift your eyes to the upper reaches of the other—undraped—walls, there you will see the happily preserved and annotated old murals of the Village as it was in the days before there was a Minetta Tavern. There is Mori's, one of the fanciest and most expensive supper clubs in all of Manhattan, doing business on Bleecker Street near West Broadway (God knows what is doing business there now), and in front of the place, a uniformed chauffeur at the wheel of a luxurious sedan, reading, waiting for the revelers. There is Washington Square North, with nothing behind the row of houses but open sky, and with horse-drawn carriages passing through the uncluttered street. There is the Washington Square arch high over a park that looks nothing at all like a jungle. There is the Sixth Avenue El. The whole panorama is rendered with such innocence! Certainly the El could never have been anything but a noisy nuisance. And Mori's was something of a clip joint. But whoever painted it all, when it was not yet very old, apparently knew that to future eyes it would be seen, most easily, as a fairyland.

When you turn your thoughts to the purpose of your visit and your eyes to the bill of fare, you will find that Minetta Tavern offers a conventional, albeit lengthy, Italian menu. What you will not learn from reading the lists is that this is a sauce restaurant —*good* sauces—wherein the ingredient to be sauced is not invariably the equal of its liquid garnish, unless that ingredient is pasta. Accordingly, you may wish to come here for a simple dinner of a cool appetizer, a big plate of spaghetti, dessert and coffee— and if you do, you will not be disappointed. But the meat and fish dishes are not disasters, and a number of them are more than decent.

To begin there is a not bad stuffed artichoke—the stuffing is an oily, herbed breading, the vegetable itself is perhaps overcooked; but it is cooked in consommé, with considerable oil, and this flavorful liquid is what you dip the leaves and heart in. The cold appetizer called Mixed Sea Salad is composed of small chunks of crisp shrimp, circlets of tender squid (cones, if you get the end of the little torso), the odd sardine, anchovies and stretchers of tomato, and diced celery, all in a bright garlic dressing, with lots of parsley and oregano.

The pasta courses are the best. Rigatoni Sorrentina is a thick, tubular noodle in a meat sauce that has been mixed with ricotta cheese. This particular combination has a mysterious succulence that seems to derive from the sauce being at once creamy and meaty. Spaghettini Caruso is a dish made of thin pasta with perfectly sautéed chicken livers, onions and thinly sliced fresh mushrooms. Another good pasta dressing in this restaurant is the sauce Matriciana, here made with tomatoes and onions, plenty of red and black pepper, considerable salt (which it takes on without tasting excessively salty), and lots of sage and bay.

Among the veal dishes there is a very decent Veal Pizzaiola—the red sauce is fiery and heavily flavored with oregano—but the veal itself is not first-rate. The Calf's Liver Veneziana is also pretty good—chunks of liver, sautéed so that they are pink in the middle, and lots of onions—but the liver itself is not perfectly delicate. The scungilli served here comes in a terrific red sauce—peppery and oily and abundantly flavored with garlic—but the scungilli (conch) itself is mature and rather tough. None of these main courses is less than good to eat, but each of them suffers a little from carelessly selected basic ingredients.

The zabaglione seems to be a mistake. You order it once, and it is snow-white for lack of Marsala, and you order it again and it is exactly the same—it is sweet, hot, frothy and liquored with something or other, but it does not taste like zabaglione. The cheese cake is better; made with ricotta and plenty of lemon, it is moist, and somehow, at once filling and refreshing. Good espresso.

○ O. HENRY'S STEAK HOUSE

345 Sixth Avenue (at West 4th Street)
LUNCH AND DINNER.
Reservations, CH 2–2000.
Credit cards: AE, BA, CB, DC, MC.
Medium-priced.

When Di Lucia & Di Lucia, despite concerted community opposition and support, elected to preserve and transform an erstwhile meat store into a so-called restaurant, it was in the then new spirit (now so forgotten and revered) of Destructive Rehabilitation (which anticipated, before its time, the movement toward Preventive Restoration which has now engendered the Retrospective Futurism of tomorrow) that they—with a financial hindsight and a commercial foresight rarely encountered in brothers who are at once restaurateurs and patrons of an architectural style that can, thank God, be called singular—elected to provide the northwest corner of West 4th Street and Sixth Avenue, Greenwich Village, our City and the World not only with an eating place wherein (and whereout during the summer months) one could in fact eat but also with a visual encounter, the reverberations of which are yet to be fully ventilated, beyond the oft-recorded impressions of quasi-historic unsanitation, intramural optical sexual review and (particularly in re the garb and manner of the professional staff) medical manhandling, both inpatient and outpatient.

Still to be explored (surely Cockshell and Stutts, despite the diligence of their research—an actual meal actually consumed in the actual room—cannot be accepted— he wore sunglasses, she is blind) are the repose and strength of the Northwest Walk-In Refrigerator Room, with its floor-to-ceiling, wall-to-wall original icebox tubing, shrewdly preserved in a cigarette-ash white to suggest, without slavishly capitulating to, the frost of yore (some say the coolant rests yet within), against a grotesque but stimulating field of lamp black. The strident and touching rendering of the overhead carcass chains, in a straightforward ventricular red, eliminates the need for further inquiry. With a rare openness (so useful), the initial essay in this area, the *South*west Walk-In Refrigerator Room (which fronts, or backs, on West 4th Street) is left as was. It tackled the problem with the more timid leverage of ornament, giving us the *loops* in red, the meathooks in putty (!); only the bold sooty walls were perfectly to the point and ultimately carried over to the climactic Northwest treatise.

The main Saloon, with its gargantuan serving counter (ingeniously spotted alongside fifteen stools), and the elegant simplicity of its table distribution (one behind another, another behind that, and so on), is ringed by the Sidewalk Café, which faithfully follows the store frontage, traversing as it does a reversed L, the trunk of which adheres rigorously to the north-south axis of the Avenue of the Americas, the leg to West 4th Street's not yet deviated east-west course. The border of flat-topped tables, under a fringe of flag-striped canopy artfully positioned to keep out the sun while letting in the rain, attracts a bizarre and colorful clientele of popeyed bipeds occupied with the study and mental notation of the physical characteristics of all erect females the circumstances of whose lives bring them past this now historic corner.

The total complex is unified by a dry slush of well-trod sawdust, constantly redistributed by the sliding shoes of straw-hatted waiters, their long white coats, from waist to ankle, gilded with a butcher's patina of coal-black and blood-red.

No shrimp cocktail; the tomato juice is chilled; the grapefruit juice is unsweetened; the Sauté Mushrooms seem stewed; tough, inaccurately prepared steaks cooked over "real live charcoal"; baked potatoes steamed to powder in aluminum foil; French fries with the texture of noodles; noodles with the texture of gum; golden-brown, crispy, crunchy, tasteless "Confederate" fried chicken; good hamburgers (ground meat cannot be tough); cheeseburgers that taste like hamburgers (the yellow stuff is visible but not tasteable); sugary-sweet apple pie on a ginger-snap crust (sans snap); the cheese cake is insipid and gluelike.

In recent years the Di Lucia brothers have had the opportunity to reevaluate, and to rededicate themselves to the refinement of their opus. With reluctance, but with fierce purpose, the butcherblock cocktail tables were removed when it was determined, once and for all time, that American adults will not manipulate their knees under a tabletop that is eighteen inches thick. But more important, the release of the long-coveted storefront property directly to the north of the Saloon has made possible a fresh approach to the original challenge. White, all white, has been their clear response, except for the sawdust, the waiters' coats and a green trellis that echoes the diamond pattern of the stamped-tin ceiling and walls. This is the first Di L. & Di L. environment in which it has been possible actually to see after sundown, and the visibility of the food has precipitated certain difficulties which, eventually, will have to be dealt with as firmly as the inflexible cocktail tables. Many of the pilgrims who climax their voyages here are from the Land Between the Hudson and the Pacific, and of her illuminated goulash, one said, "Christ, it's stew."

★ ONE IF BY LAND, TWO IF BY SEA

17 Barrow Street (near West 4th Street)
DINNER.
Reservations, 255–8649.
Credit cards: AE, CB, DC, MC.
Expensive.

There was a dingy candlelit restaurant at this Village location for many years. You surely will not recognize the place. The old carriage house has been transformed, with only a few false notes, into a spacious, airy Colonial hall.

You enter into the huge two-story front room, handsome bar to the left (an ancient, gilded cash register behind it), a couple of fireplaces to the right, under gleaming copper hoods. There are a handful of casually placed cocktail tables. It is all a luxurious waste of space.

Space is allotted more economically at the back, where the double story is divided into two stories. If you are seated downstairs, you are in the back of the big front room; if you are upstairs, you look down on it, a grand and lofty view.

Much brick, many old wooden beams, lovely patterned carpeting throughout the place. Early-American paintings mingle with modern ones. There are a couple of pseudoprimitives, both huge, one in the upstairs dining room, the other hanging behind the bar. They were probably commissioned for the restaurant, and they are ludicrous in these otherwise handsome surroundings. A bust of George Washington stands over the display of desserts; he averts his gaze from the tray of used dishes at the other end of the table.

OibL TibS, to give it its jazzy acronym, is not frequented by the full spectrum of Greenwich Village's motley populace. These are like the customers at the Coach House, but not quite so stuffy. You will see a unisex shirt here and there, but if you look closely you will spot the marks left by the tight collar worn during the day; there is some long hair, but very clean and expertly tonsured; the denim is tailored. Many tables of stylishly dressed, attractive men, discussing their creative pursuits with much arch humor.

The waiters are tuxedoed and somewhat inept. You ask for a full bottle of an ordinary Beaujolais; there is no full bottle, and you are brought the two remaining halves, with the assurance they are of the same year; a glance at the labels shows that they are four years apart, the older of them therefore over the hill. You settle for a regional Bordeaux, and your servant, in a charming accent, asks if you would like it to "breeze" for a while. You explain to him that while it breathes, you thirst, and as you are paying, it will have to do the suffocating.

Fortunately things are smoother in the kitchen, and this new place wisely essays only a brief range of dishes. You may begin with Pink Shrimps and Crab Claw. This is a frightening-looking dish, the shrimps and claws protruding menacingly from a wineglass, a pool of cocktail sauce in the bottom of the bowl. The shrimps are perfectly good, as is the sauce, but the crab claws are frozen and water-logged. (One demerit.) Instead, have the Snails by Land by Sea. Either way they are delicious, the plump snails thoroughly imbued with the flavor of the good stock they were poached in, served in a strong mixture of butter, parsley, garlic and shallots. (One gold star.) Every day a different soup of the day, some days a cream of mushroom soup that has a heavy scent and flavor of fresh mushrooms—it is creamy, hot and satisfying.

A good veal steak is served with strips of bacon, sautéed fresh mushrooms (rare and crisp), in a lemony sauce that is based on a good stock. Problem: the lemon juice is squeezed directly into the pan when the sauce is made, and a few seeds get in, too. There is little in creation that is more bitter than an inadvertently chewed lemon seed, and lemons should always be squeezed through a sieve. (One free advice.) There is only one fish on the menu—filet of striped bass. It is fresh, the skin is crisp, the meat flaky and at once sweet and salty (someone here tends to be a little heavy on the salt); altogether a rather sparkling dish.

This is an odd point for anything as hefty as a spinach salad, but there it is, on the menu, and it is really first rate—the spinach crinkly and strong, slabs of raw mushroom, lengths of soft, succulent bacon, all in a mustard dressing made with lots of salt.

There is an assortment of cheeses; they are at room temperature, and they appear to have been at that temperature several times before. It is true, cheese should not be cold, but it is better cold than frequently thawed. (To serve cheese in a New York restaurant, the house must be ready to discard a lot of cheese.) It is served with good fruit. The chocolate cake is moist and almost black, and heavily flavored with chocolate. The mousse is light and sugary, decorated with a dollop of pretty good whipped cream.

Late at night there is a pianist and mobs of tipplers.

★★PARIS BISTRO

48 Barrow Street (near Bedford Street)
DINNER.
Reservations, 989–5460.
Credit cards: AE, BA, DC, MC.
Medium-priced.

A hectic Greenwich Village restaurant, casual, relatively inexpensive. Two rooms, connected by a passage through the kitchen—in front a nondescript den, a bar at one end—brick walls, ornate mirrors, low ceiling, late-night joviality, comfort; in back there is outdoor dining (indoor in wintertime, when the overhead roll-away green-and-white awnings are un-rolled-away, and the heaters are turned on, and the fire in the fireplace is lit), under hanging white globes, hanging plants, very gay. The food is good and medium-priced, the wine is cheap, the service is positively in-passing.

The snails are plump and tender and served in a buttery sauce that is thick with parsley and garlic. These are not the greatest snails—they were not cooked in a profound stock—but they are totally satisfying. The Crevettes à la Marinade are perfect shrimps, big and firm, the surface a shiny flamingo pink, served with lemon. These shrimps seem to have got most of the cooking in the marinating, rather than in boiling water, and they retain a bright, clear taste. The Moules Ravigote are almost as good—the mussels are plump, tender and fresh, and the sauce ravigote is a nice variant—lots of mustard, fresh dill, and a sprinkling of capers. The pâté is the least of the appetizers, but still it is livery, loud and good.

The onion soup is good in all but its broth. The melted cheese on top is an excellent Swiss product, the crusts of bread that protrude from the cheese have been nicely toasted when the cheese was browned, but the stock is a bit thin, though more than palatable. Onion soup is a simple thing—the stronger and deeper the stock, the better the soup, and it should not take much to improve this version.

Your waiter drops by to chat, caressing his beard as he does so. He allows as how he likes the food here too, as he picks up the plates from your first courses and heads away with them. He returns with an afterthought—"Should I order your main courses now?" "Good idea." And off he goes to the kitchen to order your main courses, having taken an order for a second bottle of wine, as you figure to need a little something to hold you in the interim. Perhaps he knew what he was doing.

The steak au poivre here is really sturdy stuff. To some tastes this thick coating of peppercorns (barely ground) may be excessive, and the strongly brandied sauce may be, too, but the meat is good, the brandy is cognac, and it is thoroughly cooked down to make a rich, thick sauce; and the broiling is accurate. There is also a more than decent Carbonnade à la Flamande served here, the oddly sour beef stew made with beer —this version is thick and tender, and the serving is ample. Pretty nice vegetables, including excellent boiled new potatoes, cooked in their skins, bursting from them, coated with butter; tender rice, parsleyed and buttered; carrots that are barely cooked so that they are crisp—unfortunately this treatment is disastrous when it is applied to hefty, old carrots.

An utterly nowhere, commercial-seeming mocha cake, tasting refrigerated and feeling hard. You are better off with the pear poached in red wine—the wine is thickened in the process, and the good, fresh pear is firm and infused with the wine and sugar.

Careful attention to the limited number of items on the menu, sensible prices and the contented clientele that contributes to the light-hearted air of the place are the principal assets.

★★★ LA PETITE FERME

189 West 10th Street
LUNCH, TUESDAY TO FRIDAY; DINNER, TUESDAY TO SUNDAY.
Closed Sunday.
Reservations essential, 242–7035.
No credit cards.
Wine.
Expensive.

This place is still one of the most distinctive eating experiences in New York. The food is simple and elegant, the surroundings (can a minuscule room be so designated?) simple and studiously rustic, the service simple and charming. (The curly-headed slender young waiter has perfect French, if necessary, and boyish charm, needed or not; his maidenly partner makes do with a fetching smile. Though there are only five tables and no more than twenty chairs, their serenely measured attention to their tasks spins out your four-movement dinner into a five-act operetta, complete with leisurely inter-missions; no matter, for in this fairy-tale restaurant time seems to stand still, though only for the second sitting.) But its charms have been at least slightly sullied by success, and though every original stick is in place—the doves cooing in their wooden cage, the strings of onions and garlic hung starkly against the white plaster wall, the irregularly shaped and almost flat pine tables, the casually placed bunches of wild flowers, the little blackboard menu and wine list—the food is not what it once was, which was perfection within limited ambition, and it is its perfection, after all, that argues for the cameo in place of the full-blown portrait.

Not every facet has been flawed, however, and the artichoke you get here is still the irreproachable standard for all poached/cooled/dressed green vegetables, cooked to the point where undesirable rawness and hardness have been eliminated, without any loss of flavor or texture, and served with a dressing in which the mustard and vinegar are in perfect balance in the smooth, refined oil; well-bred teeth have been known to make several sets of passes over the tender leaves during long entr'actes, spooning up more dressing before each desperate scrape. You get tiny artichokes here, but perhaps that is part of the secret, or else part of the style of the place—everything here, with one exception, is small-scale.

The exception is the famous huge wooden bowl of mussels, served in a vinaigrette that has been laced with coarsely chopped Bermuda onions. But the mussels these days are not invariable at a stage of perfect, sweet freshness—definitely not over the hill, of course, but short, by a bit, of the bright and briny juiciness that used to obtain. There is an important trick to eating these mussels—the dressing, by the time the bowl reaches you, has flowed to the bottom, and when you spoon some of the mussels onto your plate with the large wooden spoon that is provided, you must tilt the bowl until you can also spoon out some of the onions and vinaigrette to pour over them. It is the tart dressing and crisp onions that make the dish—particularly these days, when the mussels themselves may be short of excellent.

M. Chevillot (the estimable chef/proprietor) has a way with a bass, matched only by the way another bass might have with a bass. He reduces it to its most edible self, supple, firm, slightly tangy, just the least bit fibrous, so that you experience the least bit of resistance when you chew it; and it is served with a smooth sauce made on a fish-stock base, with just a bit of mustard. He has a lesser way with a chicken, but not a way that is so easily resisted. His Poulet à l'Estragon is not the expected sautéed chicken in a tarragon sauce, but something akin to Chicken Paprikash, with a creamy sauce infused with excellent sweet paprika and fresh tarragon. The dish does not seem French, but that in itself is surely no sin, and the bird is nicely browned, the sauce velvety. The accompanying vegetables for these things are not invariably what they once were. Barely cooked carrots should be barely cooked *tiny* carrots, otherwise they should be more than barely cooked. The zucchini, however, grated to thin strands and sautéed in butter, is superb.

When this restaurant was new, a salad containing raw mushrooms in among the greens was a rarity in New York restaurants, and in those days, moreover, the mushrooms were impeccably fresh, crisp and sliced as thin as the leaves of the greens, which is a nice touch. Today they are coarsely cut, they may be a day old, and the lettuce itself may yield up a bit of sand. Still, it is a good salad, mainly on the strength of its dressing, and as it is no longer something of an experience, you may want to have it with a wedge of Brie—ripe but not overly runny.

Orange à l'Arabe: slices of skinned orange, strands of outer rind, and Grand Marnier —too little of the last and too brief a marination so that the dessert is little more than raw fruit. You are better off with the strawberries—plump, red, juicy, in a variant of zabaglione in which Grand Marnier has been substituted for Marsala—can't complain at all.

Wine from a brief, high-priced, select list.

★★ EL RINCON DE ESPANA

226 Thompson Street (near Bleecker Street)
LUNCH AND DINNER.
Reservations, 475–9891.
Credit cards: AE, BA, CB, DC, MC.
Medium-priced.

Buried among the garishly fronted restaurants and joints that make up the mini-strip along Thompson Street near Bleecker is this almost unnoticeable place; its little red awning protrudes hardly at all over the sidewalk. If you casually stroll the strip with the intention of eating in a place that catches your eye and takes your fancy, it is unlikely that you will end up here. Too bad. This is the best restaurant of the lot. You can eat well at Rocco's or New Port Alba or Portofino or Livorno, but you can also get some terribly ordinary food at those places. This Spanish restaurant has it all over its Italian competitors—you almost never get a bad dish of food in this humble establishment. The Greenwich Village locals know it, and the place is pretty busy—on weekend nights, right until midnight, you may find every one of the closely packed little tables in use, with customers waiting at the bar.

The bar. After hanging your coat on the makeshift coatrack just inside the entrance, repair to the bar. Behind it there is, of course, a bartender. Also a picture of the bartender, as well as pictures of the chef and of friends and relatives, and cluttered shelves of bottles, glasses, bills, reminder pads, an old-fashioned bedside alarm clock, the telephone, the chromed cash register (keys hanging from its buttons), the *pischkeh.* When things are slow it is the bar the waiters hang around, each of them red-jacketed, black-haired, long-sideburned, mustached, handsome. From the bar you can see into the kitchen (when the door swings open), and you see that it is the size of a shower stall and contains three full-size men. At the bar you also make a wise decision about your dinner beverage (you watch the bartender compound a pitcher of sangría, with *a lot* of ice, half an orange, several heaping spoons of sugar, about half a cup of brandy, and the very small amount of cheap red wine, from a giant jug kept under the bar, necessary to fill the remaining interstices between the ice cubes, all for $6), namely, to drink straight wine, from a labeled bottle, instead of sangría.

The restaurant proper is dungeony, the red walls hung with the required bullfight pictures, the rough plaster ceiling adorned with nonsupporting beams, the air filled with talk, and, at dinner, with the plinking and strumming of a flamenco guitar, and, at all times, with the fragrance of garlic—the specific Spanish persuasion here is Galician, which means food that is very much like other Spanish food, plus garlic.

Garlic, for example, in Mejillones à la Carlos, translated as Mussels Specialty of the Chef. The mussels arrive in a smooth oily sauce flavored with hot red pepper, sautéed onions, fresh parsley and the garlic, many slivers of it; the mussels may be big, but they are fresh and clear-tasting and tender, and very few customers fail to capture the residual oil at the bottom of the dish with a spoon or with bread. For something considerably milder you may have Jabas à la Plancha—shrimps sautéed in butter and white wine. The excellence of this dish derives from the fact that the shrimps are prepared in their shells, which strengthens and sweetens the flavor of the crunchy white meat. It is no tribute to the kitchen, but the Spanish ham you get here (the menu calls it Spanish Mountain Ham) is exceptional. Your large plate is covered with about a dozen thick slices of the slightly fibrous but tender, pink marbled meat—it is salty and loud, and you can make excellent little sandwiches of it if you are not prejudiced against sandwiches as a first course. Pretend you are at a picnic.

You may expect meat and/or sausages in your Caldo Gallego. You won't find either of them here. But the firm white beans, chunks of potato, and sharp greens, all in a buttery liquid, make for a decent soup just the same. Of course there is gazpacho. There is no such thing as correct gazpacho. If you have eaten gazpacho in restaurants in Spain, you know that there is approximately one version per cook. The bulk of the liquid you get here is solid—crisp little dice of green pepper and onion awash in an oily cold broth aggressively flavored with strong red pepper and garlic. You will note, but probably not taste among these pungent elements, plenty of chopped fresh parsley, too.

Your hosts, the menu informs you, are Carlos and Julio, and the former apparently works in the kitchen, as his name is appended to the dishes that are specialties of the chef. Among them is Pulpo [octopus] à la Carlos. First of all you have to not mind either the idea or the reality of eating octopus, that is to say, short lengths of a firm, slightly rubbery pale-gray meat, to which are attached unsightly little suckers; surmount that hurdle and you can treat yourself to a quite delicious dish, consisting of a substantial mound of the aforementioned stuff in an oily sauce that is thick with sautéed onions, slivers of garlic, parsley that is wilted in the hot oil, and a seasoning of strong red pepper; it is the taste of almost burnt onions that distinguishes this sauce from the many similar ones on the menu. There is also a very good Cangrejo con Salsa Verde (crabmeat in green sauce, to you). There are huge chunks of the tender crabmeat in a creamy sauce that is slightly winy, laden with parsley and strongly flavored with garlic. What makes the dish is the good crabmeat—probably not fresh, but certainly not canned—frozen, but still moist, tender, firm and sweet.

To avoid garlic, if that is your wish, have Filete de Cerdo Barbacoa con Salsa de Almendra, which is pork with almond sauce. The slices of pork are tender and blackened at the edges, and the sauce is thick, sweet, flavored with citrus fruit juice and laced with slivers of almond. You might understandably suspect that Breast of Chicken with Almonds is much like pork with almonds. However, in among the almonds in this dish are slivers of garlic, disguised as slivers of almond; the sauce is white and thick and laden with parsley; and you get two immense quarters of the very good chicken. A lot to eat. There is also a hearty veal dish, made with green peppers and Spanish sausages, all in a thick gravy. It is called Ternera a la Estremena, and it is winter food.

The usual desserts: firm flan, with a sauce of caramelized sugar; guava jelly with cream cheese and saltines; etc.

Late at night there is occasionally a bit of boisterous gaiety—streams of laughter from the bar, energetic clapping in rhythm to the guitar. No dancing.

★★TAVOLA CALDA DA ALFREDO

285 Bleecker Street (near Jones Street)
LUNCH AND DINNER.
Closed Wednesday.
No reservations (924–4789).
No credit cards.
Wine.
Medium-priced.

This is Alfredo's third Greenwich Village restaurant, and at this writing it is the best of them. Not that he has climbed to a loftier pinnacle of excellence than he reached before, rather that the Trattoria da Alfredo and the Caffè da Alfredo have been left to the erosive uses of time—the Trattoria in particular is now but a foothill in the Alfredo chain. But don't worry about Alfredo. Reputation outlives the good life, and Alfredo's first two essays continue to thrive, even though their offerings are now often little more than derisive echoes of the sensational food that once made them instantaneously successful. Do you remember, when the Trattoria was new, how, at the end of the evening, Alfredo the Exhausted would emerge from his kitchen swathed in his kitchen whites, fall into a chair, sup and smoke. Well, them days is gone forever. Al's an executive now, he makes surprise visits to his restaurants, he is dressed in spiffy duds, and his social life has improved.

"Tavola Calda" is Italian for cafeteria, and the place does have a functional look. There are rows of little square tables in the front, a display and serving counter at the back. The walls are hung with blown-up photos of garishly costumed revelers cavorting in the presence of, and sometimes *with,* various forms of Italian food. What with green plants busily filling the front window, casually dressed waiters stretching themselves thin as they squeeze between tables, much calling and waving across the room between friends and enemies, and the traffic in and out of the kitchen colliding with the restless and hungry in the small waiting area at the rear, Tavola Calda da Alfredo is a jolly circus all around. In that waiting area, by the way, one waits not only for tables, but also for food to go—Tavola Calda was billed as mainly a take-out place when it opened, but it has not caught on as such—now it is 90 percent restaurant with (a first for Alfredo) a wine list, at, believe it or not, liquor-store prices. Drop by for some splendid food at reasonable prices, Italian wine at deflationary ones.

The menu reads "Stuffed Eggplant(3)," but if you are sharing with a friend, your thoughtful waiter will bring you "Stuffed Eggplant (4, small)." Sections of eggplant shell, like four-inch canoes, the exteriors blackened by a thorough baking in oil, are filled with a deeply browned and oily mixture of cheese, bread and ham, lightly spiced and sweetened. "Tomatoes Capricciose (2)" is a refreshing and simple dish consisting of two *halves* of tomato, filled with cool rice, lightly oiled, studded with bits of prosciutto ham and fresh parsley. Though listed further down on the menu, the Insalata Marinara, also served cool, is an eminently satisfactory first course—chunks of squid, whole scallops, slices of fresh mushrooms, and circlets of raw but tamed onion, translucent and slippery, all in a marinade of lemon and oil that is flavored with parsley and bay; it is a sparkling dish, astringent and brightly flavored, appetizing.

The "salads" are not what one usually thinks of as salads, and accordingly, they will often be eaten at odd junctures in one's meal. They are referred to, simply enough, as string-bean salad, cauliflower salad, broccoli salad, and asparagus salad, and depending on the whim of the proprietor, the season of the year, and the condition of the available produce, some or all of them are available daily. Of them the broccoli and cauliflower salads consist of the lightly poached vegetable, crisp and cool, in herby dressings of oil and garlic—simple and elegant food, of fresh ingredients respectfully prepared.

Alfredo's pastas are among the best in New York, at least in this one of his establishments. In addition to the half-dozen pasta dishes on the menu, there are usually a couple of specials of the day. To begin with a couple that are on the menu, there is, first, something called Cold Pasta e Fagioli alla Trasteverina, a version of the famous chickpea-and-pasta soup, here served cold. The beefy broth is a bit thin if you get here when the soup is still new and tepid; thick and grainy if it is a bit older and chilled. Either way it is powerfully salted, herbed (principally with Italian parsley) and teeming with crunchy chickpeas, lengths of husky tubular noodles, and shreds of meat. And then there is the Cannelloni della Trattoria, the double sheets of macaroni filled with a mixture of meat and herbs that is spiced with a heavy dose of cinnamon. The little bundles are baked in a thick meat-and-tomato sauce. Every texture is right, the pasta neither chewy nor soft, the sauce viscous without being dry, the filling tender and moist without being wet. The effect of the dish is at once nutlike and vibrant, its diverse flavors unpredictably yet perfectly blended. Among the occasional pasta specials of the day is a version of ravioli in which the pasta is filled with parsley and ricotta cheese, and served in a sauce of strong cheeses and walnuts—a singular and startling compound. And sometimes there is available a spaghetti dish in which the sauce is composed of tuna fish, tomatoes and olives—somehow it does not work well, perhaps because canned tuna is used.

As usual, Alfredo's veal dishes are the least successful items he sells, including a Veal Française that is nicely flavored with lemon, but soggily crusted and drastically over-salted. His Chicken Scarpariello, on the other hand, consisting of chunks of chicken sautéed in oil and rosemary and served in a pan sauce made with white wine, is tender, the meat nicely browned and crisped. And sometimes there is a really extraordinary chicken dish in which the roasted and stuffed bird is served under a thick fruit sauce of black and white raisins, peaches and lemon rind. The chicken and veal dishes change from day to day—none is listed on the printed menu.

Not every restaurant offers a cheese cake of the day. You never know what you will find in or on your cheese cake at the Tavola Calda. First of all, this cake is more American than Italian—it is made with cream cheese rather than ricotta cheese, and it is baked on a graham-cracker crust. If the cheese cake is spread with blueberries or some other fruit, avoid it, for the heavy and dry cake is not made any lighter or moister by a topping. But if you have lucked out, and the cheese cake is filled with candied fruits and raisins, have it, for the moist fruits that have sunk down to the crust are the perfect juicy foil to the solid cake. You can also have strawberries and cream.

★ TITO'S

125 Seventh Avenue South (near West 10th Street)
DINNER.
Closed Monday.
Reservations, 691–5827.
No liquor.
No credit cards.
Medium-priced.

Italian cooking, as we all know, is divided into two factions, the reds against the whites, the tomato worshipers *vs.* the cream-and-cheese fanatics. Until recently almost all local territory was in the hands of the reds, but the whites waited until decades of power brought on overconfidence and decadence among the reds, and they are now establishing beachheads in areas that were once impregnable red strongholds. In Greenwich Village, for example, where the noisy kitchens and colorful dining rooms of the traditional Italian restaurant were almost universally governed by temperamental reds, suave whites, long passive, are asserting themselves. Comes, thereby, Tito's, among others, so decorous an Italian restaurant that it may be accused of masquerading as a little monastery mess hall.

The effect is of an earthen jewel, all ochers, olives, browns, with a bit of gold here and there. Even the courteous waiter wears the stable's colors (his mustard-hued shirt is unbuttoned from the neck down to his dark trousers, revealing a triangle of bronzed chest), the china is the tan of the walls, as is the handsome menu, as is the linen, as is the carpeting. Prints on olive mats hang within gilded frames. The room is softly illuminated by old-fashioned opaline chandeliers. It seems a desecration to wear bright clothing to the place, or to raise your voice.

There is little meat on the menu, also not much fish. Substantial first courses, thick soups, pasta dishes and vegetable dishes, salads and simple desserts are what the menu is all about.

You may begin, for example, with Lingua Tonnata—four slices of cool tongue, covering most of the surface of a good-size platter, the tongue hidden under an ample spread of a salty tuna fish-mayonnaise which is studded with pickled capers. This is a lovely cool dish, more so with cold white wine. As this restaurant is very good about serving one dish at a time, the platter of food at the center of the table, empty plates to each diner, you may follow this cold first course by the hot one called Cavolo Pacco, a delicately seasoned mixture of ground meat and rice that is wrapped in tender leaves of cabbage and served in a light lemon sauce. Your bottle of cold white wine will serve you well.

There are soups and there are soups, which is to say that there are minor soups, served before a main course, and major soups, that is, main-course soups, like Brodetto di Porto, a bouillabaisse-type thing, complete with a red broth that is heavily flavored with saffron, in which are cooked scallops and sea bass, shrimps and sole, clams and halibut. If there is anything left of that cold white wine, it is perfectly appropriate with this spicy mélange.

By this time you have drunk all of the white wine, and you switch to something heavier, Chianti, for instance, or a Barolo, either of which are just right with Cappelleti al Forno—discs of pasta stuffed with ground meat, folded to the shape of little crescents, and baked in cream and cheese. Cream and Italian cheese, as you can imagine, make a thick and pungent sauce, very nice on the firm little cappelleti. That wine is equally appropriate with Tagliatelle alla Bolognese—myriad strands of a very eggy noodle, cooked *al dente,* and served in a dark sauce of tomatoes and ground meat. And Tito's is also right in there with Spaghettini con Pesto—thin spaghetti in the anti-red (green) sauce made with fresh basil, plenty of garlic and strong grated cheese. The thin strands are firm, and the viscous sauce is heavily scented, powerfully flavored.

There are vegetable dishes, including perfectly simmered asparagus, firm and crisp, drenched in butter and cheese; unfortunately, the asparagus is not peeled, and some of that crispness borders on the fibrous, particularly in the thicker spears. The string beans (Fagiolini alla Pomodoro) are a bit overcooked, but they are fine with this simple tomato sauce.

For something cool before dessert, you would do well to try the Insalata di Sedani, which consists of lengths of raw celery and lightly browned mushrooms and a splendid mayonnaise made on the premises.

Most of the desserts are centered around fruit—fruits in Marsala wine, fruit and cheese, strawberries in cold zabaglione.

LATTER-DAY BOHEMIAS

Greenwich Village, New York's haven for starving artists, starving idealists, and starving hangers-on, has for years now harbored no more of the city's educated poor than its statistically proper share. The Village has become, in fact, a fashionable middle-class, and, most important, high-rent district. As you would predict, the creatives formed new communities nearby. As no one expected, these neighborhoods seem to be going straight in no time at all. And the professional downtrodden, determined to stay that way, plod on in the search for permanent slums. As the Village begat the East Village and SoHo (so named because it is *So*uth of *Ho*uston Street), these have an offspring of their own, called NoHo (you figure it out). Naturally, in New York, where there are people there are restaurants.

★ BERRY'S

180 Spring Street (at Thompson Street)
LUNCH AND DINNER.
Closed Monday.
Reservations, 226–4394.
No credit cards.
Inexpensive.

A lithe young man in jeans and a skin-tight navy-blue T-shirt brings you a few chocolate-brown bagels on a plate, twenty bread sticks in a beer mug, a dish of semisoft (semiwarm) butter, and a leather-bound wine list. It is in the nature of SoHo restaurants (and perhaps in the nature of SoHo itself) that the only Bohemianism practiced is comfortable Bohemianism and that the only conformity studiously eschewed is conformity that constricts. Art makers of the seventies are not masochists, they do not take moral positions that end up as frostbite. Well, the rest of us have been that way for a long time. The trappings are here in this new sleek saloon, but the absence of ceremony is itself ceremony, the civvies on the help as *de rigueur* as an uptown tux.

Berry's is a small place with a big bar. Through the dim light, rendered misty by a haze of tobacco smoke, and undisturbed by the old-style, four-blade ceiling fans hanging from stamped tin, you glimpse an intricate, colorful wallpaper, carved mirrors, old prints, chalked menus on brown slates; through the restrained din you catch an eclectic juke box—the plinkings of ragtime, the wisdom of Billie Holiday, John Denver. What it has to do with this tailored denim, these meerschaums hanging under thick handlebars, these berets perched on Afros, or these Afros perched on pink-cheeked soubrettes, no one knows for sure, but it looks very much like the young art world and its hangers-on loving itself to distraction. The rest of the world is invited to come on down and love it, too.

There is food, but what goes on between courses is much better.

He: "I'm losing you to Ron. I can just feel it. And it's crazy, because I have everything he has."

She: "It's not true. You're not mentally ill."

Well, perhaps the food is better.

To begin, you may make the right choice or the wrong choice. There is no other choice. The wrong choice is the salad. Dressed yesteryear, it is limp and sodden if you get there much after sundown, which is a pity because the fresh greens are comingled with circlets of shallots, and the dressing would be fine on crisp lettuce. But the so-called Relish Tray—a plate of crisp celery stalks, carrot spears and green-pepper collars, all adorned with long-cured Italian olives and served with a dollop of a thick cheese-and-cream sauce which has been laced with chives—tastes as if it was cut up for you the second before it was served.

There are three or four main courses listed any given day. The descriptions suggest much, the preparations are ambitious and not invariably successful, but the ingredients are fresh, and the food you get is good to eat. A chicken in wine sauce is a whole breast of chicken that has been braised in butter and wine. This cannot hurt chicken, and if you love chicken, you will appreciate this—the meat arrives awash in the liquid, surrounded by boiled spinach and unexceptionable rice. There is an even more ambitious striped-bass dish in which an effort has been made to duplicate a Dugléré, in which the fish is steamed with wine, tomatoes and onions. Usually the cooking liquid is then made into a thickened sauce, but here it arrives thin. The bass, however, is huge, it is fresh, and it has been cooked to just the right point. And if you want the flavor of a Dugléré, pile your fork with a bit of the bass, some of the tomato and a few strands of the sweet onions, and consume them as a trio.

These places will get cute. Banana Spice Cake we understand, but what are they telling you when they say it is "with Penuche Icing"? So at least they should tell the waitresses, who, not having been told, tentatively venture something like "It *looks* like brown sugar." Whatever it is, it's a great cake, just a couple of clove and cinnamon strides beyond bananas and sugar, moist and redolent of the ripe fruit. The Creamy French Apple Pie is a mound of spiced cooked apples, bits of crust here and there, moistened in a sauce of heavy cream and sugar—very nice.

★★ EAST-WEST COOKERY

105 East 9th Street
DINNER.
Closed Sunday.
Reservations, 730–9082.
No credit cards.
No liquor.
Inexpensive.

Natural food, health food, organic food. Who is not put off by the antiseptic phrases? Yet this stuff need not taste like undoctored shredded wheat. Set aside for the moment the fact that the terms are vague at best, meaningless most likely, that they suggest plain food, unsauced food, intact food, unbleached and nonchemicalized food, berries and nuts, salads of weeds and stews of tubers—in short, medical repasts; and call to mind for the same moment your knowledge that things take on identities only when they are given names: had the pizza parlors leaped onto the health-food bandwagon at the beginning (whole-grain crust, vine-ripened tomato sauce, certified-milk cheese), we would associate lithe bodies and clear eyes with the red-and-white pies. But no particular kind of food has monopolized the fad, and though there is a pretty consistent tendency in the movement to eschew red blood, there are natural-food restaurants in New York where you can get steaks and chops with your seaweed. Perhaps because Japanese food, as perceived by Americans, has a Spartan quality, it is a natural for the sound-body freaks, and this restaurant serves up its health à la Japanese, with a preponderance of tempura on the menu. Tempura, of course, is deep-fried food, usually shrimp, fish, vegetables. Wasn't fried food once the antithesis of health food?

East-West Cookery is a low-luxury but comfortable little place, perfectly suited to its youthful clientele. They come in their sandals, jeans, long flower-print skirts, sleeveless tops, splendiferous hair; they park themselves on the ledge under the hanging plants at the front window to wait patiently for one of the little tables, even more patiently for one of the burlap-upholstered booths along the side. The walls are of raw redwood clapboard, the slat ceiling is vaguely Japanese, there are white paper place mats on the red-clothed tables. Your hostess is birdlike and cheerful, she knows "just how you feel" if you give up your turn to opt to wait longer in hopes of getting one of the commodious booths.

This is a bring-your-own-wine or- beer establishment, but the innocents drink mostly tea (no charge for tea) or tap water (no charge for tap water) or spring water from the water cooler, just like the one in your office (10 cents for spring water) or mineral water (the Perrier is 65 cents).

The food is rather elegantly made; it has, it cannot be denied, freshness, purity, life; you eat it with chopsticks (the little Japanese ones that come joined and wrapped) unless you want to advertise yourself as an alien.

There is a charge for bread, 40 cents, a dime more if you have it with miso spread (soybean paste). Pay the charges. The bread is extraordinarily assertive in its vibrant scent and flavor of wheat, and the miso, warm and oily, is the perfect succulent foil to the dry bread.

Begin with shrimp tempura. The shrimps (several) seem to be fresh, as are the broccoli, carrots and green peppers, and they are all very artfully battered and rapidly deep-fried in very hot and, it must be, frequently changed oil. The ingredients of the dish are just barely cooked, and the batter is crisp and airy, all in all the equal or superior of the same dish in Japanese restaurants that are actually run by Japanese. Move on to a soup of the day, which, when it is split-pea and zucchini soup, is a substantial bowl of thick pea soup, rather heavy, relieved by chunks of moist zucchini —a nice idea.

In line with the "East-West" theme, there is a dish called Scallops Champignon, the Orientalism of which is in the dish itself, the Westernism in the title. This is a gigantic stew of scallops (the big ones from the ocean, not the little ones from the bay), mushrooms and other vegetables, in a briny broth. The food lacks character, but the excellence of the ingredients and the straightforward preparation yield a pretty satisfying plate. Better is the broiled fish—immaculately fresh bluefish, for example, broiled in butter and flavored with rosemary; flaky and moist, the rich fish retains its robust character, and the browned skin, crisp and buttery, is like a built-in sharp seasoning. As a garnish to whatever you eat, there is (are you ready?) seaweed du jour.

Domestic desserts, displayed on a counter just below the window at the back of the room, through which you may observe the activity in the bustling kitchen. The banana cake consists of a dark, moist, banana-flavored cake, a banana-flavored icing and chunks of banana-flavored bananas. Excellent. Good pies, and pretty good apple strudel, with crisp apples and lots of cinnamon, wrapped in a flaky pastry.

★ LADY ASTOR'S

430 Lafayette Street (near Astor Place)
LUNCH AND DINNER.
Reservations, 228–7888.
No credit cards.
Expensive.

Like parti-colored clowns in a cathedral are these SoHo Bohemians and off-Broadway theatrical types in the men's-club solemnity of these plush, spacious halls. Lady Astor's sports pretty girls and pretty boys, dreamy onlookers and slumming voyeurs. When things are busy the bowling alley–length bar, which runs along one side of the main dining room, looks like the rear view of a multiple-edition mummers' last supper.

It is unfortunate that some of the loving care that went into the selection of appointments for this grandiose conception was not set aside for the appointment of dining room and kitchen staff—the former are amateurish and without pretension, the latter merely amateurish.

Lady Astor's is situated in a grim old commercial neighborhood. At night one is confronted on these streets by the huge bleak façades, behind which by day light industry industriously throbs. But in recent years Off- and Off-Off-Broadway have established beachheads, the so-called East Village is only a couple of blocks off, SoHo and the real Village are not much farther; these are the cultures that are the culture on which a handful of new restaurants down here feed.

The small, dimly lit yellow canopy barely calls attention to the place. Up a few steps and through unpretentious apartment house–vestibule doors into the grandeur that was your grandfather's rarely used musty library and study. The dark maroon walls are illuminated by crystal chandeliers and graced by great and ornately framed mirrors. Dark-green linen on the tables, dark-green leather and brass nailheads on the comfortable armchairs, deep carpeting across the vast floor. Through it traipse the waiters, waitresses and busboys, trancelike, as though just released from solitary to be pressed into this service, barely awake to the world around them; behind it sounds the background music—late Beethoven quartets followed by the Benny Goodman Quintet followed by Billie Holiday.

From the international selection of first courses you choose a seviche of scallops, in which the "cooking" of the scallops is accomplished by marinating them in lime juice, bits of red and green peppers, a modicum of Tabasco or another hot liquid pepper, and parsley and chives. The scallops retain their strong oceanic flavor, and what might be an excess of richness in raw scallops is offset by the sharp flavors of the spices and herbs. Nuggets of calf's brain, cool and in a good vinaigrette, make up an equally rich appetizer—the house sprinkles them with fresh parsley and you squeeze on the lemon juice. There is a livery pâté, well fatted, and studded with pistachio nuts—it would probably be terrific if it weren't refrigerated right up to the time you order it. A handful of hot appetizers, including a Greek feta cheese and spinach pie—the filo pastry is oily and flaky, and its contents, strong cheese and fresh spinach, are pungent, almost loud. Unless you ask for a postponement, you will be served a green salad with your first course—the Boston lettuce is unspotted and crisp, and the dressing, made with lemon and fortified with grated cheese, is tart and fresh-tasting.

The main courses are more ambitious and not invariably successful. Lady Astor's has discovered the "tenderloin of chicken," and they sauté these small sections of the chicken in butter and flame them in brandy. To sauté the breast of chicken is an exacting proposition—you must cut off the cooking at the moment the meat has become cooked, just before it begins to dry out. With only that objective in mind, the house is to be praised. Moreover, the dish is good to eat, the lightly brandied lengths of chicken served on a mound of buttery rice that is, rather startlingly, sweetened with an admixture of white raisins, warm and juicy. Sweetbreads are prepared in a pretentious way—they are braised, the braising liquid is thickened with foie gras and flavored with bits of truffle, and the meat is served in a pool of the sauce, amid chunks of pastry crust (pâté brisée), with which you soak up the remainder of the thick polished sauce.

Everyone is offering steak au poivre these days. This one is studded with abundant black pepper before it is broiled and served in a creamy and brandied pan sauce. The peppering must be done well in advance, for you discover that the treatment has implanted a potent pepper flavor to the unsuspecting beef. The sauce is creamy and strong, but the meat itself is not first rate—a little tough and not particularly tasty. Something styled "Calf's liver à la Bordelaise" comes in a nice winy sauce, but you cannot be certain you will not receive the most sinewy slices of the liver.

Naturally there is chocolate mousse, and here it is served in a large stemmed wineglass. It is loaded with concentrated chocolate flavor, it is so thick it is almost sticky, and if you are really flying, you can have yours with a huge dollop of whipped cream. There is an equally solid cheese cake, American style in that it is made with cream cheese and strongly flavored with lemon, Italian in that it is soaking wet—good stuff. Eschew the fresh-fruit desserts, because they are frigid, almost frozen.

★★ OH-HO-SO

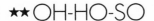

395 West Broadway (near Spring Street)
LUNCH AND DINNER.
Reservations, 966–6110.
Credit cards: AE.
Medium-priced.

But that the kitchen produces some terrific Cantonese food, Oh-Ho-So is most of the things New Yorkers have come to think of as what a Chinese restaurant is not. Where, please, just to begin at the beginning, is your big, bold and brassy Chinese menu, complete, as we have come to expect, with endless lists of available dishes, rendered in both ornamental Chinese characters and garbled English. And what of these surroundings? How are the skeptics to be persuaded that Oh-Ho-So is in fact a Chinese restaurant, when not a gilded ornament catches the eye, not a gewgawed chandelier, nary a square inch of pink Formica, nor a swatch of gold-flecked hanging cloth (parted to reveal a mural of bamboo forest or a wallpaper of cavorting dragons)?

You are about to leave, of course, having obviously come to the wrong place, when an alert Oriental in platform wedgies and illustrated stockings sprints up to you, smiling prettily, and with delicate fingers caressing your flaccid bicep, coaxes you back into what looks like Penn Station—the *old* Penn Station, the one with the lofty ceiling you could see on a clear day; for this Sino-SoHo renovation is in the South of Houston mold, sure enough, but on a Kennedy Airport scale.

Oh-Ho-So is a lofty carving out of old commercial-loft space. You enter a dim, roomy saloon, a long bar cutting through it diagonally, behind which a lengthy mirror, from shoulder-height to ceiling, tilted into the room at the top, reflects the scene: a polished hardwood floor, small tables randomly distributed thereon, brick walls that reach up to a complex of rafters. The house and the customers provide the sound—the management installed the juke box, the customers insert the quarters—and you get gentle strumming of soft rock against the hard-edged quarters. The cleanest Bohemians of our day lounge on bar stools and loll contentedly at table, beside their imported beers. There is not an unwashed hair in the crowd. You spot Hell's Angel tops over Ali Baba pantaloons, velvet suits and velvet shoes, sunglasses with a blue lens and a red one, glimpses of denim foundation garment, denim umbrellas, denim denims. All squeaky clean.

You proceed through that cool, carefully staged theater of casual chic to the capacious dining room, dozens of vintage wooden tables, row after row of refurbished oak surrounded by a hundred sizes and shapes of straight-backed chairs; at the back of the room, a second level, a mezzanine, with more rows; all in this giant box of earth-colored walls under a dark, electric-blue ceiling of conduits and pipes, from which, on long cords, hang the simple shaded lamps that cast islands of light on many of the tables.

The Orientals who greet may be the only ones you will meet, for this is one out of perhaps one Chinese restaurant in town where you are waited on by locals, in this instance youngsters of just-out-of-college age. But not just any such—these, as befits SoHoers, are the avant-garde, and this is the first place in town in which *unprinted* T-shirts have been sported. Also in style is a bit of surreptitious munching while they bus tables, and intersexual flirting (*this* is the avant-garde?) among the working boys and girls before the fashionably late 9:30-on diners and revelers arrive, flashing the snazzy duds that are the signs of freedom from constraint among the topsy-turvy dissenters of our day. But do not, because of these signs, hold in suspicion the merchandise dispensed at Oh-Ho-So. For one thing, you will from time to time encounter Chinese family parties within these walls, so the place passes New York's traditional test of Chinese authenticity; and for another, the ardent young waiters and waitresses inform you, when you try to pin them down for more information about the food than is provided by the menu, that the sources of additional info are the chaps in the kitchen, and they, you learn, merely gesture and giggle when addressed in English, so recent is their arrival from old Hong Kong. Chicky, the immigration cops!

For no reason at all, the printed menu appears on circular pieces of paper affixed to paper plates. For good reason, to the left of each listed dish there is a number, for it is by numbers that the dining room staff communicates the patrons' orders to the kitchen. You may begin by ordering *1. Oh-Ho-So Spare Ribs (the asterisk next to this and other dishes denotes "First time served in New York"), and you conclude that this is precedent by presence of a very subtle ingredient, for these seem to be your standard ribs, moist, slightly crisped, in a barely present sweet and syrupy sauce. Much more interesting is *3. Oh-Ho-So Barbecue Pork, which consists of sturdy chunks of meat and sections of green pepper impaled on a skewer, and served in a pool of a meaty broth that is principally soy sauce, beside a garnish (a peculiarity of the place) of lettuce and tomato. This is not a subtle dish; it is strong and satisfying, the meat well-salted and spiced, the peppers oiled and, here and there, blackened.

You move forward to what the menu mysteriously calls "Entries," and after viewing the parade to the post, you decide to risk $5.50 on number 12, Coconut Chicken, and your choice, though out of the money (finishing fourth behind Braised Flounder, Crazy Drunk Chicken, and Rice Noodles"), performs creditably enough and could be a winner in cheaper company. Coconut Chicken is coconut candy made out of chicken, the large cross-sectional slabs of bird little more than carriers for the sweet coconut sauce. Everything seems to be just as it is meant to be—the meat of the chicken moist and tender, the sauce smooth and polished—but this is a dish you would have to grow up with to want twice. On the other hand, *13. Crazy Drunk Chicken appeals even if first encountered late in life. It is a many-flavored, many-textured scramble, like innumerable Cantonese dishes, and like the best of them it has individuality despite the range of its ingredients. The singularity of this dish stems from its abundance of peanuts. Unlike many Chinese peanut dishes, as they are served in New York, the nuts in this have neither the taste nor texture of the thirst-making things you find in converted ashtrays on New York bars. These peanuts are cooked *into* the stew until they have the soft flaky texture of moist chickpeas, and it is the breakdown of the peanuts that thickens the Chinese-wine–flavored sauce in which there are, in addition to the chunks of chicken and peanuts, Chinese cabbage and parsley, that mysterious mushroom called cloud ears, and occasional stimulating strands of fresh ginger.

Because *27. Baked Stuffed Crab Shells is listed under "Sea Food," you leap, without looking, to the conclusion that the crab shells are stuffed with seafood. *Au contraire.* The dish is simply a meaty method of not wasting the shells of hard-shelled crabs after the crab meat has been used in something else. The five shells per order are stuffed with a spicy forcemeat of pork and herbs, they are moistened with an almost black sauce that has a concentrated and briny flavor of strong fish, and they are sprinkled with an abundance of sharp chopped scallions and fragrant Chinese parsley. This is a far-out dish by domestic standards, principally because the flavors of fish and meat are so closely juxtaposed.

You will be relieved to learn that under the heading "Sea Food" there are actually a number of seafood dishes, though in the nomenclature of some of these there are other puzzlements. For example, *29. Braised Flounder is not braised, though it is a splendidly prepared flounder. The fault here probably is with the expert brought in to provide the English equivalents—he may know English, he may know cooking, but not both. In any event, what you get shortly after ordering this dish is a browned, crisped and fish-shaped item spread on a platter. The biggest mistake you can make is to permit your young server to bone it for you, unless you are happy to let 25 percent of it go to the cat in the kitchen. Filleters they are not yet. Within the apparently deep-fried shell there is a tender and perfectly fresh flounder, garnishing it strands of strong ginger and sprigs of Chinese parsley.

The fish tanks in the dining room are not merely decorative, the carp swimming within are doomed according to your order. There is an unnumbered item on the menu, indicated by the suggestion "Try our live fish . . ." Be not afraid, it is dead when you get it, and you can have it killed either by deep-frying or by steaming. Either way, this is a very bony fish, served with nothing but clumps of the very strong fresh ginger it was prepared with. This is simple, elegant food, the steamed version rather spare, the fried one providing a bit of crust next to the tender meat of the fish.

Under the brief listing of "Rice & Noodles" there is mentioned a cold dish of Rice Noodles w. Bean Sprout in Wine. This is a copious serving of cool, inch-wide, cloudy-white strands of rice noodle, slippery in their slightly sweetened oil, accented with sesame seeds and crisp bean sprouts.

The menu announces, "We have desserts." They haven't, unless you accept canned lichees and such as such.

★ 162 SPRING STREET RESTAURANT

401 West Broadway (at Spring Street)
LUNCH AND DINNER.
Reservations, 431–7637.
No credit cards.
Medium-priced.

You get into a cab and you remain in the lean-forward position after instructing the driver to take you to the corner of Spring Street and West Broadway, because you assume that he has heard of Broadway, but not West Broadway, and that he has never heard of Spring Street. But if your driver is young and bearded, he may turn and ask, eagerly, "Are you going to the *Spring Street Bar?*" (the place is known as the Spring Street Bar), and you will have begun to discover that this out-of-the-way SoHo tavern is to the SoHo community what your local OTB office is to your local horse degenerates —not only a hangout, but where the action is.

To call it the Max's Kansas City of a decade later is glib and false. Studiously groovy ambience and all, this place is a real restaurant, serious about the wine and food it serves, if not invariably successful with it; and the best meal you got at Max's cannot compare with an average one here.

You enter into an oddly laid out barroom, through which the gleaming bar cuts a diagonal line. Lots of people hang around, glass in hand, talking or looking for someone to talk to. The rest of the establishment is dark-brown: two dining rooms, one with brick walls, one with dark-brown painted walls; strings of the world's dimmest spotlights offer a pale glow from the distant ceiling; the tables are dark-brown; the china is dark-brown. The dining rooms fill late, and they become noisy and cheerful. The prices are high, and the customers can afford them; no starving artists; everyone is clean; SoHo's struggle was brief (it is now a middle-class neighborhood), and the struggle is now out of style.

The former strugglers often begin with the Quiche Lorraine—a pretty terrific, very cheesy pie on a dark crust with chunks of dark ham throughout. On other occasions they enjoy their new-found prosperity with ratatouille (hot or cold)—an oily, wet, heavily garlicked soup of sautéed vegetables, including oily slices of green pepper, strands of sweet onion, and chunks of tomato. Continuing to enjoy themselves, on their next visit they learn about saucisson with potato salad—the loud sausage wrapped in a pastry and sliced thin; the cool, crisp potatoes mixed with strong, freshly chopped raw onions and fresh parsley. Then they discover that this prosperity thing isn't all roses, because the snails here are, atypically, inadequately seasoned, though they are nice and buttery.

The regular *nouveaux* have learned about the pork chops and skip them; the trichinosis scare is at work, so the chops are pre-cooked and then re-cooked, and they arrive dried-out and fibrous. Sensibly, they order the roast leg of lamb—many, many slices of pink lamb arrayed on a large platter, the meat well flavored with garlic and moistened with good gravy. Eminently American roast chicken, with a moist, peppery stuffing that will remind you of Thanksgiving. Something called John's Lemon Steak is a dissonance of beef, lemon juice, dried thyme and dried oregano. The meat is good to begin with, and it is cooked carefully, but the concoction is artless; dried herbs are always a poor excuse for fresh ones, and no dish that calls for herbs in abundance should be made with them.

Nice vegetables: Tomato Provençale—tomato halves under oil-soaked bread crumbs, with garlic and parsley, browned and hot; sometimes cauliflower under browned, melted cheese, nice and salty; often scalloped potatoes, layer on layer of thinly sliced potatoes, thoroughly greased with the melted fat of the bacon that is part of the dish.

Puzzling salads: A huge $3 bowl of watercress sprinkled with lemon juice (you can't get half a bowl for $1.50, or even $2), and half the watercress is yellow and shriveled, and there are lemon seeds hidden among the greens! (Nothing more bitter than an unexpectedly chewed lemon seed.) Your free-with-the-price-of-the-entrée salad ordinaire, on the other hand, is made with good Boston lettuce and a few slices of tomato, all in a good vinaigrette.

The waiters and waitresses here are nothing if not opinionated, and less if not outspoken. "How's the fruit salad?" "It *can* be boring." "The pecan pie?" "Doesn't make it." You are given a strong recommendation for "David Eyres Pancake, for two —30 minutes to order $4.00."—a deep, pot-shaped popover filled with stewed apples (flavored with lemon and cinnamon), and about a pint of perfect, airy whipped cream. Can't miss. If you don't want to wait, the fruit tarts are warm, made with fresh fruit and served in warm fruit syrup. Good chocolate cake with dark-brown icing.

If you get a table near a West Broadway window, you have a beautiful view of the Goldman Pressing Machine Corp. at No. 402 and the Hoffman Boiler Co. at No. 400. When the Hoffmans and Goldmans have gone home, there is not a domestic car at the curbs. Getting here by cab is easy, but finding one in this neighborhood late at night is a little tougher.

★ RAOUL'S

180 Prince Street (near Sullivan Street)
LUNCH AND DINNER.
Reservations, 966–3518.
Credit cards: AE, MC.
Medium-priced.

You are wandering up and down Prince Street, looking for a restaurant. No restaurant. You enter a neighborhood saloon, in search of a telephone, to call for instructions about how to get to the recommended Raoul's. There you are. *You are in Raoul's.* Can you believe it? The place with the red-and-blue neon Ballantine Beer signs in the two front windows is Raoul's. Even if you walked right up to the storefront and pressed your nose against the window right under the Ballantine three rings, so that you face, as seen from inside, is bathed in a gaudy glow, you might still not know that this is Raoul's. Yes, now you notice, the name is painted on the windows, but one's sight does not pick the dim letters out under the gleaming neon.

Raoul's subtitles itself "The Bistro de SoHo." One might quarrel with "The," but not with "Bistro," for this is the Platonic Bistro à l'Américaine, a "small, unpretentious tavern or café," as the dictionary has "bistro," in the local manner, complete with elbow-worn bar along one side of the front room, opposite it such unlikelies as a hoary Frigidaire (the one that did away with the blocks of ice) and a rack bearing a roll of butcher paper (from which waiters tear off lengths of tablecloth), not to mention an ancient upright with eighty-eight black or yellow keys. The serving and eating, however, are done in the back room, where you will find not only the stamped-tin ceiling which stamps the premises as genuine, but even stamped-tin walls! (Sorry, the floor is of asphalt tiles.) The upholstered settees that form the booths are of two-toned plastic, and they are a little lumpy, what with these springs struggling to break through and attack the seated. Pipes of long-forgotten purpose wander along the ceilings; here and there pathetic, *fin-de-siècle* electric fans jut out from the walls, at the ready, should the leaning air-conditioning machine finally fall over. Murky paintings, prints and travel posters are hung with such seemingly random placement that one automatically suspects wall deformities behind them. A few plants and the kinds of overblown table lamps your grandmother had in the old place in Brooklyn complete the wreckage. You can't see the radio (which seems to play always), but you assume it has one of those bands of orange light with a center shadow which narrows as you sharpen the tuning. A house dog (shepherd) and cat (black) wander about.

You are approached by a muscular youth in a printed T-shirt who addresses you in a husky whisper and stands on one foot, then the other. Hurry up and order some of the pâté so that he can fetch it for you, with some good bread and a scrape of sweet butter which seems to have been gouged out of a vat with a wooden spatula. You notice for the first time the helter-skelter of the assorted china patterns, and you also notice that the substantial slab of pâté is not only enough to eat, but also moist, heavily herbed, abundantly fatty without being excessively so; moreover, it is served with those crisp *cornichons* (tiny pickles) that have the anise-flavored sparkle which attests to their having arrived in these parts in French jars. On various tables around the room, pâté eaters are having their pâté with various kinds of mustard. One of the mustards is Pommery—see if you can get that one.

There is usually a navarin listed on the blackboard menu, and it is made here in a coarse and satisfying version, composed of chunks of strong, muttony lamb in a thick and heavily seasoned gravy, with carrots and celery added well along in the stewing, so that they retain their flavors and crispness, and slivers of mushroom, added right near the end, so that they are still a bit crisp and faintly woodsy. You can also get brains in black butter, the tender and extremely rich innards delicately browned, served moistened by the black sauce of butter and vinegar and ornamented by a copious sprinkling of sour capers—solid stuff. Something listed as Poulet à la Moutarde is, surprisingly, hardly à la Moutarde at all; but the well-browned and moist bird has the clear, sweet flavor of never-frozen chicken, in itself a reward for your money, and the dark sauce traces back to a sturdy stock, mustard or no. If it is your habit to pass up all "amondine" dishes, because they are almost invariably made with canned almond slivers which have lost most of their almond flavor and impart little to the dish, your judgment is to be praised. But, though the almonds in the Filet de Bass Amondine are just what you expect, the fish is so perfectly fresh that the foolish nut-crust can be ignored—a squeezing on of lemon adds zest to the perfectly broiled and flaky fish. Such garnishes as zucchini in a slightly thickened tomato sauce seem to be held in large quantities in a steam table—they add nothing to your meal. And the hugh salad you get as a built-in course of your dinner is of iceberg lettuce, and none of the head is wasted.

There is a selection of cheeses, and your eye or nose should be able to help you to select those that are fresh from those which have been refrigerated a few times—when the cheese tray is brought to you, the cheeses are at room temperature. Pretty good cakes, including a Gâteau aux Pecans—a moist nut-flavored cake under a mocha icing and a sprinkling of pecans.

There are eminently drinkable wines available for less than $6!

Neighborhood Restaurants

These restaurants are integral parts of their communities. They draw much of their trade from within walking distance. The food they serve often reflects the national origin of the neighborhood people. These places are mostly small and moderately priced; one or two are humble. Many of the customers are regulars, they chat with the owner and the staff and with other customers. For many, these dining rooms are second homes. People read newspapers, sometimes even when they are not alone.

The enemies of the neighborhood restaurant are the restaurant freak and the mass publications that cater to him. You can't blame the individual freak, but when a restaurant's business quadruples overnight because some widely published clown with a typewriter liked its meatballs, the meatballs and everything that went with them are compromised as the owner of the favored spot demonstrates that he has, in the face of the windfall, retained his humanity— that is, he raises the prices and devises shortcuts in the kitchen.

Many of these places may appeal to you. But go only when you happen to be in the neighborhood.

★★ ANGELO'S

146 Mulberry Street (near Grand Street)
LUNCH AND DINNER.
Closed Monday.
Reservations, WO 6–1277.
Credit cards: AE, DC, MC.
Medium-priced.

Just inside the door is a hatcheck facility, the simple appearance of which is no clue to the turmoil that can develop around it. We have here an aisle, three feet wide, formed by the door and the wall opposite. Mounted on the wall are coat hooks—six feet of them, about fifty in all. About fifteen inches from the wall (we are still in the three-foot aisle) there is a Formica counter, long as the row of hooks, and six inches deep. The condition between the counter and the wall, when the coat hooks are all in use, is one of not enough space for anything more, certainly not for the plump young thing whose post is, technically, between the counter and the coats. (Conditions on the other side of the counter are equally dense when customers arrive in groups of more than two normal or one stout. And as customers not only arrive here but also leave, the scene is frequently one of direct confrontation, unalleviated by right-of-way guidelines.) What happens, of course, is that the attendant must contort herself wickedly to hang or retrieve a coat. As she stretches, her short sweater rises above her skirt, revealing a band of well-filled skin. This attracts the attention of the waiter at the front table, whose customers, in a moment, find themselves giving their order to empty air because the waiter has stuck his pencil behind his ear, to free his right hand to caress the revealed skin as he shares a whispered country thought with the harried soubrette. When things ease up she comes out from behind her counter and parks on a chair near the door—here she scratches herself a lot (perhaps she is allergic to coats) and pretends to read the *News*. The natty host (he constantly buttons and unbuttons his velvet jacket) keeps her company with suggestions about what they might undertake after work. She levels a look of transcendent boredom, then giggles and turns a page.

Farther inside is a restaurant. It is a comfortable if overdecorated place. There are three rooms, back to back, and a kitchen that is visible from the street through a steamy window. The front room is red-flocked; the second one is done in crazed mirrors and illuminated, framed beachscapes; and the back room is dóminated by a hazy mural, the central feature of which is a mosque—it's hard to figure. The food is good, the service serviceable, and the price tolerable. The customers are expansive and well-fed.

Before you get to the pasta and main courses you may want to have something light —the Angelo Special Antipasto di Mare (served for two people at $4). It is light stuff, but you get a heavy amount of it—a foot-long platter of squid, conch, shrimp, scallops and celery cut into small pieces, dressed in garlicky oil and a little lemon, and sprinkled with coarsely chopped fresh parsley. The ingredients are fresh-tasting and the dish is stimulating, but you can't be sure that the conch will not be leathery—but for this occasional flaw, the salad is a wonderful and stimulating first course. If you don't wish to take a chance on tough conch, or if you want hot food right from the start, the hot first courses include Eggplant Provenzana (thoroughly sautéed eggplant, browned, soft and oily, in a tomato sauce flavored with garlic and herbs); there are also stuffed mushrooms—they are fresh, and the stuffing of bread crumbs, oil and chopped red peppers is tasty without overpowering the mushrooms; as part of the Home Made Hot Antipasto you also get a couple of whole bell peppers, sautéed in oil until there are little black spots here and there, which add a strong accent to the hot, limp and oily vegetable.

This place has something of a reputation for its linguine with clam sauce. It is served here with the clams still in their shells, the pasta dressed with oil and plenty of garlic. Theoretically this should be a wonderful dish—as the clams are steamed separately from the preparation of the sauce, they can be tender; and because they arrive still housed in and attached to their shells, you know they are fresh. But despite the advantages, the clams are sometimes tough, which makes the whole dish an absurdity. The linguine, however, is good and not overcooked, and the garlic has not been browned, so it has the strong flavor of the barely adulterated genuine article. There are also some quite eggy homemade noodles here, served in a variety of sauces, including a frankly southern mushroom sauce—a thick tomato sauce, very spicy, combined with plenty of sautéed fresh mushrooms. (About 90 percent of New York's Italian restaurants now call themselves "northern," no matter what kind of Italian food they serve —it's the fad. In Little Italy that fashion would be suicide, as the population down here, after lifetimes of powerful sauces, is largely unable to detect the flavor in anything that lacks garlic and/or hot red pepper.) For a noodle made with potatoes instead of flour, the Gnocchi di Casa alla Napoletana are pleasantly gummy and amorphous little morsels—the sauce is, of course, strong and red, with sautéed onions, and over the whole dish there is a layer of melted cheese. Hard to beat.

The Veal Pizzaiola is served in a hearty sauce that is made with lots of red peppers and oregano and mushrooms; but you can't be certain of getting tender veal in the scaloppine dishes. The fish, on the other hand, is reliable—fresh, moist and flaky—and the Bass Livornese, in its sauce of capers, olives, onions, tomatoes and, you guessed it, garlic, is a good choice if you have already had a couple of courses, because there is room for a light fish where a heavy meat will not fit. If you are not having that problem, then try the Calves' Brains Arreganata—the brains are white, rich, tender, lightly breaded and browned, and they are served with a sauce that includes *whole cloves* of garlic and an abundance of oregano.

Some of the vegetable dishes at Angelo's are well above average, and in the city-wide deep-fried-zucchini contest, the crisp and moist zucchini you get here maintains a respectable position. For an item you will not encounter all over town, try the Escarole alla Monachina—the strong green leafy vegetable is sautéed in oil with garlic, black olives, pine nuts, strong and salty anchovies, and sweet black raisins. The result is an amazingly well balanced dish, despite the unbelievable diversity of its elements.

The pastries come from Ferrara, of course, so if you have been to Ferrara, you know that the cheese cake is a compromise—the menu refers to it as Torta di Ricotta, and sure enough, there is a little ricotta cheese in it, but mostly cream cheese. The cake is fairly moist, studded with candied fruit and flavored slightly with lemon. The rum cake is a rum-moistened sponge cake with whipped cream on top—a meaningless item.

This is a spotty restaurant with a mixed clientele: families, with children; hirsute East Villagers on a spree; the gay; SoHo artists and hangers-on. It is just for a few hours, so they all get along.

★★ BENITO'S

174½ Mulberry Street (near Broome Street)
LUNCH AND DINNER.
Closed Sunday.
No reservations (226–9007).
No credit cards.
Beer and wine.
Inexpensive.

Tiny, as brightly lit as an operating room and as garish as a five-and-dime, Benito's is an uncompromisingly Sicilian restaurant, the brash assertiveness of the food matched by the blunt service, all appropriately set in this adult nursery of a restaurant. The toys include a tiny Swiss clock, strands of plastic onions, a small sign reading "SMILE, God loves you." Dusky still lifes of expired fish and a sunny oil of a South Italian coast block out portions of the yellow wallpaper. Under the golden curtains at the front window, little baskets of fresh fruit are on display, and through the interior window at the back of the restaurant (through which the prepared food is passed to the waiter), Mrs. Benito kisses some of the arriving guests. There is a homey white refrigerator at the rear, in which both red and white wines are stored, along with the beer and 7-Up. Near it are displayed some of the appetizers of the day. The tables are fairly small, but yours can be made more commodious if you stash your giant red Alitalia plastic ashtray under your chair. The formally attired, erect waiter is assisted by a slouching youth in civvies. One senses that the little enterprise is rather closely supervised by the morose-looking, hatted gentleman in the kitchen who is busy at the stoves—he says little, leaves the public relations to the missus, and all runs smoothly. There is no gnashing of operational gears when a group of twelve surprises the restaurant, takes up a third of the tables, and requests a dozen orders of Veal Rollatine—by and by, out come the little packages, on a giant metal platter, and the happily gluttonous and casually dressed stouts (who seem to make up 90 percent of the clientele) fall on their food.

Come on Friday, when there is an unlisted appetizer of cold seafood salad—crisp shrimp; soft purple-and-white lengths of octopus; chunks of chewy conch; celery; and crushed garlic, fresh and loud; all in an oily dressing. Come virtually any day, when there is an unlisted appetizer of caponata, in one of New York's best versions of this variable dish. Caponata is a spicy and oily amalgam of peppers, olives and capers, sometimes reduced virtually to a homogenous paste, which is OK if you like it that way, and sometimes barely married, which is how it is served here—huge slices of red and green peppers, lightly sautéed and crisp; coarse black olives; plump sour capers; and garlic; all in a thick oil that is brown with spices.

Hot appetizers too: the ready-and-waiting Sautéed Eggplant is part of the appetizer display, and when you order the Eggplant Parmigiana, which is absent from the printed listing and almost always available, a portion is covered with cheese and tomato sauce and stuck in the oven—what reaches your table is pully of freshly melted cheese, moist with a tart tomato sauce, and succulent of oily eggplant, all freshly browned and steamy. One item the menu does mention is the stuffed artichoke, and presumably for that reason, it is not always on hand; if it is, try it. The stuffing is a singular mixture of croutons, almost leathery little black olives, and capers, oiled and spiced; the vegetable is packed with this mixture and heated—on occasion insufficiently, so that the heart of the artichoke may not be as hot as the oily stuffing, which is a pity. Suggest that it be left in the oven for sufficient time.

Spaghetti Meitro di Otel is a big four bucks, which is a lot of money for a plate of pasta in so otherwise unpretentious a place. But this is a special sauce, the waiter informs you, and you would do well to drop the extra dollar on this selection if you want noodles. The spaghetti itself is cooked to order, and it arrives firm and slightly chewy; the sauce is an elegant blend of tomato, its tartness softened with an admixture of cream, fresh mushrooms, bits of ham, slivery sautéed onions and lots of parsley— it is at once mellifluous and slightly biting. Several ranks lower down are the Home Made Gnocchi—Potatoes Piemonte Style. It is doubtful that Piedmont or any other region of Italy will leap to claim this dish—the little dumplings are rather leaden, and the sauce is as gross as it is bright-red, strong and wet and sour, seemingly the right foil for the heavy shell-shaped knobs of potato, but somehow it just doesn't work.

Nowhere on Fifty-sixth Street will you get better Chicken Scarpariello than you get for a modest $3.25 at Benito's. The chunks of chicken on the bone are sautéed until the skin is crisp to the point of being noisy, and not only is the chicken thoroughly imbued with the flavor of fresh garlic and amply sprinkled with herbs, but the meat itself is utterly moist, almost as if it were steamed, rather than browned in hot oil. The Veal Rollatine is unusual in that it is breaded—the stuffing of ham and soft cheese is the usual thing, but the outer crust adds a note of frank coarseness to a dish that often fails to be either delicate or strong. The veal is surrounded by sautéed fresh mushrooms, and these and the veal are moistened by a sauce that is fragrant of bay and Italian parsley. Many, many sausages the size of a large man's small finger are the feature in Sausage, Mushrooms and Peppers; secondary roles are played by fresh red peppers and green peppers and equally fresh mushrooms. The sausages are rich and fatty and heavily seasoned with fennel, the red peppers are sweet and the green ones strong, and the tomato sauce that graces them all is livened up with the marvelous, heady flavor of fresh basil.

Your waiter makes a speech in explanation of the fact that as Benito's is a small restaurant, they cannot stock many desserts. He explains that the usual cheese cake and rum cake are eschewed in favor of cannoli, because cannoli are Sicilian, and, he adds, the cannoli you are about to eat are made in the true Sicilian style. There seems to be something to what the man says, because the custard that is packed into the crusty pastry tubes is not the usual cloying thing—it is thick and rich, but in an artfully airy way which gives it a texture that is far more pleasant than the sugared Hellmann's mayonnaise that is often passed for custard in Italian pastries; it is studded with candied fruit and laced with anisette, and they help too—the thick espresso served here is indispensable if you are determined to consume an entire tube. For something with less staying power there is a good zabaglione—very frothy, warm, with just the right amount of Marsala.

The choice of wines is limited and dreary—the Sicilian wine on hand is sugared and watery; the Bardolino and Valpolicella are the usual things; there is beer in cans.

★★ CAFÉ EUROPA/LA BRIOCHE

347 East 54th Street
LUNCH, MONDAY TO FRIDAY; DINNER, MONDAY TO SATURDAY.
Closed Sunday.
Reservations, 755–0160.
Credit cards: AE, BA, CB, DC, MC.
Medium-priced.

This is one of the simplest and most straightforward neighborhood restaurants in New York. It is also reasonably priced. The present site is its third since the restaurant first opened as Peter's Café Europa more than a decade ago. The present expanded name reflects an expansion of the menu by an additional menu of large, stew-filled brioches which are good value for some imaginative food.

There is a quasi garden wherein it never rains—a small room in the back which, with its skylight, glass wall, floor of simulated red tiles, and plants, feels very much like a garden. The main dining area, with space for about twenty tables, has the dim, soothing atmosphere of a cool, deeply shaded house in some hot part of the world. The walls are of bare plaster, overlaid here and there with stripped cabinetry, tapestries and cracked oil paintings. The illumination is from a couple of pewter chandeliers with dim lanterns, and from candles on each table. Oriental rugs fail to absorb the shock of the heavy-footed; the wooden floor is creaky, and when a customer or waiter goes by, you may feel it through your chair.

Mussels Marinière are the always-available appetizer, and they are well made—in a buttery broth of wine, seasonings, abundant fresh parsley and, adding an unusual tang, minced scallions. The alternate first course varies from week to week, and it is rarely a humdrum item: on occasion there is something the house refers to as Shrimp Castillo—a little hot sandwich of minced shrimp, flavored with spices and lemon, between two slices of well-browned French toast; at times a very decent ham-and-asparagus quiche. The invariable soup is gazpacho. This dish has too often been called a liquid salad, but the version made here really merits the description. It consists of very finely minced vegetables—tomatoes, celery, cucumber, onions, etc.—in their own juices, with very little oil, no thickening of bread and hardly any garlic, all very fresh, refreshing, nourishing and thinning, but it should be listed as V-8 Maison. Among the alternate soups one is likely to prefer are a mulligatawny that is sometimes available cold, sometimes hot, sometimes both ways; but hot is best because the soup is a thick, curried, puréed vegetable made with a chicken base, and curry when it is cold is a little queer. There is also, on occasion, a cucumber soup (sometimes hot, sometimes cold) which is very thick and has a strong flavoring of dill.

Broiled lamb chops, it would seem, should not be tampered with. Get some good chops and broil them, but not too long. The result, as everyone knows, is a simple, perfect dish, and anyone who can't consume sixteen baby ribs at a sitting is a sissy. Well, you don't get sixteen ribs here, and they are tampered with, but in such a way that the simple dish is actually improved. The chops are marinated in soy sauce, sake and ginger before they are broiled. The marination lasts only long enough to flavor the outside of the meat, and the subsequent broiling creates a brilliantly flavored crust—the lamb on the three-rib chops is excellent, but even better are the highly flavored bits and pieces one finds when the nearly denuded bones are finally picked up and nibbled at. Amazingly, the chops are served with *fresh peas.*

The Duck à l'Orange here, as in almost every restaurant, has a sauce that is too candied; its sweetness is not as exaggerated as in some places, but it is a bit excessive. The bird is perfectly roasted, however; the sauce is served in a separate dish, and using just a little helps. There is also Chicken Kiev (yes, the butter spurts out when you cut into it), and Beef Wellington (no, it is not overcooked).

Then there is this matter of the brioches. Each one is the size of a cantaloupe. The conical top is pulled out of the brioche, the center is hollowed and filled with the stew of your choice, and the plug replaced. Among the available fillings is an excellent Chicken Basquaise—chicken cooked in wine, with strong ham and green peppers. There is also a good Veal Marengo, made with fresh sautéed mushrooms, onions, celery and tomatoes; a spicy Curried Beef (with nuts, fruits and chutney); Crab Gumbo; and something named Shrimp & Mushroom Polonaise. In all of these the flavors of the ingredients are preserved, and the combinations are well balanced. You will get more brioche than gravy with which to moisten it—spread the remainder with butter and eat it that way.

The salad is nothing special. Among the desserts, there are several good reasons to pass up the chocolate mousse. It must be on the menu because it sells well, and it is made with good, dark chocolate, but it is airless, like a pudding rather than a mousse.

Have, instead, the macédoine of fresh fruit—the apples are crisp, as if they were just cut; the strawberries are ripe and juicy; the blueberries are large and firm; the orange sections are seeded and sweet; there is no sugar added, and the fruit arrives in the juice that comes of cutting it up—very pure, though a little bloodless. Better still are the crêpes, in a sauce of wine, lemon and sugar. Best of all are the bananas au rhum—bananas baked soft in a custard—very sweet, with just a suggestion of the edgy flavor of cooked milk, and a strong flavor of dark rum.

Some of the waiters here are a little goofy, though they seem to mean well. One kicks a chair in retaliation for having bumped into it. Another describes tarragon chicken as celery chicken—it is a new special, and by the end of the week he has it right. They wear long-sleeved shirts, four-in-hands, beige vests, and assorted sculptured head- and face-hair creations. All this, with their mixed casual postures, is reminiscent of an early scene in a forties comedy about draftees.

If every part of New York had a handful of sensibly priced neighborhood restaurants like this one, the supermarkets would be reduced to their natural commerce—dog food and soap.

★★FORLINI'S

93 Baxter Street (near Canal Street)
LUNCH AND DINNER.
Reservations, 349–6779.
Credit cards: AE, BA, DC, MC.
Medium-priced.

Forlini's has been here for almost twenty years. It was a seedy place at first, but almost immediately successful, and each year a portion of the profits is invested in improvements—one year the fake wood paneling, another year the nondescript murals, another time the color TV—so that the locals who drink beer and eat meatball sandwiches at the long, massive front-room bar will keep coming back. Forlini's is one of the best restaurants in Little Italy. The solid food is served by brusque but competent waiters to solidly built customers, their trailer-truck physiques maintained by habitual ingestion of the rather heavy stuff that is the stock in trade of this restaurant.

The first courses are not particularly interesting. There are the usual baked stuffed clams and mussels, and stuffed mushrooms (listed as a vegetable). The clams may on occasion be a little tough from being cooked too long, but the mushrooms are excellently sautéed, and their breading is herby and well seasoned. The broth here is strong and salty, almost briny, and it is a nice setting for the little tortellini you can have in it—these are stuffed ring-shaped pouches filled with ricotta cheese, farina and fresh parsley.

Good pasta, including an item listed as Linguini Clam Shrimp Crabmeat Fra Diavolo. And sure enough, the casual syntax notwithstanding, that is what it is—the linguine is *al dente,* each of the three kinds of seafood is present, each retains its own flavor, and the sauce Fra Diavolo is strong and heavily flavored with garlic. The lasagna is firm, stuffed with gooey, melted ricotta cheese and covered with a red, peppery meat sauce that is studded with discs of hot Italian sausage. For an extra half a dollar you can have it with extra sausage, by which is meant not a few more discs, but two substantial lengths of the strong stuff, which converts this dish into a complete dinner.

You will not find a better saltimbocca than the one you get here—tender white veal, strong red ham, melted cheese that seems to be Emmenthal, all served on a pile of fresh spinach that has been sautéed in oil with plenty of garlic. Every element is delicious, and it adds up to an extremely hearty dish. There is an item here called Diced Shell Steak—it consists of more steak than one normally eats, in chunks the size of children's blocks, sautéed with celery, mushrooms, green peppers and onions. The beef is tender, the vegetables are rendered very tasty by their sautéeing, and the strange dish can feed you and a friend and a small dog.

When it is in season, this restaurant serves Broccoli di Rapa, that tender wild broccoli which is pleasantly bitter—a little like a cross between broccoli and escarole. Forlini's variant in the deep-fried-zucchini competition is to start with thick cross-sectional slices of the vegetable instead of with strands; this makes it possible to brown the outside batter very thoroughly and still retain a moist, barely warmed interior. The little side order of salad is made up of chicory, onions, fresh Italian parsley and bits of tomato and green pepper, all in an oily dressing with a bit of garlic—very good.

Good cheese cake (very creamy and smooth, with graham-cracker crumbs on top), and zabaglione (very thick, intensely sweet and loaded with wine), and the usual ice cream desserts.

★ GROTTA AZZURRA

387 Broome Street (near Mulberry Street)
LUNCH AND DINNER.
Closed Monday.
No reservations (CA 6–9283).
No credit cards.
Beer and wine.
Medium-priced.

To love the Grotta Azzurra, as many do, you must suspend half a dozen common predispositions about comfort and courtesy. Except at off-hours, you must wait in line to get a table at this restaurant. If you're near the front of the line, you're one of perhaps eight people in a five-by-five vestibule just inside the front door—photographs of celebrities, plastic flowers, unspeakable writhing when, simultaneously, customers attempt to leave and those up next are summoned to the just-vacated table. Farther back in the queue, you wait on a marble stairway which descends to the aforementioned waiting room at an angle that is not quite sheer. You join with your neighbors in applauding the departing customers as they leave, bleary and contented, cigarettes hanging from their lips, each of them one obstacle less between food and you. At the very rear you're on the Broome Street sidewalk, under a plastic canopy—you regret not having brought a book; you discuss alternate restaurants within walking distance, and customers behind you tell you of the joys of Luna's, Forlini's, Angelo's; you try not to think about food. Once inside and seated, you ask a nearby waiter for a bottle of wine. He's not your waiter, so he just forgets about it. Five minutes later you ask another waiter, pointing out that you tried once before. He explains, with only a trace of contempt, that if you ask a waiter who is not your waiter, you can't expect to get what you ask for or anything else for that matter. You proceed to ask *him* ("your" waiter) for the bottle of wine, but it's sort of late, he yawns broadly while you ask, shudders, shakes off the sleeps and looks at you quizzically, so you ask again for, say, a bottle of Bardolino. On a good night he asks if you want it at room temperature or if you want it cold; on a bad night you just get it cold. On a good night you get Bardolino; on a bad night you get something else, already opened. On a good night the something else is Valpolicella, which is at least from the same country; on a bad night you get a bottle of something the label describes as "Claret wine" (from France), and, in fact, it is red, and it may have reached this country by way of France, but no more can be said for it.

The Grotta Azzurra is just a little hole in the ground that turned out to be a gold mine. It is small, low-ceilinged, garishly lighted, mirrored and muraled. There is sawdust on the tile floor. At the rear a handful of impassive, well-disciplined kitchen men are visible through a semicircular hole in the wall that is framed with copper pans. At the nearby register, Mama, under fifteen inches of copper hair, takes the cash. The boss, a couple of hundred very healthy pounds, barbershop-tanned, wanders around. He has grown into his diamond-studded ring so snugly that the stones barely peak out

—only the most bloodthirsty mugger will ever get it off him. His tailored suits fit him more lightly, and his silver ties match his hairline mustache.

Although forty million New Yorkers can be wrong, in this case they are not entirely. With all its grotesqueries, this manages to be a good restaurant, partly as a result of the undampable good spirits of the customers (for them d'Grotta, as they call it, is a wondrous treat), and partly because of the sturdy, highly flavored food. Here heavy-duty eating and drinking are the thing—the terribly audible conversations are mostly between courses or between the waiters and the customers. One waiter to a large party: "Oo wants cannoli?" (six hands); "Oo wants chisscake?" (eight hands); "Oo wants spumoni?" (a chorus of boos); "Oo wants coffee?" (fourteen hands). The figures check.

The Steamed Clams Italian Style (they don't come any other style) are served in a sauce you will hear much of here—thick tomato sauce studded with chunks of garlic. The clams themselves, however, are of three generations, and in a seafood restaurant the grandfathers would be reserved for clam chowder—here it is not on the menu. The stuffed pepper is a huge red vegetable sautéed in oil, stuffed with a loud combination of capers, eggplant, chopped meat and chunks of garlic, and served under the Universal Sauce. If you tire of the sauce, you might try the stuffed artichoke—the vegetable itself is overcooked, so that the ends of the leaves are rather mushy, but the bread stuffing is nice and oily and spicy, and the heart tastes pretty good when you dip chunks of it in the pool of oil and garlic the thing is served in.

Of course there is pasta, with the usual sauces. But for an unusual sauce there is mussel sauce—good oil, fresh mussels, a few sautéed fresh mushrooms, the unavoidable garlic, and a handful of fresh parsley, served over carefully cooked linguine. Or you can have your pasta Sicilian style, which means with eggplant, and here the eggplant is battered and deep-fried before it is combined with the tomato sauce, blanketed with cheese and baked; not bad, and the dish contains a lot of garlic.

You ask that your "Calves Liver, Sauté Garlic & Oil" be served rare. "Of course," Mr. Waiter says, not exactly in polite acquiescence, rather in tones of disbelief that such a thing need even be mentioned. When it arrives you find you have no fork. And the waiter is gone! Presently he reappears, his arms burdened with gleaming metal casserole dishes, huge china platters, bowls of pasta. All for some other table. But he approaches to within three inches of *your nose.* Why? Then you perceive that from among the solidly balanced pyramid of plates protrude the tines of a fork. He knew! You extract it, he proceeds to the big table, and you proceed to eat what is a good change from the usual Liver Veneziana—garlic instead of onions, and the liver is tender and tasty.

For something really solid, and for at least three people, there is Chicken, Steak and Sausage Contadino—a monster platter of sautéed chicken, strong sausages, chunks of beef (not your prime sirloin), red peppers, fresh mushrooms, and you guessed it, large pieces of garlic; to make the whole dinner "family style," you order Mixed Fried Vegetables—battered and deep-fried: zucchini (good, but not up to the best deep-fried zucchini in town—too much taste of batter, too little crispness of zucchini); mushrooms; fresh cauliflower (it, too, could be crisper); rice balls mixed with cheese; pieces of mozzarella cheese that are gooey and pully inside their crisp wrapper; and potato croquettes.

The famous cheese cake is nothing much. The cannoli are filled with a thick custard that is flavored with anise. The coffee is good and comes in a glass, spoon standing within.

Get out your low-cut, bare-midriff whatever, your dark glasses; make sure your hair is blue; a couple of over-the-shoulder pelts would be nice. His glasses should have half-inch-thick frames; his fingernails should be shiny. And wait in line. Before six-thirty and after ten you can usually get a table promptly. Frank Costello no longer comes here. When he did, he did not wait in line.

★ JOHN'S

302 East 12th Street
DINNER.
Closed Monday.
Reservations, GR 5–9531.
No credit cards.
Medium-priced.

After being in the hands of one family for more than half a century, this out-of-the-way place changed owners a few years ago. The new management is intent on maintaining the traditions of the old. To maintain the trappings is easy, and they have succeeded completely. To continue the quality of the food is not so easy, and, in fact, John's is not quite the restaurant it used to be, though it is still dependable. And if you are in search of unimpeachably decent food in this remote territory, you haven't much choice.

This is the grandfather of all the Italian restaurants that are illuminated by candles stuck into the necks of wine bottles. The rules of the game call for the formation of pyramids of wax around the bottles, and, sure enough, every table has its paraffin monument. There is even a monument to the monuments: in the back room there is a *clump* of monuments, on a table all its own, consisting of bewaxed bottles that have grown together. You might think that for oddness this would take the cake. Perhaps. But the aluminum-foil ceiling is a sharp contender. You don't get too many of those. If aluminum-foil ceilings make you nervous, don't worry—only the back room has one. The floor is of barbershop tiles, the walls are a vague gray, there seem to be paintings, draperies, and fans here and there. It is difficult to say, because that candlelight is virtually the only illumination in the place save for the cigarette machine.

Another tradition of old: it was the way of the former proprietor to seat himself at your table to discuss the menu with you; he probably had flat feet and rested more comfortably folded than erect-on-fallen-arches. At any rate, the new management *trains its waiters to sit* during the ceremony of the taking of the order. They are mostly young fellows (in shirt sleeves and clamped-on bow ties), and they will have some unlearning to do if they pursue their careers elsewhere in this line of work. Absurdities aside, the reception at this restaurant is friendly and straightforward, with no pretension. John's is the epitome of the comfortable neighborhood restaurant.

The cold appetizers are the usual things that make up cold antipastos in Italian restaurants, including some pretty good ham and melon, fresh clams, and such nourishing stuff as celery and olives. You are better off with some of the hot ones, including the Shrimp Marinara, which consists of carefully prepared shrimps that are crisp and fresh-tasting, served in a thick and sour red sauce that is abundant with garlic. This place also varies its stuffing to the stuffee, which is to say that what stuffs a pepper does not stuff an artichoke. As between those two, the former is better: two halves of a huge green pepper, sautéed in oil until there are black and leathery spots on the vegetable, filled with rice, slivers of ripe olives, and mushroom stems, and covered with the standard but good red sauce. The artichoke, on the other hand, is filled out with a heavily oiled mixture of bread crumbs and oregano—the flavor of the stuffing is not good enough to justify obscuring the flavor of the artichoke.

The pasta is served in perfect *al dente* condition, and the simple rendition of spaghetti with garlic, oil and anchovies is elemental and satisfying. The Baked Homemade Lasagna, a hefty stack of layers of pasta, meat, ricotta cheese and mozzarella cheese, intermingled with tomato sauce, is not your most elegant noodle dish, but eminently solid and convincing.

The Calamari in Casseruola is more interesting than pleasing. The squid itself is pretty good, which means it is firm without being tough, but the modification of red sauce that the calamari are served in really doesn't work. The sauce is heavily flavored with powdered *cloves,* believe it or not, which may well be some time-honored way of Italian squid, but to the unaccustomed palate it is merely odd.

Sausages are available a number of ways, and these are the kind which, odoriferous and crackling, used to be sold from wagons, the way hot dogs are now. If you liked them, you will like these. But more elegant meats are sometimes less well rendered here—the Bragiola, for example, is rolled beef around a stuffing; the meat is dried out, and the mostly-cheese stuffing is indifferent.

The vegetable garnishes are OK. The escarole sautéed with oil and garlic is crunchy and strong. The fresh mushrooms with garlic and oil are quite terrific—a huge oval platter of crisp mushrooms that are moist with oil, fragrant with parsley.

There is a pretty splendid house salad here, made up of a broad assortment of crisp vegetables—cucumbers, radishes, mushrooms, watercress, arugula, green and black olives—in a strongly vinegared dressing that is appropriate to this kind of mélange.

Good cheese cake, pebbly, liquored and moist, its blackened top sprinkled with sugar. Good rum cake, made up of two layers of sponge cake, a layer of preserves between, *real whipped cream* on top, the whole thing saturated with rum. Good zabaglione, made with enough Marsala wine to render the thing a deep shade of café au lait.

★★★ MON PARIS

111 East 29th Street
LUNCH, MONDAY TO FRIDAY; DINNER, MONDAY TO SATURDAY.
Closed Sunday.
Reservations, 683–4255.
Credit cards: AE.
Expensive.

Mon Paris goes on and on and improves. Nothing changes, except for the better. Mon Paris has progressed through stages. Once it was that little-known, relatively inexpensive, out-of-the-way-and-humble secret place—few customers in total, but all of them so given to the place that their repeated visits kept it packed, as if its popularity were city-wide. Then it made a bit of money, refurbished, hideously, its interior, received praise from the local press and guidebooks, and was, for a period, known, stylish. Finally its fashion passed, as its gaud tarnished, and Mon Paris is something of what it started as—a top-notch restaurant which, blessedly, lacks vogue; we must be thankful for our town's uglies, as it is the presence of inelegant patrons, their voices as noticeable as their duds, that assures the continued non-chic of this valuable establishment. One envies the customers' manifest contentment, and one contents one's self, as best as one can, with inner enjoyment, which is, unfortunately, wholly inappropriate to the food served here—its flavor is flagrant.

Mon Paris is a busy restaurant, but not as it once was. Only rarely are they standing two deep at the bar waiting for tables. And the cozy little booths, called "Ninon" and Suzon," are sometimes available just for the asking. Traditionally one has had to reserve them days in advance.

The menu has not changed. There is still the Terrine de Canard, a gamy amalgam of duck meat, fat, strong flavorings, including sweet spices, and bits of sharp pickle embedded here and there, the whole thing garnished with a potent beef-stock jelly. And the leeks rémoulade are as cool and tart as ever, buried in a generous dollop of the thick, mustard-based sauce. As always, the snails in this establishment, plump and powerfully flavored, are among the best in New York.

There are things one comes to know. One comes to know, for example, that the menu lists, in among the other soups, a "Potage du Jour," and that the listing is a deception, because no matter what *jour* it is, the *potage* is always lobster bisque. For years the *potage* varied with the *jour,* but when customers asked about the soup of the day, they rarely agreed to order some unless it was lobster-bisque day. Ergo, lobster bisque became the *potage* of *tous les jours.* You will be glad. This restaurant serves lots of lobsters, and the discarded shells are accumulated and used to strengthen the bisque, which has an overwhelmingly vibrant scent and flavor of the lobster shell, in addition to an abundance of meat and sherry, and a smooth and creamy texture. This is the best lobster bisque in town; it is surely one of the best cups of soup of any category, and it must not be passed up.

Good kidneys, styled as Les Rognons Sautés Bercy—the kidneys, in little chunks, are clean-tasting and crunchy, in a pungent sauce made of a heavily herbed stock. Le Filet de Boeuf Bordelaise consists of two substantial slices of beef (in this place the portions are never skimpy). The meat is artfully sautéed, so that it is lightly blackened and cooked to the desired doneness; and it is served in a thin, dark, brothlike sauce that is strong and winy, and with a dollop of tender marrow on each slice of the excellent beef. It is served with the little puffed potatoes for which the restaurant has something of a reputation—they are browned, airy pillows of potato, and if they do not automatically come with the dish you order, arrangements can be made.

After the hearty food served here, a salad of endive is appropriate. The endive arrives prettily, six sixths of an endive lined up on a plate, moistened just before serving with a pure, clear-tasting, oily dressing with a touch of mustard in it, and sprinkled with fresh parsley—the slightly bitter endive in the mellifluous dressing is very refreshing.

Nothing surprising in the way of desserts: sharp and fresh pineapple chunks awash in kirsch; a dark, heavy mousse of chocolate, topped with perfectly fresh whipped cream. It is not mentioned on the menu, but the man in the kitchen knows how to make dessert soufflés, and if you plan ahead, you can impress the customers at nearby tables by arranging to have a chocolate soufflé delivered to your table, with a touch of ceremony, as ordinary customers make do with pastries or custard.

The waiters have been here forever. They know the menu. They know many of the customers. They are always upon you, with their ladles and big pots, spooning out some more of the Lobster à l'Armoricaine or Le Poulet au Vin Rouge, always a pleasant surprise, as you get plenty on the first serving.

★★PATRISSY'S

98 Kenmare Street (near Mulberry Street)
LUNCH AND DINNER.
Reservations, CA 6–8509.
Credit cards: AE, BA, CB, DC, MC.
Medium-priced.

Patrissy's is not far from the old Police Headquarters building, and it was always a policemen's hangout. You still see a lot of men in hats. They wear them at the bar and when wandering about, though the chapeau *is* removed at table. A jacket not removed despite profuse perspiration over a Lobster Fra Diavolo suggests that your suspicions about the bulge under the left shoulder are sound. You are well-protected here.

The dining room has the look of the thirties, though the black and crimson overlays of paint and wallpaper, undertaken in more recent decades, add a men's-club note which is supported by the heavily framed paintings, mounted sailfish, scimitar over the doors to the kitchen, solid captain's chairs surrounding the linened tables, massive lobster tank near the passage to the bar. Among the waiters a pattern has been observed —the locals are gruff and brief; those from the old country will talk as long as you want. They all know the menu and their jobs. It's just that domestic courtesies, unlike the imported, are extended grudgingly. These domestics have not been domesticated; perhaps they are policemen *manqués*.

Patrissy's is principally a Neapolitan restaurant, which means that the Zuppa di Mussels (their Italian) is made by steaming in the presence of tomato in addition to the usual wine, garlic and herbs. Fresh mussels and a strong and briny sauce—good stuff. But for a restaurant of the southern persuasion, this Frutti di Mare is surprisingly mild—chunks of octopus, squid, shrimp and conch, plus black olives, in a lightly garlicked and oily dressing with lots of parsley—also good stuff.

Marinara sauce is a basic industry in restaurants of this sort, and Patrissy's version is nuggety. The soft part of the sauce is a thickness of vegetables, the more solid ingredients chunks of tomato, and less frequently encountered and pleasantly startling, chunks of garlic; the heady flavor of basil pervades. Whatever shape of pasta you have it on, the noodles are cooked to order and arrive properly *al dente*. The wide noodles here are not the commercial, dried variety, and the sauce Carbonara you can have with them is thick with cheese, accented with bacon, and livened with parsley.

Those lobsters are carefully prepared, and, happily, the Lobster Fra Diavolo is very much Lobster Marinara, with the same potent sauce you can have with pasta. The Striped Bass Livornese is of good fish, and you will even enjoy the sauce, though this version, with its millions of capers against mere hordes of olives and oodles of tomato, is a bit unbalanced.

More cloves of garlic in the Chicken Scarpariello, not to mention sections of crisped and oily chicken and sautéed fresh mushrooms. Garlic yet again in the Special Contadina Dish, a hectic assortment of charcoaled slivers of beef, joints of chicken and lengths of strong sausage mingled with fried potatoes, mushrooms and peppers, the whole mélange flavored with oregano—sturdy stuff. To accompany the miscellany with a medley, have the Mixed Fried Vegetables—in addition to the expected cauliflower and zucchini, fairly crisp within their crusts, you will find a deep-fried clump of spinach and a hot, crusted-over hard-boiled egg.

Wonderful cheese cake, thick and heavy, soaked in liquor that has sunk through the browned top, through the cheese, to the bottom, where it moistens the many bits of candied fruit. Little else of interest among the desserts.

If you do not specify, your red wine may arrive cold.

★ PAUL & JIMMY'S PLACE

54 Irving Place (near 17th Street)
LUNCH AND DINNER.
Reservations, OR 4–9463.
Credit cards: AE, BA, CB, DC, MC.
Medium-priced.

Paul & Jimmy's is a straightforward place—a rectangular room containing three rows of tables. The appointments are a trifle garish (wallpaper of red flocking on a silver ground, chairs painted gold, askew oils in the rosy hues of sunny Italy, and one odd wall of mirrors and varnished travel-poster collages), but none of it is jarring, and anyway, Paul & Jimmy's is not exactly a rendezvous for delicate social or business negotiations, but just an eating house at which it is virtually impossible to have a bad meal. The menu is long and interesting, and the prices are sensible. Only the wine and beer are ridiculously expensive.

You might well begin your dinner with the splendid stuffed mushrooms. The stuffing includes the usual bread crumbs, but also sautéed onions, minced red peppers, the chopped stems of the mushrooms and plenty of butter. The stuffed clams are also good —little clams, with flavored bread crumbs and oil, baked until brown, without toughening the clams. And the Shrimp Fra Diavolo, though not unusual in any way, are quite notable for the frank intensity of their flavoring—lots of garlic, oregano and hot red pepper.

The pasta portion of the menu is not particularly interesting reading (you have read it all before), but the pasta and sauces are carefully prepared, and there are a couple of specialties—notably Cannelloni Fiorentina and Lasagnette all' Alfredo which should be sought out in their obscure corner of the menu, away from the other pasta dishes. The cannelloni are stuffed with ground chicken, spinach, garlic and pine nuts, and are served under a very rich, creamy béchamel that is sprinkled with a thick layer of strong Parmesan cheese. The lasagnette are little noodles, tender but firm, served in the usual Alfredo sauce of butter, cream and cheese—good, but the whole idea of Alfredo is that it be outrageously rich, unspeakably creamy, and from that point of view this dish does not quite make it.

Lots of very good meat and fish dishes: Bass Livornese in a vibrant sauce of black and green olives, capers, tomato, the ever-present parsley, anchovies and chunks of garlic (you know, like half a clove on this forkful, half a clove on that). The fish is fresh and flaky, the garlic is thoroughly cooked, so it is not really overpowering, and the dish is so strongly flavored that it is as stimulating as it is satisfying, and splitting it as a first course is not a bad idea. If you don't like fish, not to worry. You can have Steak

Pizzaiola—in this dish even the garlic is cooked rare; the meat is good beef, covered with a sauce of tomatoes, fresh mushrooms and the garlic, and you get, as they say, enough. Something called "Chicken, home style" is sautéed chicken, made with lots of pepper, and served under layers of rich béchamel and mozzarella cheese—browned under the broiler. Such dishes as Veal Marsala are distinguishable from what you get in most Italian restaurants by a clear taste of Marsala wine in the buttery sauce, and by the tenderness of the pale veal. The sautéed escarole is made with a handful of the house garlic, and the deep-fried zucchini is tender, moist and crisp.

At Paul & Jimmy's you get salads that are of fresh greens, and cheeses that are imported from farther away than Brooklyn, which means provolone that is a little loud, flaky, faintly peppery, and more than you can eat.

As in nine Italian restaurants out of ten, you're assured that the pastry comes from a man who "used to work at Ferrara's." This may or may not be, but the pastries are pretty good, including a sfogliatelle, which is a rather dry cake studded with candied fruit, flavored with anisette and cardamom, and wrapped in dozens of layers of thin, crinkly pastry.

One is greeted here by a chap who seems displeased with his station in life. He does not stoop to provide a menu when he seats you, and is distinctly irritated when you ask him a question, as if he were a waiter or something. But once you get him out of the way, the service, by industrious and intelligent waiters, is excellent and friendly.

"Ah, you want some wine? Very good. My grandmother drinks half a bottle of wine every day, and she's ninety-two years old."

"She'd feel even better if she drank a whole bottle."

"I don't think so."

★★ LE TOURET

132 Lexington Avenue (near 29th Street)
LUNCH, MONDAY TO FRIDAY; DINNER, MONDAY TO SATURDAY.
Closed Sunday.
Reservations, 683–2089.
Credit cards: AE, BA, CB, DC, MC.
Very expensive.

Le Touret is a jewel-like restaurant with Tiffany prices. It belongs in the Fifties near Fifth Avenue, where the tariff would be competitive with the most pretentious French restaurants in New York, and the food with some quite competent ones, which, of course, would rob it of all distinction, as there are dozens of that kind. But here it is, in what is not quite Gramercy Park, surely not Murray Hill, along a semi-seedy stretch of Lexington Avenue, a fallen star—well, starlet.

When this place was far from brand new, a few years back, it had the kind of rough edges you expect during a start-up period of, say, a few months, but those have finally been ironed out, though it is difficult to determine whether the current smoothness of operation is the result of a slow learn or the natural fallout of sluggish commerce. True, Le Touret is kept pretty busy at lunchtime by the upper echelons of the lower–Madison Avenue insurance industry, but the dinner hour is slow. At an $18.75 prix fixe for dinner, with supplemental charges on many dishes, you can be sure that the local residents are not going to crowd the place; and if adventurers are going to travel for their dinner, why travel here? If, however, cost is not a consideration, and you like to try them all, Le Touret has its virtues—food that is good, occasionally exceptional; a few rarities on the menu; and an attractive room (sometimes close to deserted at dinner hour during the week, busier on weekends).

That room is small, mirrored, rimmed by a plush crimson banquette; little vases of fresh flowers adorn the tables. Almost everything in the place, from the polished bar at the front to the room at the back, seems reduced to slightly less than human scale. It is all, somehow, crystalline.

The food, however, is full-size, though from a short menu. A Gallantine de Canard Truffée is, despite its promising name, but a slightly overcooked and dried-out terrine of duck, too much of the fat baked away and much of the flavor of duck with it, but the slightly unfortunate dish is partially rescued by a garnish of glistening jelly, almost mahogany-colored—it is made of a potent stock. The house still produces a good salmon mousse, freshly made of fresh salmon, served with a green mayonnaise which is perhaps a bit cloying in its extreme richness and thickness, but of perfect flavor, and its cool and creamy quality is excellent with the slightly dry mousse, if it is used sparingly. A sharp slap on the wrist for a watercress soup served at dinner that seems to have been made for that day's lunch. Watercress soup, to be worth bothering about, should be consumed no more than a few minutes after the watercress is added to the base. That way the distinctive, lively flavor of the green is retained. To serve a soup of *cooked* watercress is to serve just another soup. The soup is thick and buttery, but it might as well be spinach soup or lettuce soup.

Now for the good news. Squab Périgourdine. A plump, moist little bird with a sauce that is smooth and polished—winy, sharp with the flavor of the bones that were simmered in the stock, fragrant with herbs. Underneath the sections of this here bird you will find a couple of chunks of toast, elegantly browned French bread, spread with a foie gras that is accented with a generous chunk of truffle. This is a dish which is rich but without a trace of excess, and the garnish of grainy, slightly dry wild rice is the perfect foil for the moist bird.

Tournedos Béarnaise. Perfect beef, perfectly grilled, with a sauce Béarnaise that is a bit thin but redolent of the mysterious, vaguely smoky flavor of fresh tarragon. The meat is served with cubes of sautéed potatoes, soft inside, crisp and lightly browned outside. Which just goes to show what meat-and-potatoes is all about.

Simple and brilliant desserts. Perfect berries covered with a Crème Chantilly (does not rhyme with Aunt Tilly) to which Grand Marnier has been added in just proportion. Perfectly poached pears in wine, the delicious syrup given an added zing with a dash of cognac.

At its best, worth the high price, and if you seek *haute cuisine* on lower Lex, you have no other choice.

★ VINCENT'S CLAM BAR

119 Mott Street (at Hester Street)
LUNCH AND DINNER.
No reservations (CA 6–8133).
No credit cards.
Inexpensive.

This institution offers one of the briefest menus and some of the freshest seafood (in a couple of the simplest of preparations) in all of New York.

Vincent's is a garish two-room restaurant/saloon in which the most tasteful element is the color TV. In the front room there is a bar, at which you drink, and a clam bar, at which you eat and drink. Behind the clam bar there are mounds of fresh seafood, battered, ready for the deep-frying that much of the hot food here gets. In the back room there are rows of Formica-topped tables, each adorned with containers of paper napkins. There are brick walls, tan plaster walls, a bright-red acoustical ceiling, yellow lanterns. A blue note is provided by the police. They parade in and out, having decided that Vincent's offers the finest men's room in Little Italy, which—as this place is sometimes very mistakenly taken for *Umberto's* Clam House, a few blocks away, where Joey Gallo got, as they say, his—may provide a feeling of security. The late-night customers are casual locals on dates, guys on the way home after the four-to-midnight shift, Greenwich Villagers who have learned that the fifteen-minute walk to this spot will provide them with better food of the kind than they can find anywhere in their own district. You can tell who's who: at the Villagers' tables there are bottles of wine; the four-to-midnight men drink beer; quarts of Pepsi are the hallmark of the neighborhood youth. You are served by gravel-voiced waiters in red vests—you have the impression that not long ago they were here drinking the Pepsi.

The menu lists littlenecks and oysters. The former are big for littlenecks, and the latter are available only in the "R" months, even though the pointless prohibition against oystering between May and August has been lifted—it seems that New Yorkers simply will not order oysters in what they consider the "off" season. Whichever you get, they are perfectly fresh and freshly opened, and the juice that remains in the half shell after you have eaten the meat is at once sweet and briny.

Then there is the hot food, all of it served with one of two sauces—medium-hot and hot. These are thick and red, indistinguishable one from the other except by the intensity of their spicing, and it is a common and accepted practice to order your food with medium-hot sauce with a plate of hot on the side, so that as your palate is numbed by the extremely hot "medium-hot" sauce, you may rouse it with a dose of the searingly hot "hot" sauce.

The sauces may be applied to deep-fried calamari—firm squid, ringlets and tufts of filament, lightly battered and crisped in hot olive oil. Like all the cooked food here, it is served with a slice of hard bread that has been dipped in water to moisten and soften it. Yes, it sounds terrible, but it is the perfect accompaniment to the unrelenting sauce and the fried fish. When soft-shell clams are in season, come here for them if you want them with a red sauce. The clams are sweet and crinkly, fried to the perfect point. There are also steamed mussels (plump and tender), steamed conch (soft, slightly rubbery, and vaguely gamy in an oceanic way), deep-fried shrimp. Everything is served in small orders or large orders, so it is possible to sample most of the menu on one visit.

No desserts.

Beyond Veal Parmigiana

There are hundreds, perhaps thousands, of Italian restaurants in New York. Most of them are terrible, but there are some that do more in their kitchens than break open pasta packages and tomato cans. Some of them *make their own* pasta. Some of them serve sauces that are *not red*—at least not all of them are red. (A handful offer Italian wines other than Chianti and Bardolino.) And a few that do stick to the southern and Neapolitan styles of cooking provide evidence that the food from these regions, though almost consistently red in color, need not be monotonous.

Unlike the general run of New York's decent French restaurants, which almost all look alike, there is usually a bit of idiosyncrasy if not fantasy to the look of the better Italian places—one is a posh grotto, another a millionaire's hunting lodge; this one a humble trattoria, that one a besilked and chandeliered palace hall, a third a rustic summer house.

The places to avoid (there are exceptions) are the ones with the red-and-white tablecloths, Chianti bottles with candles in them, and rotund Papa or Mama greeting you at the door. The table linen is chosen for its natural concealment of the stains of this cuisine; the paraffin illumination in discarded-bottle-bases is the cheapest atmosphere obtainable; and the girth of the staff is testimony to their jollity at the number of locals and visitors who take copiousness and color for good food.

★★ ALFREDO

240 Central Park South
LUNCH, MONDAY TO FRIDAY; DINNER, MONDAY TO SATURDAY.
Closed Sunday.
Reservations, 246–7050.
Credit cards: AE, DC, MC.
Expensive.

In this sanctum of convention—not tradition, *convention*—the movement for women's rights has apparently been heard of, and a little backlash (if so violent a word can be used to describe the reaction of so staid an establishment) has been engendered. Two perfectly civilized-looking women are seen arriving, with each other, and with the effrontery to be unassisted, in their search for sustenance, by so much as one man. They are led to a poky niche and seated at a bantam table, while a dozen commodious accommodations stand unused in the center of the room, where, if the need arose, they would be in a position to signal and be seen by a waiter or captain. Since they are not fully accustomed to their rights, they make the error of *explaining* their objections; but they know their rights, so they insist.

One of them: "We don't want this table. It's too far back."

Their host: "The food is the same."

The other of them: "It's right near the kitchen. There's too much traffic."

Their host: "Don't worry about the traffic. We don't seat anyone else back here."

Both of them: "Exactly!"

He considers that the growing dispute is more unseemly than the awful vision of unmanned women at table, and they are transferred.

Gold-on-gold wallpaper, golden draperies, mirrored pillars, fresh flowers, pale, starched lemon-yellow linen, carpeting, an interior portico leading to an ornate cocktail lounge—just what you think of when you think of Central Park South, except for the view of the park. The customers will not surprise you. They are prosperous and well-fed, bejeweled and besilked, cuff-linked and starched. Only the opera singers who frequent this place flash a little style.

Though tastelessly posh, the place is comfortable; the service is polished; and the portly tenors and sopranos have found that the food is eminently good enough to preserve their figures, and the short walk to Lincoln Center a painless gesture to the health of the lung.

To stretch the skin you might begin with Spiedino alla Romana—layers of bread and mozzarella cheese, fried to a nice brown exterior, in a sauce of wine, lemon juice, capers and anchovies. It is at once solid and stimulating, but when you think of this familiar dish, you think of anchovies; lots of people do not like anchovies, and there are only traces of the salty fish in this version. Pass up the Scampi alla Griglia—the menu provides the clue: "Broiled Jumbo Shrimps—Barbecue Sauce." Barbecue sauce? In an Italian restaurant? Sure enough, the three large shrimp are served in a plain tomato sauce that is barbecue-ized with Worcestershire and Italianized with oregano—an international error. The menu lists Cozze alla Posillipo, but if mussels are not available, or simply if you prefer, you may have Vongole (clams) instead. In either event, you get a good, briny tomato sauce, flavored with parsley and lots of red pepper, and the mollusks are fresh. The Zuppa Celestina is far from celestial, which does not mean that it is far from good—its goodness, however, is quite earthy, deriving, as it does, from a strong chicken broth in which there is plenty of chicken fat, and slices of a simple, breadlike, lightly browned omelette, made with lots of parsley.

Of course there is pasta, including a number of interesting preparations. Chicce alla Bergonzi, for example—a green pasta in the shape of short lengths of string bean, but with a very discernible flavor of spinach. The sauce is a creamy tomato mixture, with aggressive doses of black pepper and grated cheese. If that color scheme offends, there is Tortelli Fatti (fat tortellini, presumably)—little donut-shaped pasta dumplings filled with meat and cheese, flavored with rosemary and parsley (lots of it, the filling is quite green), sprinkled with cheese and browned. Both of these dishes are exceptional.

If you are a purist and don't wish to have your salad at what is sometimes called this point in time, betray your inside knowledge of the place by asking for some marinated zucchini to dawdle over. It is not listed on the menu, but it is usually available, and the captains suggest it to the people they feel like suggesting it to. It consists of very thin slices of zucchini, cut the long way, each slice the shape of a wide tongue depressor. This, however, you swallow, and *then* say "Ah." The vegetable is roasted with garlic until its edges are blackened, and is then marinated in oil; the flavors of the blackened skin and the garlic, the texture of crinkly seeds, and the smoothness of the oil combine into a singular dish.

If you are wild about brains, and under no other circumstances, try the Cervella Dorate. The dish consists of brains that have been deep-fried in an egg batter, and a couple of slices of lemon which you may squeeze on. The brains are perfectly cleaned and poached before they are put through the final preparation, and they are rich and oily—all very pure. The Steak Pizzaiola is good, though the sauce is milder than what goes by this name in restaurants that are frankly Neapolitan; the steak itself is of good beef, accurately grilled. There are several familiar veal dishes, and also one called Involtini alla Partenopea—thin veal slices rolled around a stuffing of bread crumbs, chives, parsley and oregano, served with a strong, winy mushroom sauce that is flavored with rosemary—a nice, solid dish. Suprema di Polla Veronica is a boned breast of chicken (one bone is left in, and the dish arrives with the bone standing up, as a decoration) served with a thick cream sauce and grapes. The whole thing is browned before the dish is served, and it is not bad. There are pretty good à la carte vegetables at $2 to $3. This restaurant is not above serving a salad, on occasion, that is of old greens.

Mostly simple desserts: an excellent caramel custard; a chocolate rum cake that manages to seem a little sinful despite the use, or at least the taste, of artificial rum; good zabaglione. The big dessert deal here is Sorpresa alla Colzani, a rum-and-pineapple creation that belongs in Trader Vic's, at the other corner of the park.

★★ APERITIVO

29 West 56th Street
LUNCH, MONDAY TO FRIDAY; DINNER, MONDAY TO SATURDAY.
Closed Sunday.
Reservations, 765–5155.
Credit cards: AE.
Expensive.

Of the more prestigious Italian restaurants in midtown Manhattan, Aperitivo is one of the least formal, and though it is popular, it is not inundated with business the way, say, San Marco and Giambelli are. So if you want to be in a right place and you also want to be comfortable, Aperitivo may be it.

On the other hand, the menu at Aperitivo is humdrum, and among the appetizers in particular, there is very little to choose. Of the nine antipasti listed (one of which consists of two of the others), one finds such delights as pimentos and anchovies (*not* roasted fresh peppers and anchovies, but canned pimentos and anchovies); Pâté Aperitivo, which, it develops, is from a French can; fresh fruit cup; and shrimp cocktail. So you are left with baked clams (tender little clams baked with bread crumbs, oregano, parsley, pepper and oil, to which you add lemon); and Shrimps Aperitivo, a refreshing cold salad of shrimp, celery and endive in Russian dressing.

Probably the most idiotic aspect of the menu has to do with what is translated and what is not. We are told, for example, that Prosciutto e Melone means "prosciutto & melon," but not what is meant by Rigatoni Amatriciana; similarly, we are informed that Coppa di Frutta Fresca means "fresh fruit cup," but we are left in the dark about Tagliatelle Aperitivo—on one occasion the genius who was taking the order defined "Aperitivo" as "the way we make it here."

So, though you may have to go to some trouble to find out that Linguine Marechiaro is linguine with white clam sauce, when you get it you will also find out that it is perfectly made, with very coarsely chopped fresh clams, garlic that is sautéed but not browned, and abundant parsley. And though you may understandably suspect that Cannelloni Aperitivo is a secret house invention, you'll find that it is a good version of the standard cannelloni recipe (stuffing of meat, spinach, cheese and oregano) in green instead of white pasta pillows. It is served under the equally standard béchamel sauce and grated Parmesan cheese, which is not to say the dish is bad—it is delicious —just that "Aperitivo" hardly means anything. There is also a good Spaghetti Carbonara served here, with crunchy bacon, Parmesan cheese grated into the pan while you watch the action, freshly ground black pepper (a moment later), and egg yolks and butter to make certain you don't go hungry.

This place has a deserved reputation for the quality of its veal. It is as white as breast of chicken, and extremely tender, which makes it perfect for a dish like Piccata de Vitello—veal in a limpid, lemony sauce. Oddly, for New York Italian restaurants, Aperitivo does a superb job with kidneys and with liver. The kidneys are perfectly rinsed of their acid taste, sautéed with onions and garlic, and a bit of sauce is created in the pan by the addition of lemon juice; Liver Veneziana is a simple dish of liver and onions sautéed in oil, but it is made here with excellent calf's liver that is sautéed very rapidly, so that it is browned but still tender.

At this point you order Key-West Lime Pie because it is the best lime pie in New York—brown, flaky crust; a chiffon that is powerfully flavored with fresh lime (and not made kelly-green with coloring); and two inches of the airiest whipped cream imaginable. A few deviates have tortoni, or spumoni, or zabaglione, or fresh fruit cup, or rum cake. No one knows why.

Glazed brick walls, wine bottles in straw baskets hanging thereon, a twelve-stool bar at the front, with pictures of movie stars, baseball stars and Vatican stars. The customers are a casual crowd, of whom the most formally dressed are the Catholic priests who often eat here.

★ BARBETTA

321 West 46th Street
LUNCH AND DINNER.
Closed Sunday.
Reservations, CI 6–9171.
Credit cards: AE, CB, DC.
Expensive.

At one time Barbetta was just one of New York's innumerable Italian restaurants, like the others in the simplicity of its interior, better than many by a degree of superiority in cuisine, and unlike most in a clientele that included writers and artists who were attracted by the fair prices, good food and relaxed ambience.

The enterprise was so successful that the proprietors were able to send their young daughter to what are known as the finest schools—Brearley, Bryn Mawr, and all that—from which she emerged tainted by worldliness, which, in turn, when she took over management of the restaurant, tainted it. Now it is not only one of the most elaborately appointed eating places in town but also one which attracts some of the most elaborately appointed customers: gents in tailored shantung, accompanied by hard-coiffed ladies at night; suited matrons for the pre-Wednesday matinée lunch/fashion show (on this day the place is a field of hats through which lissome lovelies wander, displaying the current wares of this or that shop or house).

Within, there is silk wallpaper, a bar of *green onyx,* a terrazzo floor, giant crystal chandeliers in the main room, arched windows with silk shades, large and well-spaced tables, and brocade upholstery on the comfortable chairs—all very splendid. Without, in the garden, there is a pool with statuary of spouting fish, cherubs astride; overhanging shade trees and smaller, decorative ones near the brick or stucco walls; inset arches, with roses here, a Roman goddess there.

The prices are what you would expect in such grand surroundings, though lunch offers some reasonable possibilities. The food is not invariably what you hope for. And the service is the kind of service that is sometimes called Italian: an almost unbelievably unctuous host who wears an expression of such focused seductiveness that the matinée ladies, when it is turned on them, seem to shudder; a Franco Corelli captain who gestures grandly with his arms simply to accompany a "Very good," as he betrays no annoyance at your selection of a French wine for your Italian dinner; businesslike waiters who divide people into two categories—those who are going to the theater and must be served at once, and those who are perfectly happy to sit around long enough to see the theatergoers return for dessert (you may, if you wish—house policy).

Lots of eel served here, including, at lunch, a delicious Eel Carpione—discs of breaded and fried eel, marinated in vinegar and seasonings, and served cold. The prosciutto and melon is excellent, but such items as "Grande Antipasto Piemontese—served from the wagons—$2.95," which is printed in red on the menu to indicate it is one of the "Specialties of Piemonte," is all in all one of the most misleading menu items in print. It is a disgrace consisting of Progresso caponata, a canned artichoke heart, a Portuguese sardine, and several items from several other packages, with the exception that the zucchini is probably boiled in the kitchen. Perhaps this mess is "served from the wagons" but the service takes place out of sight, and one's selection is made by one's waiter.

The Bagna Cauda here (also in red) consists of a plate of raw vegetables (plus a canned pimento) and a pot of hot oil-and-anchovy mix, over a candle. One dips the vegetable into the mix and eats. Very good.

The Fritto Misto is described as "a variety of fried meats and sweets," so you shouldn't be surprised when it consists mostly of vegetables and variety meats, largely sweetbreads, which is perhaps what is meant by "sweets" (self-starter etymology on 46th Street?). The mislabeling aside, it is delicious; the frying perfectly timed so that the different items—zucchini, mushrooms, liver, veal and sweetbreads—are all at their best.

Game in season. A so-called Venison Steak in Civet not long ago was tough and rather bland—a sautéed steak with an undistinguished deglazing sauce, and wild rice that was not only wild but raw.

The veal dishes are generally good, made with tender, white veal. There are such standards as veal Marsala—very sweet, lots of wine; and at lunch there is a really unusual and fabulous dish of raw Veal Steak Tartare alla Piemontese—a huge pancake of cross-hatched ground veal covered with lemon juice and olive oil, and served with a mound of sliced raw mushrooms, a smaller mound of minced fresh garlic and a pepper mill. There are many vegetables on the menu, including an outstanding asparagus—the stalks are peeled, poached just a little, sprinkled with butter and Parmesan cheese, and briefly broiled and browned. There are very good salads, and when they are available, a salad of arugula and raw mushrooms, moistened with a rather strong wine-vinegar-and-oil dressing, is really something.

The pasta dishes are very good, but at the dinner hour, cheapskates who want pasta as their main course must pay extra for their preference, which, when added to the cover charge (smallest typeface on the menu) can really put you in the position of paying something for nothing.

The desserts are not bad—the Zuppa Inglese is an ordinary sponge cake moistened with rum and covered with very fresh whipped cream. Many cooked fruits, including an orange served in a caramel sauce that has been thinned with orange juice, and garnished with strips of tart orange rind.

If the wine list says '64, you're just as likely to be brought a '66. But the French wines are mostly good bottles.

A wonderful restaurant in many ways, with a unique feel to it, but its occasional failings are cataclysmic.

★★ DELSOMMA

266 West 47th Street
LUNCH AND DINNER.
Closed Sunday.
Reservations, PL 7–9079.
Credit cards: AE, BA, CB, DC.
Medium-priced.

The brilliant neon sign is an incongruous beacon on this dingy block. This is an incongruous restaurant in this rundown neighborhood, something like Reverend Moon posters on abandoned buildings, or a forties Warner Bros. Technicolor musical in a Bowery movie house. But once you are inside, behind the hanging strands of huge beads that fill the front windows, you are not inside the Bowery movie house, but in the musical. Delsomma is a slickly appointed joint—solid shining bar in the dimly lit drinking section (lounge) off to one side (TV at the ready for major sports events), in which well-heeled and well-fed gents in snug suits drink and discuss deals while their ladies silently sport their duds and diamonds, and from whence their occasional boisterousness and the perpetual background music emanates. The dining room gleams—slick white plaster walls, walls of wine bottles, walnut-paneled walls; a gleaming patent-leather butterscotch-yellow banquette rims the room; the linened tables are large and well-spaced, fringes of dark-green cloth showing beneath the white; and under all, plush red carpeting. There are nautical notes: a sailfish leaping up one wall, nautical plaques, and at the center of the room (where the gleaming red espresso station forms an oasis of warmth in the frigid air conditioning), a model sailing ship in full red sail.

The nautical theme augurs a seafood emphasis—not in the written menu, which is burdened with the usual encyclopedic listings of pastas and veal dishes, but in the urgings of your host, a gravel-voiced toughie with an overlay of politesse, who suggests, "Read da menu fa fi' minutes. Den we talk." Meanwhile you sip some of the red wine you ordered ("We'll have a bottle of Chianti." "You want dat at room temperature?"), and enjoy the commodiousness of your well-placed huge table—with all his gruffness Mr. Gravel does not lead strangers to obscure corner tables when better ones are available, which is a good sign.

The secret of Delsomma (big secret) is that after you read da menu fa fi' minutes, you discard whatever decisions you may have arrived at in favor of Mr. G's recommendations. He advises, for example, that you pass over the listing of appetizers (good advice, for it eats as dully as it reads) and begin with Shrimps Fiorentina, an easy thing to do, as the dish consists of an even number of shrimps, six, which is divisible by either two or three. This quite superb delicacy consists of huge shrimps that have been battered and then sautéed in butter, wine, lemon and parsley. They are served in the delicious and well-seasoned sauce this preparation yields, the shrimps crunchy, their batter crusts soaked in the liquid, with plenty of additional sauce left over for improvement of the excellent bread.

Delsomma makes a good Lobster Fra Diavolo, but what is perhaps more important, you can get in on someone else's lobster, if one is in preparation, to have an unlisted spaghetti and lobster sauce. G will keep you informed. The pasta here is cooked when ordered, so it is never gummy, and the lobster sauce is a sparkling harmony of the flavors of clear, fresh lobster, hot-peppered tomatoes and good, strong garlic.

Old Grav will try to steer you toward more seafood, including some good striped bass or squid, but if you insist that you would like to return to land, he knows his way around the veal and chicken dishes, too. He suggests that you might be amused, whatever your deepest feelings, by Scallopine of Veal Pagliacci, an asymmetric sandwich of sautéed eggplant and sautéed veal between melted cheese and escarole—two stacks to an order, excellent for noncombative sharing. The veal is tender and white, the eggplant browned and soaked in the sautéeing oil, the cheese pleasantly gooey and loud, the escarole sharp and lightly metallic. A dish difficult to fault. On second thought, better get two orders.

The secret chicken is Chicken Arreganate, unlisted—chunks of moist chicken, on the bone, browned in oil, served in a dark and salty sauce that has been flavored with oregano. All the sauces are good here, and this is another one that will make you glad there is bread.

No cheese cake! Well, occasionally there is cheese cake. The rum cake is the usual excessive confection; the pastries are mediocre; the zabaglione is fine. Order the good espresso, and a bottle of anisette is placed on the table, with which you may improve the coffee and your disposition.

★★★ GAETANO

242 East 58th Street
DINNER.
Closed Sunday.
Reservations, PL 9–4660.
Credit cards: AE, BA, CB, DC, MC.
Medium-priced.

Gaetano serves a six-course dinner at a fixed price. You have no control over the first four items (appetizer, soup, pasta, salad) and none over the last one (dessert); these are invariable, from table to table, from Monday through Saturday. A choice is offered from among three main courses (usually one chicken dish, one of veal, and one of fish). Each week, after one day of rest, the menu is completely revised and the new one is then served for six days. This system would be unbearable in a restaurant that serves ordinary food, but at Gaetano everything is impeccably prepared, and most of it tastes good, too.

Gaetano is a comfortable spot, with dark-pink walls of rough plaster, a little barroom at the front, and a couple of smallish and low-ceilinged dining rooms to the back, their ceilings lowered still further by wall-to-wall, hanging wine bottles in dining room One, a trellis with artificial grapes and vines in Two. The place is dimly lit, the ample tables are spaced well apart, and the customers, casual and relaxed, are under the care of waiters and a captain whose efficient service varies from courteous to positively sweet. If anything, they are *too* efficient (you probably don't want your clams until you have finished your gin, and if after greedily chewing down every sliver of pasta you captured the remainder of the sauce on a few slices of hot garlic bread, you would probably appreciate a few minutes with your wine before the salad and chicken are delivered), but this pace can be adjusted if you inform someone at the start that the courses should not be brought until each one is asked for.

There is no predicting what you will get, but some of the things that have been got include, as first course, a fantastic Eggplant Parmigiana, made of eggplant that has been sautéed in olive oil until soft and dark, fresh mushrooms and slivers of crisp zucchini, all in a thick and herby tomato sauce, under strong melted cheese; and firm meatballs of chicken and veal, for some reason served in a scallop shell, in a winy sauce with lots of mushrooms. At this point you get soup—if it is onion soup, too bad, because it is merely decent onion soup, but if it is minestrone, three cheers, because it is a clear, strong and fragrant vegetable broth with bits of meat, celery, tomatoes, onions and lots of parsley therein. It's nice to eat half the bowl as is, and then, for a change, strengthen the rest with grated cheese.

The pastas here are almost invariably perfect: Conchiglie Alfredo—glistening shells, soft but firm, in a thick cheese sauce, with slivers of ham (the usual) and slivers of browned sweetbreads (a rich addition to an already creamy sauce); fusilli (spindles) in a remarkable garden sauce—about ten different vegetables, including leeks, radishes, onions, tomatoes, zucchini and eggplant, browned in olive oil and then combined with butter and a well-herbed consommé to make the amazingly fresh-tasting yet rich sauce.

Sometimes there is striped bass, in a garlicky marinara sauce, with a garnish of sautéed shrimp—the fish is fresh and moist, the shrimp crunchy. And sometimes there is boneless chicken inundated in a thick vegetable sauce that is something like a heavily garlicked ratatouille, with sautéed green peppers, tomatoes and onions. The chicken seems fresh, neither stringy nor pulpy; it is floured and browned before it is covered with the sauce. The Chicken Sorrentino that is occasionally offered is a bit heavier— the same chicken, baked under layers of sautéed eggplant, melted cheese and strong tomato sauce. This place starts with good veal—white and tender—and when they convert it to Veal Zinghera, they do so by covering it with a long-cooked meat sauce, laced with slices of egg white and black olives—substantial stuff.

Italian desserts are Italian desserts—usually heavy. If you hit a night when cannoli are it, you may as well appreciate that these are good cannoli—crisp, cylindrical pastries, with a cool and very thick custard inside, each end studded with nuggets of good, black chocolate—perfect, but rather leaden for most tastes. On luckier nights there are Fritelle de Ricotta—sweetened dumplings of cheese and bread crumbs, deep-fried and crisp, moistened with a crème Anglaise. The coffee comes in handsome crystal glasses that are rimmed with sugar and anisette.

Very little choice, it is true, but even with careful selection you cannot match the food you get here in more than a handful of New York's Italian restaurants.

★★ GIAMBELLI

238 Madison Avenue (near 37th Street)
LUNCH, MONDAY TO FRIDAY; DINNER, MONDAY TO SATURDAY.
Closed Sunday.
Reservations, 685–8727.
Credit cards: AE, BA, CB, DC, MC.
Expensive.

This is a rather garishly appointed restaurant. You enter by way of the well-trafficked bar; beyond it, down half a dozen steps, are two rooms into which are crammed an inordinate number of tables at night, and that many plus a few extras at lunchtime. (The lunch menu, by the way, is like the dinner menu, but with no appetizers of interest.) The illumination emanates from crystal discs flush against the ceiling, and there are prints and paintings along the walls which, unfortunately, have lights of their own. By day this is a businessmen's restaurant in which businessmen take businessmen to lunch. At night it is a businessmen's restaurant in which businessmen take business-women to dinner.

There are few dishes in any cuisine that consist of a fish sauce on meat. The cold Italian dish of Vitello Tonnato is probably the best-known, and the version served here is very hard to beat. It is made with tender, pale veal; and the tuna-fish sauce, flavored with anchovies and lemon, and rendered creamy by thoroughly blending it with olive oil and stock, is at once sparkling and rich. And if the blandness of veal is not what you are in the mood for, there is a completely different order of cold meat served here called Bresaola Valtellinese, which is a smoked, dried beef, served in thin slices over a large plate. You pour oil, squeeze lemon and grind pepper over the delicious and tender meat, and the prejudice you developed against dried beef in your army days will be wiped away; if there is a single good reason for coming to this restaurant, the dried beef, smoky and salty and only slightly gamy, is it. The list of first courses is long here, but the only others of real interest are the fried baby squid and the Mussels Riviera (in a delicious, garlicky broth).

Rice is a nice occasional alternative to pasta. But the risotto with mushrooms served here is a big comedown; compared with the version served at Mama Laura, it is an insult. And when you realize that they give it to you for $6.50, it's a triumph of materialism over mind that they ever sell any. On occasion the rice is not merely *al dente* but pebbly, and when that doesn't happen you find that the dish consists merely of coarse grained rice that has been boiled in an undistinguished chicken broth, and then combined with sautéed mushrooms.

The pasta dishes are generally better, including a good version of Spaghetti alla Matriciana, which is made here with the thinnest of spaghetti and a heavily parsleyed tomato sauce in which the onions are only lightly sautéed and still firm, and in which there is an abundance of tiny slices of good ham. Plenty of red pepper makes the sauce very lively. You can also get those little containers called tortellini, here filled with ground chicken and served either with meat sauce or with a creamy sauce which you complete with a heavy dose of grated cheese and fresh pepper.

Excellent brains are served here—they are carefully prepared by marinating and poaching so that they are rich and vaguely sour, and then dipped in flour and eggs and rapidly sautéed in hot butter. You can also get Veal Piccata, and so on, but as in lots of Italian restaurants, the veal scaloppine dishes are disappointing because the various sauces all start with the same beginnings, to which a little lemon is added for piccata, or a little Marsala for something else, or a few vegetables for yet another dish. Try, instead, the Veal Paillard, in which the veal is flavored with garlic and grilled very rapidly, so there is a pattern of lines on the outside of the veal that is almost black, while the inside is creamy white and tender—the garlic is delicate, but not lost. There is a chicken dish here called Pollo dei Castelli Romani which is made with fresh artichokes and mushrooms. There is a minor miracle in that the chicken actually takes on the flavor of the artichokes, but there is a major idiocy in that the slices of artichoke reach you with the choke and the inedible, hard portion of the leaves still attached.

The cheese cake is the real thing, made with ricotta instead of cream cheese, but it lacks moisture. The otherwise competent captains are not particularly careful about their zabaglione—they make it right there before your eyes, and they spoon it into your dish, and it is cold. Perhaps the best dessert here is the Banana Vesuvio, an adult sundae, made with ripe bananas that are sort of sautéed in simple syrup (to which Grand Marnier and brandy are added) and flamed. All that is then combined with vanilla ice cream. As a rule such concoctions do not add up, but this one does, and it can make you forget the sins of the recent past. At best, one of the better Italian restaurants in New York, but there is carelessness in the preparation of the food at almost any meal.

★★GIAMBELLI 50TH

46 East 50th Street
LUNCH AND DINNER.
Closed Sunday.
Reservations, MU 8–2760.
Credit cards: AE, BA, CB, DC, MC.
Expensive.

The bartender chews while he pours, laughs merrily, says "Wrong again" every time he gets the drinks mixed up, shakes his head and smiles with tolerant indulgence at his little faults, and tries again. Well, this is only the bar, you say, but on visits to this restaurant you almost invariably spend some time here because your table is not ready for your reservations. *Unless,* big unless, you are willing to sit *upstairs* (Coventry), where no one will see you, and you will see no one. *But,* big but, where the place is not populated to within a millimeter of the swinging door leading to the kitchen, and where there is service, not only when you trip up a waiter, but sometimes if you simply catch his eye. The service downstairs, which is simply terrible, suffers not from lack of help, but from lack of room for help. A few more people downstairs, and the traffic, which now has two speeds—slow and stop—would have one speed. Rule No. 1: Eat upstairs. Rule No. 2: Bring plenty of money.

Rule No. 3: Don't eat the Antipasti Variati. These so-called "Italian Hors d'Oeuvres" come from American, Portuguese, Spanish and Mexican cans, with a few items in domestic casing: a slice of ham, another of salami. Instead, have the Spiedino

Valdostana—a series of squares of ham, Fontina cheese, dough, ham, cheese, dough, etc., impaled on a skewer, fried and served under a strong sauce of tomatoes, peppers, capers and anchovies—an eminently Italian dish, strong, heavy and satisfying. Or have the Mussels Riviera—mussels steamed in their own liquid, oil, parsley, garlic, onions and tomatoes, and served on toasted Italian bread—tender mussels, and a delicious broth.

Or if you wish to start with a pasta, have the Trenette al Pesto. For "Trenette" read "Linguine," as it is simply the Genoese term for that particular shape of macaroni. And for "Pesto" read one of the best basil sauces in New York, made with garlic sautéed in oil, chopped fresh basil, a little cream, consommé, pine nuts and grated cheese, all warmed together with the pasta, lots of parsley added near the end. The captains here, particularly upstairs, where they have the time, put on elaborate shows of twirling in the sautéeing pan, as if they were coiffing the head of a great lady. It does not hurt the food, and they seem to enjoy doing it. The high flavor of the pesto seems literally to vibrate.

The Tortellini al Sugo di Carne, on the other hand—pasta tubes filled with ground dark meat of chicken (the white meat is reserved for a couple of $7 Chicken Suprême numbers)—tastes not of chicken under its overpowering and not particularly brilliant sauce of cheese, cream, tomato and garlic.

But the pasta should be shared, or eaten in small portions, to allow for such main courses as Red Snapper with Clams. The snapper is done in the same sauce as the appetizer of mussels, but with little necks, which add a sharpness that changes the sauce slightly but significantly, making it brinier, though the clams are added only at the end of the cooking of the fish, so that they are still tender when you get them.

The Osso Buco is tender, falling off the knuckle, served with a fettuccine, all under a simple tomato sauce—not bad. And the Pollo Napoletano—chunks of chicken and chicken livers, sautéed with shallots, is a plain, rather heavy dish which should perhaps not be preceded by pasta; it's good, but it's an awful lot of solid meat. A long, slow sautéeing in olive oil makes the Eggplant Parmigiana almost intolerably rich, under its layer of melted cheese. It is listed as a vegetable, but if it is ordered for one person, little else may be needed.

Ricotta is the cheese used in the cheese cake here—not Philadelphia cream—so the cake is dry but tasty, and moistened with rum and candied fruits. Strawberries Portofino is a simple sweet of strawberries. They are warmed in butter and flavored with Grand Marnier, which yields a honeylike sauce. This is served over ice cream and whipped cream.

Posh surroundings; a different perfume at every table, so you may have to keep your nose to your plate to enjoy your food. There are more than 150 items on the menu, of which most are nothing, but the English translations make clear what is what— Coppa di Frutta Fresca, you understand, is fruit cup, and Sofiiola alla Mandorla is Sole Amandine. Order items whose English definitions seem to speak in Italian—like Veal Scaloppine with Prosciutto, Sage, Artichokes and Peas, or Disjointed Chicken with Peppers and Mushrooms, and *not* Sogliola Inglese Gratellata al Burro, which is not Heart of Grateful Donkey, but English Sole Maître d'Hôtel.

The French wines are priced for comic relief. A spotty restaurant, but sometimes the food is inspired.

★ GIRAFE

208 East 58th Street
LUNCH, MONDAY TO FRIDAY; DINNER, MONDAY TO SATURDAY.
Closed Sunday.
Reservations, PL 2-3054.
Credit cards: AE, BA, CB, DC, MC.
Expensive.

The wild-animal theme (giant head-on photos of rhinos and elephants; a photomural of the veldt, complete with creatures; animal statuary, and so on) is an irrelevance. The place is an intimate hideaway in the traditional mold, with solid comfort, dim light, and soft music. The ceiling is low, there is dark wood paneling, red carpeting, potted palms. The service is so discreet that it is suggestive.

The customers, however, are among those by whom the digital watch was first tried. It is clear they enjoy knowing the bartender by name. They wear their success in bold plaids, they like to order fresh drinks and push aside stale ones that have not been drained, their intimacies are uttered too loudly: "I don't sit down and ask you what you want for Christmas. It's like writing a blank check. And anyone can buy a girl a mink. I don't know, maybe I'm too sophisticated." You guessed it—she got a cloth coat for Christmas, the wife got fur.

But the house is not responsible for its customers. Nor is it required that meals here be taken illicitly. Legally available men have been seen with singular women, and no one was the wiser, except, of course, that one was surely a little wiser than the other.

The food is good, never great, never bad. The menu is steakhouse/Italian—solid stuff that is brought to the table in sparkling condition. You will enjoy eating it, but with a few exceptions, you will not remember it for very long.

One of the exceptions is the Crostini alla Romana, a combination of fried bread and strong cheese, melted and pully, in a meaty sauce that has a pungent beef-stock base. The Baked Stuffed Mushrooms are not quite up to that standard. The mushrooms are of different sizes, stuffed with a pretty good mix of oiled bread crumbs with herbs. Naturally, the big mushrooms are not as thoroughly baked as the little ones, but none are better than others—just that some retain the flavor of raw mushrooms, others have the taste of thoroughly oil-soaked sautéed ones. They come in an oily and bubbling sauce made slightly tart with tomato.

The lobster bisque is an exaggeration of itself, but delicious. It actually seems to have too much lobster, too much cream, and too much sherry. It is so powerfully flavored from all directions that it lacks refinement, but it is very satisfying, and perhaps this is a sensible version of this soup for this restaurant, because most of the other dishes are so inherently strong that a quiet bisque would be unheard amidst all the noise.

The Mussels Marechiaro are a quite remarkable dish—the mussels are sautéed in garlic, oil and white wine, and they are served in a vibrant marinara sauce that is thick, loaded with minced garlic and made fragrant with plenty of chopped parsley. The restaurant must be praised for the quality of its veal, even if the preparation is not always first rate. The meat is pale, almost white, and very tender. But what they do to it to come up with something called Côte de Veau Chevalier is superfluous—they bread it, and sauté it, and cover it with a not very flavorful sauce Mornay, and they serve it over green noodles. This is a production rather than a dish.

The salads are of good greens, but there is an unfortunate tendency to drench them in dressing.

As you would expect, the desserts are *rich,* including a napoleon of several layers, each the size of a deck of playing cards. The pastry is flaky, but the creamy filling is a little cloying. A good conclusion to dinner here is the orange sherbet—sparkling and slightly acid.

★★ITALIAN PAVILION

24 West 55th Street
LUNCH AND DINNER.
Closed Sunday.
Reservations, JU 6–5950.
Credit cards: AE, CB, DC.
Expensive.

This is a gracious and comfortable restaurant with food that is always reliable, occasionally excellent. It has long been a lunchtime hangout for the publishing world. Nobody knows why. More mysterious is why they choose to eat in the commonplace, albeit comfortable, front room, when the year-round garden room, with its tall windows, is bright and airy and pleasant, despite the inelegant vista of a New York backyard planted in vines. Perhaps the dim interior is a fitter setting for the cunning proposals that lure literary talents into the traps of the book industry.

Between lunchtime proposals you might try the Fonduta—a thickened mixture of cheese and eggs, cooked together and then fried, to form a nice brown crust; or perhaps the thinly sliced, pale, slightly smoky ham, with a couple of slices of ripe melon. Since most of the appetizers here are items you can get anywhere—clams, oysters, shrimp, smoked salmon or trout—the pastas are a more interesting beginning. The linguine with white clam sauce, for one, is made with an abundance of fresh clams, added to the sauce just as it is being completed, so that they are tender and briny. If you like this dish made with lots of garlic, you had better so specify because the inclination of the house is toward a rather pure but slightly bland version. A specialty of the house is Fettuccine Pavilion—the noodles are carefully prepared, so that they are neither gummy nor hard, and the sauce is a thick and oily tomato sauce, heavily flavored with garlic and mixed with chunks of smoky ham. The Cannelloni Bolognese are stuffed with herbed veal and covered with a mature meat sauce that you can awaken and improve by adding a couple of ample spoons of the good grated Parmesan cheese that is served here.

In season the Italian Pavilion offers shad roe, and as in most restaurants, it is cooked too long, so that the rich and oily quality is lost. You're better off with some of the dishes for which the place is known. What is Suprema di Pollo alla Doria? It is tender, white chicken, sautéed until it is nicely browned, served in a thick, thick sauce of cream and cucumbers; it is very intelligently served with perfectly made white rice on which you spoon your extra sauce when you have finished your chicken. What is the Osso Buco like here? It is tender—falling off the bone, as they say—browned outside but still moist, and served with Risotto Milanese—rice heavily flavored with fragrant saffron.

Good vegetables: the asparagus is carefully peeled, so that it is tender, not stringy, and it is served under a filmy layer of melted cheese and a lightly fried egg; if you order your spinach with garlic, it is made to your order, and the distinctive mineral taste of the fresh spinach is well seasoned with fresh garlic.

The desserts are few and traditional. A moist, rummy Zuppa Inglese, carefully prepared zabaglione, and the usual ice cream and custard things. Better to order some more red wine and dunk your Amoretti. It takes about 150 Amoretti to soak up one bottle of wine, so you may wish to drink as well as dip.

There is an abundance of help at this restaurant, strained only when every table is taken, and the service is professional—available, polite, friendly. The captains wander around in search of wishes to fill.

★ MAMA LAURA

230 East 58th Street
LUNCH, MONDAY TO FRIDAY; DINNER, DAILY.
Reservations, MU 8–6888.
Credit cards: AE, BA, CB, DC, MC.
Expensive.

Certain restaurants transcend their elements. In them you will never shake your head in wonder over a stunningly contrived dish. Their rooms are perhaps no more than neat and clean; the service is possibly too slow or too noticeable. But these places develop followings of loyal customers who check their acumen with their coats, ensconce themselves as if in a warm corner of their mother's kitchen, and proceed to take sustenance with a contentedness and security unknown since the days when the old lady herself was handing out the hot meat on familiar plates.

One of these restaurants is Mama Laura, the suchness of the place perhaps owing something to the late proprietor, for whom it is named. World War II servicemen used to visit this restaurant before leaving for overseas duty, and many of them left military insignia with Mama Laura for luck; there is a display of dozens of these in the entrance foyer. When they returned they brought foreign money, and there is a framed collection of exotic currency in the dining room. Apparently the place has always had a homelike appeal.

The restaurant has a familiar layout, with a short bar at the front, rows of immaculately laid, well-spaced tables in the two small rooms to the rear, brown walls, somber Italianate paintings, carpeting.

The food, barring a few dishes, is unexceptional but decent. You are presented, first, with an abundant dish of raw vegetables and olives—on one day the carrots are small and sweet, another day coarse, hard and tasteless; today's celery is green and crisp, tomorrow's may be flecked with brown. Well, it's just something to hold you while you read the menu and select, if you are well advised, the Vitello Tonnato to start—tender, white veal, cold, overlaid with a thick, tart purée of tuna fish, lemon juice, oil and seasonings, and sprinkled with capers. If you prefer a hot appetizer, the best one is the Mussels Marinara. When the huge bowl of them is on the table, nothing else can be smelled within a radius of about five yards—the fresh mussels have been steamed with the very garlicky marinara sauce, and when the mussels are gone you are left with a pungent soup of strong sauce laced with the juice of the mussels.

Among the pasta dishes there are a few unusual items, including Fettuccine with Prosciutto—very thin homemade noodles that are combined with butter, fresh tomato sauce and the minced ham just before serving; and green lasagna stuffed with a sauce of coarsely chopped beef and a fresh, creamy cheese.

You don't find many rice dishes in New York's Italian restaurants, though in Italy a rice course sometimes takes the place of pasta. The Risotto with Mushrooms may be the best dish served in this restaurant—the rice is baked in broth and then combined with fresh mushrooms that have been lightly sautéed in butter, bits of minced prosciutto, parsley and strong onions. Sprinkled with the good grated cheese served here, this is a simple and splendid dish.

The meat dishes are where they slip up. The Steak Pizzaiola is OK—good beef and a hearty sauce heavily flavored with oregano and parsley—but the Chicken Cacciatore seems to be of frozen chicken, browned in undistinguished grease and served in a dull sauce that would benefit from the wine this dish calls for. And though the cold Veal Tonnato is of good veal, for the hot scaloppine dishes and the Veal Rollatine (stuffed with bland cheese) a redder grade is often used, and the results are often coarse—the tough meat fails to take on the flavor of the sauces. The Shrimp Marinara are much better—crunchy shrimp in a creamier, less pungent sauce than the one used for the mussels.

The conventional desserts include a mild, frothy zabaglione, with or without strawberries (usually in good condition), and a rum cake that is like a child's confection—layers of sweet white cake and custard, and a colorful icing. Ask for extra rum; it gives the cake the needed zing.

No one pays much attention to the food here except in a cursory way, and questions about the preparation of this dish or that are received with surprise and occasional bewilderment.

Though newcomers are treated cordially, the staff is most at home with the regulars: a waiter intercepts a young lady returning to her table and shows her his Kodacolor prints of his son; she reviews them appreciatively. The captain recites the desserts to a table of six while standing behind the most comely of them, his hands upon her thinly clad shoulders. A portly gentleman who eats alone at a table in the rear, from which he can look out over both rooms, is greeted as "King Farouk" by the help and is joined by a gigantic chap from the kitchen with whom he shares some food.

If you are collecting menu typos, there are a few winners here: wine is suggested, to compliment your meal; you could easily read right through Vitello Tomato; the prize goes to Vitello Gordon Blell.

★★ MARCHI'S

251 East 31st Street (near Second Avenue)
DINNER.
Closed Sunday.
Reservations, 679–2494.
Credit cards: AE.
Medium-priced.

The food at Marchi's demonstrates the degree of perfection which should be achieved by a restaurant that serves a limited or fixed menu. With the possible exception of the lasagna, none of the food here suggests a particularly inspired hand in the kitchen. What it does reveal is simple preparation, with exquisite attention to time, temperature and proportions; and fresh ingredients of first quality. Anyone can do it, it would seem, but Marchi's, despite its success, has no imitators.

Marchi's has been serving its five-stage dinner in these spacious dining rooms for over forty years. The place is comfortable, the dining rooms well lighted, clean and carpeted, and the service very simple and correct; the stiff manner of the staff suggests a stern disciplinarian in the wings.

Dinner begins with a huge antipasto of celery, radishes, tomatoes, fennel (the winter celery with an anise-like flavor), melon (always ripe), parchment-thin slices of superb Genoa salami, and a mixed Lorenzo Salad of green olives, capers, chopped celery, red cabbage, parsley and a hint of tuna fish. In many neighborhoods in New York, one could go from store to store for a day and not be able to assemble the quantity of vegetables, in perfect condition, that is placed on a table for two at Marchi's. There is not a brown spot on the celery or fennel, the radishes are firm, the melon, though ripe, is not beginning to rot here and there. Even the tomatoes, virtually unobtainable in good and tasty condition in many years, are sound, if not what we remember from the days when tomatoes were tomatoes. It's best not to eat all that is served at this course, as there is much more to come, the aforementioned lasagna being next. This pasta dish, as prepared at Marchi's, is very sexy. The flat noodles are soft and firm— no hard edges, no binding together of gluey strata. The lightly tomatoed meat sauce is the single culinary accomplishment of this restaurant that seems more than simply perfect—in fact inspired.

The lasagna is succeeded by fish which has been lightly floured and fried to the point of crisp skin, and flaky, perfectly cooked flesh. The type of fish varies from time to time; occasionally one is served whole little smelts, sometimes small steaks from a larger fish. The fish is accompanied by barely cooked, crunchy, cold beets, and cooked green beans at room temperature, in a simple dressing.

Roast chicken, with skin crisped to the flakiness of parchment pastry, and roast veal, with a spoon of pan gravy, are the meat of the main course. The chicken is fresh, but the veal is rather dark and coarse. These are served with an oversufficiency of sautéed mushrooms, and a salad of very crisp greens in a clear, sharp dressing.

Dessert consists of deep-fried lemon fritters, a disc of rather mild provolone cheese (port would go nicely here), a bowl of fresh fruit (nary a worm), and a huge stack of cristoli, those twists of dough which are here deep-fried to a brittle crust and sprinkled with powdered sugar. The espresso is perfect, or you can have tea, which is made with a Twining tea bag.

One is never hurried at this very busy restaurant. 'Twas ever thus, even on Fridays when the Friday meat fast was in effect. Avoid Fridays and Saturdays, when reservations are not accepted, and the waiting time can be long.

★★ IL MONELLO

1460 Second Avenue (near 76th Street)
LUNCH, MONDAY TO FRIDAY; DINNER, MONDAY TO SATURDAY.
Closed Sunday.
Reservations, 535–9310.
Credit cards: AE, BA, DC, MC.
Expensive.

Mourn not the overdue demise of Villa Doria. A familiar face from Giambelli of 50th Street has deserted midtown, moved himself and a staff into the dreary vacated premises, and livened them up with a slight face lifting, substantial improvements in the kitchen, and as a result, abundant and contented patronage. One thin, thin page, not without its blemishes and errata, added to the very thin book entitled "Estimable Italian Restaurants of New York's Upper East Side." (Do not turn down the fragile leaves.)

So we give thanks. Also a bit of advice. Your host is a gracious gentleman, he aims to please. In fact, his good will extends even to the help, from whom he does not demand the good manners he expects of himself. He sets an example which may or may not be followed, almost certainly not by the captains. You innocently ask one of these bored officials the difference in preparation between the mussels (Muscoli Portofino) and the clams (Vongole Positano). "It's da same thing," he says to the section of wall just over your head. On another occasion you order the Misto di Pesce fra Diavolo, but as the occasion is a Friday, when the daily special is Zuppa di Pesce Livornese, you are brought the daily special, which is ready, instead of the food of your choice, which is not. You remonstrate, and you are assured, in no-compromise terms, that the food before you is precisely what you ordered. Risotto con Funghi, a rice dish, is listed under "Farinacci," to which list is appended the legend "half order of pasta served as an appetizer." You request a half order of risotto. No dice, full orders only. (He is peeved —the rice takes forty-five minutes, which info does not persuade you to change your mind.) Then there is the chap who courteously pours a bit of wine into your companion's glass, a bit into your own, and marches off with the bottle, a few ounces still at its bottom.

Il Monello is a pretty big place, plaques and crossed swords on the walls, garish chandeliers hanging from the acoustical ceiling, white linen on the tables. There is, of course, a bar, over which well-fed guys exchange wisdom with the bartender while the ladies are off powdering their noses—no quotes, this is a family publication. Though the captains are in formals, the waiters wear only long-sleeved pink shirts (open at the collar), as if they were a crew of dashing unemployed actors—on the portly and/or bald the outfit looks delusional, like aviator glasses on a spinster. But in this crowd there can be no anomalies—Seventh Avenue mingles with Wall Street; whispered, spiritual seductions with young marrieds comparing prosperities—"What was your average wedding present?" one husband wants to know of another.

Begin with Insalata di Funghi Freschi. You cannot tell from the name, even if you read Italian, that this mushroom salad is 50 percent celery, but you will know at first taste that slivered fresh mushrooms and crisp celery, in a slightly garlicked dressing of oil and little else, is a stunningly appetizing first course, particularly when the ingredients are impeccably fresh—who would have figured, mushrooms and celery? Or else divide a main course of Muscoli Portofino, in which fresh mussels are steamed in white wine and garlic. The mussels seem newly plucked from the sea, they are not oversteamed, so they are tender, and the broth in your plate, a layer of minced garlic at the bottom, is briny and strong.

Proceed to Tortellini alla Panna, those little crescents of pasta stuffed with ground chicken, each of them firm, in a sauce of thick cream and strong cheese. This is mother's-milk kind of food, warm and comforting, but it can be converted to something more stimulating by grinding on the fresh pepper. That rice you were warned would take forty-five minutes comes in half an hour and is worth the pause. The magic of these Italian rice dishes is in the sautéeing of the ingredients, including the rice, before the grain is cooked in a strong broth. To make the sauce, butter and/or cheese are added at the end. This version is close to perfect, each grain of rice separate, the thick sauce pungent and vaguely smoky, the bits of mushroom here and there almost lost among these powerful tastes, so that it is best to eat them separately.

Well, you can put up a giant fuss, or you can eat the Zuppa di Pesce Livornese (which you received in place of the Misto di Pesce fra Diavolo that you ordered). Minister to your feelings with a glass of Barbera (before your captain vanishes your bottle) and proceed with your alternate dinner. This is a Friday special, apparently made in batches, and the clams and mussels toughen a bit as they wait for your arrival. The dish also includes chunks of fish, big scallops and squid, all in a spicy and oily sauce —strong, satisfying food, in abundant amount, but without finesse. Just to prove they can do unqualifiedly ill, Il Monello is kind enough to destroy a dish that you can get good versions of in dozens of other places. The chicken dish called Pollo Scarpariello consists of chunks of chicken which have become oil-logged in their sautéeing; it is served in a milky red sauce, and it is garnished with canned artichokes, the makings of a total mistake. However, another dish you can get almost anywhere—Saltimbocca Fiorentina—is made here in an exceptionally vivid version: there is across the top the usual layer of ham, but here the meat seems to have been grilled or broiled briefly, which accentuates the sharp flavor of the red meat; the veal just below is white and buttery; the spinach the meats rest on is pure and strong; and over it all there is a smooth sauce, buttered and slightly lemony, which livens the dish. An order of deep-fried zucchini is one time soggy and limp, another time crisp and lightly browned.

Your helpful captain makes special arrangements for the delivery of menus by the busboy so that you may select desserts. Then he returns to hear your selections. Then he informs you that your selections are not available. Had he brain one, he would have told you that in the first place. You figure this is basically a good Italian restaurant, and you calculate that, therefore, the house must have real Italian Parmesan cheese in the kitchen. You are right, and it is hard, sharp, head-clearing. You may have it with melon that is not invariably ripe. You may skip the whole thing and have a cheese cake that is of the cream-cheese variety—rich, gooey, and sweet. Or you may get even with Il Capitano by ordering a zabaglione. He makes a good one, eggy, with lots of hot wine.

★★NANNI'S

146 East 46th Street
LUNCH, MONDAY TO FRIDAY; DINNER, MONDAY TO SATURDAY.
Closed Sunday.
Reservations, 697–4161.
Credit cards: AE, BA, CB, DC, MC.
Medium-priced.

There is a captain here who somewhere picked up the notion that nothing will impress an American more than a restaurant wherein the chef is also the owner. The dining room here is small, and throughout dinner you will hear the captain working the fact into his presentations that the owner of Nanni's is also its chef. These lectures seem always to begin with a reminder that in a good restaurant the menu is merely the starting point, and they then proceed with the assurance that Nanni, the chef, the owner, will make for you anything you want, which comes down to anything on the menu plus three or four specials of the day.

"You won't find it on the menu, but if you like, Nanni, the chef, the owner, will make for you a cold seafood salad as an appetizer, which you can have with some cold white wine we have which is very special." The gentleman does a Balinese hand dance as he talks, with a counterpoint of Western mime, explaining how this is delicately seasoned (he pinches off a small piece of air), that carefully prepared (he eyes an imaginary pan on your table, waiting for the moment when . . .) with some perfect ingredient (he kisses a wild vegetable with his eyes closed). At first it is sort of amusing.

Nanni's is a simple enough place. You walk along a narrow corridor past the bar, into a room decorated with Italian travel posters. There are three rows of tables—about fifteen in total—and on each table there is a small lamp with a red shade. There is little room for the waiters to get from here to there, and the place is noisy when it is half full.

Among the items which Nanni, the chef (the owner) will make for you sometimes, other than the starting points on the menu, is the brilliant seafood salad, composed of small, crunchy shrimp, very tender little mussels, bits of bass, chopped cucumbers, celery, onions and parsley, all marinated in oil and wine.

Nanni will be delighted also to make for you a pasta course of Capellini d'Angelo (angel's hair) in sauce Nanni—"Tin, tin, tin little spaghetties, with Nanni's own sauce" (a whisper that is barely a hiss, emphasizing how svelte is the noodle). Chef Nanni's sauce is a delicate mixture of creamed tomatoes, peas, sautéed mushrooms, wine and a little strong cheese. It is not just a tomato sauce, with other stuff thrown in, but a balanced mixture, with the tomato in the background. Of course angel's hair is not kosher, and if that concerns you, you may have Tortellini alla Nanni—the same sauce, on little tubes of pasta that are stuffed with spiced ground veal—very heavy going, but redeemed by the great sauce.

The owner's main courses are easily oversold by the captain. One is talked into "breast of chicken taken off the bone, and pounded very, very thin. Then sautéed. And also is sautéed some mushrooms and prosciutto ham. All together with some cheese on top, and baked." (Fifteen inches in front of your nose he is holding his vision of the breast in his hand.) The breast is actually still on the bone. It may have been petted, but not pounded, and that of course ruins the dish—it is heavy rather than tender. The veal, roasted with mushrooms and truffles, is of second-rate meat—a kind of near-beef. They hate to admit it, but their thing is veal scaloppine, and they do it all the usual ways—piccata, Parmigiana, Milanese, zingara. The bass baked with mussels is splendid. The side orders of vegetables are often superior to what they garnish—sometimes crisp broccoli, at other times barely cooked zucchini under a thin sheet of browned cheese.

Crushed garlic is the most noticeable ingredient in the salad dressing here—good greens, including arugula when it is available, strong wine vinegar, oil and lots of that raw garlic. If that's what you want before dessert, you got it. It is good for what it is, and it is best between the pasta and the main course.

Zuppa Inglese here is an excessively sweet, very rummy cake, with a barely cooked meringue. If you want even more rum, there is a straight rum cake—Sacra Pantina—so loaded with alcohol that it can literally intoxicate; it doesn't taste bad either—lots of almond paste. But for something that does not rely on excess for its effect, there is fruit (peaches and strawberries) marinated in sweetened Marsala—fresh fruit, lots of fortified wine and a long marination—the best dessert in the place. Complimentary macaroons.

★★NICOLA PAONE

207 East 34th Street
LUNCH, MONDAY TO FRIDAY; DINNER, MONDAY TO SATURDAY.
Closed Sunday.
Reservations, 889–3239.
Credit cards: AE, DC.
Expensive.

William F. Buckley Jr. has written that Nicola Paone is the best restaurant in New York. This is erroneous. However, though liberals may comfort themselves that this nonsense confirms the poverty of Mr. Buckley's judgment, and though conservatives may answer that his powers of intellect and discernment are husbanded for battles in the intellectuo-politico-socio-econo arena and are portioned stingily to gastronomo-oeno, the fact is that Nicola Paone is a splendid restaurant of its kind—a leisurely, comfortable den—serving Italian food to successful men (sometimes accompanied by successful women) who keep their jackets on but never lose their cool, and who make this place their fraternity house, albeit one in which nonmembers are quite welcome.

For the selection of food one is presented with a simulated slate on which are painted, in simulated chalk, such informative entries as Boom Boom, Nightgown, Non M'Importa (at $9 it must be at least fairly important), Serenata in Minore, Chicken Baci Baci (it must be chicken) and Primavera (it must be spring). If you're left for ten minutes with this incomprehensible document, don't fret; use the time to take in the surroundings: mock sandstone building blocks and pillars, stained-glass windows, a linoleum floor in a pattern of red clay tiles, and as in all Roman abodes, phonograph-album covers on the walls, in abundance, picturing the man of the house and his guitar.

When the captain finally returns to your table, you can find out what the slate is all about. The pre-pasta courses here are not especially mystifying and are the least interesting items available. There are baked clams in a fairly good version of this common dish, with a strong flavoring of Italian parsley in the breading; stuffed mushrooms, in which the mushroom caps are filled with a well-seasoned stuffing of minced mushroom stems (waste not); and if you try the hot antipasto, your sampling of these items will be augmented with sautéed eggplant filled with cheese and tomatoes, stuffed peppers and a lone baked shrimp. There is a Zuppa Pavese, which, it develops, is chicken soup wherein an egg has been poached (it's still there), on a slice of toast (which any poached egg deserves). A harmless broth.

The pasta dishes here are a much better starting point than the official first courses, and one of them in particular is really outstanding. It is called Serenata in Minore and turns out to be wide noodles tossed with ricotta cheese, sprinkled with more cheese on top, the whole then briefly browned under the broiler. The pasta, which is cooked to order, is tender and firm; the excellent cheese makes a delicate but extremely rich sauce, and the stronger flavor of the browned cheese on top is a perfect accent—a marvelous dish.

A man who ordered Nightgown, because he likes them, discovered that it consists of a pair of cylinders of veal, cheese and prosciutto which have been baked, then wrapped in eggplant, breaded, baked again, painted with a sauce of cheese and tomato, and browned briefly in the broiler. This is quite a production, the serving is immense, and this kind of solid, highly flavored and satisfying food calls for an adequacy, perhaps an abundance, of wine.

Chicken Coraggioso is an excellent sautéed chicken. One of the things that is really outstanding about the preparation of this dish is the superior browning of the chicken. In most restaurants so-called sautéed meats are hardly browned, if at all; they are mostly stewed in oil or butter, and liquid. This brave chicken is made dark-brown and crisp on every visible square inch of its skin before being simmered in white wine, mushrooms and Genoa salami—which makes for a very hearty feast, particularly as the portion could feed a small family.

There are good versions of more standard dishes too—Veal and Peppers, Braciola, Shrimp Marinara, and so on.

It's a pleasure not to be presented with the common litany of salad dressings— French, Russian, Roquefort, Gollic. Nicola Paone's salad of very good greens is available only with a light, tart oil-and-vinegar dressing, and nothing heavier would be appropriate after the formidable dishes served here.

The desserts are pretty—presented by a flying squad of waiters, a different edifice of whipped cream, mocha, mousse, fruit, etc., in each hand. But these lovely-looking items are mediocre in the quality of the cake, in the purity of the cream, and in the flavor of the custards—only the fruits are of first quality. To eat wisely here is to have pasta, a main course, salad and then the strong espresso coffee in squat, heavy glasses—their rims coated with lemon-moistened sugar.

The service is very leisurely (you may call it slow if you are in a hurry), but this is in part because the food is made when ordered, and it has that bright, strong quality of flavors just brought to their peak. The staff works together well, and they seem loyal to their boss:

"Who is Nicola Paone?"

The captain's face lights up. "He owns this place! He's a celebrity! He's an entertainer! He sings! He plays the guitar! He makes records! He writes songs! He cooks! *He makes the pastry!*"

"Does he make love?"

"Eh. I donno about that."

There is one large table in the small rear dining room, where the walls are lined with wine bottles. Contemplative, aimless background music of Nicola plucking. (Says the captain, "Everything is homemade here, even the music.")

★★ ORSINI'S

41 West 56th Street
LUNCH AND DINNER.
Closed Sunday.
Reservations, PL 7–1698.
Credit cards: AE, CB, DC, MC.
Expensive.

This is the famous, intensely romantic hideaway where grown men eat in the dark beside cool, slender nymphs. Why, then, does the house provide us with Muzak, specifically "Una Furtiva Lagrima" on a muted (but well amplified) trumpet, followed, even more grotesquely, by the "Casta Diva," rendered the same way? Your host, perceiving that you have noted the music, explains that not all the customers like it, and that some even ask to have it turned down!

There is a lot of nonsense about Orsini's—that the favored get tables in the front, the unknown clean in the rear, lepers one flight up; that the food you get is not the same as the food *they* get; that if you are not a tiger, this place will humiliate you and then impoverish you with its haughty treatment and high prices. This stuff is believed by people who want to believe it, to flatter themselves, or to take comfort in their imagined persecution. In fact Orsini's is a fairly straightforward place. The service is polite, the food is reliable, if never inspired, and the prices, particularly for wine, are below San Marco's, Romeo Salta's and Giambelli's. The mythology is ridiculous on its face. If this place were the private preserve of the international set, they might, it is true, not object to the sour note of the Muzak. But would they tolerate being taken for less than top dollar?

Downstairs it is dark. There are red velvet walls and red velvet love seats. There are paintings with simulated century-old grime. Dim crystal chandeliers barely cut the gloom. Wrought-iron partitions form intimate corners.

Upstairs it is sunny. The walls are of rosy brick and creamy plaster. The tall windows at the front are hung with printed curtains, tied back to reveal rows of flower pots at the windowpanes. The chairs are straightbacked and rustic, with red-and-white fitted cushions.

Scampi—good, crisp shrimp, in a fresh-tasting buttery sauce, with garlic and lots of green parsley. Mozzarella in Carrozza—slabs of mild mozzarella cheese, lightly breaded and deep-fried until crisp outside and gooey inside, delicious with squeezed lemon. Vongole Sorrentina—rather ordinary breaded clams, utterly mis-described on the menu as "clams in tomato broth." Crostini alla Romana—the familiar deep-fried cheese-and-anchovy sandwich, but the batter is a little too sweet, like a fritter.

The gnocchi in pesto sauce are rather heavy, but the sauce is oily, loaded with garlic, powerfully perfumed of sweet basil and edged with an accent of Parmesan cheese. The pasta usually comes out of the kitchen in good condition, but the sauces that are made by the captains are as different as the captains themselves—this one of the mellifluous manner gives you an Alfredo of eggs, butter and little else; that one sharply flashes his teeth under his black mustache as he grinds and grinds the black pepper and sprinkles and sprinkles the grated Parmesan cheese. The menu describes the Risotto Milanese as "rice, veal marrow, saffron and wine." Pretty fanciful. It can be made that way, but it isn't.This is good rice, cooked in consommé and flavored with saffron, but it is not the kind of rice you want as a separate course, because it is just a step removed from plain rice.

Very good Osso Buco, tender, flaking off the shank, in a lemony tomato sauce enriched by the cooking of the veal bone. The Veal Chop all'Orsini is stuffed with cheese and good prosciutto, and it is served in a nice, slightly sharp sauce of tomato, white wine, lemon and cream—the veal itself white and tender. Something called Mignonette Peperonata is an elemental dish of grilled filet mignon, sautéed green peppers and a simple tomato sauce—not a silly concoction, despite the disparity of the elements, but a well-balanced dish.

The salads are good. You ask for spinach, and you get spinach with a bonus of slivered raw mushrooms. The Caesar salad is of good fresh lettuce, but the croutons are apparently allowed to age in the dressing, and they are mushy, not crisp.

The cheese is cool (not cold), and this does not really hurt a cheese like Gorgonzola. Orsini's is, how you call, not a dessert house. The Zuppa Inglese is an acceptable almond-flavored cake, with layers of chocolate, custard and preserves, all soaked in rum —not bad.

Orsini's has one distinct advantage over many of the most popular midtown Italian restaurants. It is not a mad scene. You do not wait for your table at a packed bar. Even where the tables are fairly close together (upstairs), there is a feeling of space. The place is gracious.

★★ IL RIGOLETTO

232 East 53rd Street
LUNCH, MONDAY TO FRIDAY; DINNER, MONDAY TO SATURDAY.
Closed Sunday.
Reservations, 759–9384.
Credit cards: AE, BA, DC, MC.
Medium-priced.

Hare, quail, duck, lamb and tongue rarely appear together on one menu in New York, and never on an Italian one, that is, not until the establishment of this ambitious restaurant. Il Rigoletto serves a broad assortment of dishes from a broad assortment of the regions of Italy. As the food of one section of Italy may have as much relationship to the food of another as the food of one province of China has to that of a province of Canada, this variety is a device rather than a purpose—virtuosity, we all know, expresses the virtuoso rather than the music—but though a group of selections from the proffered numbers will not invariably yield regional harmonies, who cares? The cacophony of delicious Tortellini in Brodo followed by tender Osso Buco is surely preferable to the euphony of grits and eggs. Assonance is not all.

You are greeted in a little vestibule by an agonized clown, but fortunately one that is painted on glass. You hasten past this brilliantly colored, leering figure, past the shiny little bar, into a room that is filled with the sounds of not necessarily operatic background music. The restaurant is relatively small, absolutely low-ceilinged, unquestionably softly and dimly lit. It is put together to look like a hand-plastered cellar—the walls are not only rough but wavy, though the wood paneling and marbleized mirrors that here and there relieve the clay-colored plaster are plumb. The grotto effect is further offset by cushy carpeting, elegant ice-blue linen and glinting glassware on the tables, a lacy drapery on the front window through which, at lunchtime, a soft light falls on a couple of isolated, intimate tables that are away from the main dining room.

Lingua con Salsa Verde consists of three thin slices of cured tongue, well-marbled with fat, the edges slightly darkened, lightly dressed with oil, minced mushrooms and parsley, and garnished with hot green peppers and olives. There is of course a piquant green sauce served with it, but unless you hate tongue, in which case it must be assumed you would not order it in the first place, it is recommended you have one slice with the green sauce, two without. The green sauce is good, but it seems designed to overcome some people's aversion to this meat in its unobliterated state, and the light dressing is perfect for adding a bit of moisture and for bringing out the taste of the tongue. Melanzana Pasticciata, as of course you know, is eggplant stuffed with ham, cheese, tomato and oregano. This is a nice dish (the oregano-flavored tomato sauce buttery and mild, the cheese filling tame, the eggplant itself, in a thin rolled sheet, a little bland) but sexless, lacking that fillip of near-discord that rouses the senses to keener appreciation of the harmonies. Not so of the steamed clams (Vongole "Marullo"), in which the clam juice adds a note of briny butteriness to the steaming broth of wine, which has been flavored with a little tomato, herbs and garlic. True, the clams may be steamed a bit long, toughening them, but the dish is nevertheless both stimulating and satisfying.

Good pasta, boiled to order, and diverse sauces. The Fettucine alla Romana, for example, consists of wide eggy noodles, firm and slippery, in a sauce that is an elevation of the standard red, by the addition of bits of ham and sautéed onions; the tomato side of the sauce is so sharp that this dish, despite being pasta, raises your appetite almost as rapidly as it satisfies it. This place also makes a good pesto sauce, served on trenette, which are small flat strands of noodle. Your pasta arrives surmounted by a deep-green and pebbly dose of hot pesto on which a pad of butter is melting. Though the sauce is heavily flavored with garlic, the fresh basil is fragrant enough to compete with it, and though the sauce is made with cheese, there is not much of it, and each customer may raise the cheese quotient according to his taste.

Listed as Costolette "Giovanna," the tiny lamb chops served here are four little chops that amount to not much more than four morsels of garlicky lamb, the tender meat coated with minced garlic. On both sides. The menu alleges a presence of bay leaves, rosemary, white wine and lemon. Perhaps. You will note most the garlic and the excellence of the very young lamb—a simple and delicious dish. The hare stew with gnocchi (Coniglio all'Umido con Gnocchi, to you), is a sweet fricassee of marinated hare, on the bone, but tender and falling from it, in a thick dark sauce that is heavily scented with cloves. Herbs, onions and wine also add flavor to the heady stew, and the mound of potato gnocchi that accompanies the meat can be fruitfully moistened with the extra sauce.

The waiters push Anitra alla Paesana, perhaps, as is the way with waiters, because the customers seem to like it. But this duck stew, though a perfectly pleasant dish, is far from ducky. Amid the aroma of celery, the high taste of strong bacon, and the sturdy stock the bird is stewed in, all that remains of the bird is its tenderness and moistness. This is a good dish, but one's excitement and curiosity at the idea of a *stewed* duck are let down by the discovery that much is lost in preparing the bird this way.

Pesce in Cartoccio is translated for us as "Fish, cooked in paper cases." The paper turns out to be aluminum foil, the fish to be cod that was browned before it was steamed in the foil with marinated mushrooms and spices. The fish is fresh and flaky, and cod, being a rather coarse fish to begin with, takes well to this peppery treatment—the food is sturdy and satisfying, but with little in the way of finesse.

This restaurant's adventurousness does not extend to sweets. Almond pudding sounds interesting, but it is merely a custard with a bit of almond patted onto the exterior—excellent custard, but the flavor of the nut is gone. The Zuppa Inglese is a better than average complexity of chocolate cream, chunks of chocolate, rum-soaked cake, maraschino cherries, etc. The special coffee of the house is served in a sugared glass with anisette—good, but at $2.25 it is a steal, and not on your part.

Polite, intelligent service; a fascinating menu; prices that, for the East Fifties, are more than tolerable.

★ ROMEO SALTA

30 West 56th Street
LUNCH AND DINNER.
Closed Sunday.
Reservations, 246–5772.
Credit cards: AE, CB, DC.
Very expensive.

If all the dishes in this restaurant were as well made as the pasta, the disparity between their cost and their quality would be merely grand. As it is, if you don't know what to order here, you can drop a young fortune on some very tired food; and just to add contempt of customer to disdain of value, you're presented with a wine list that makes no mention of prices. On the other hand, perhaps this is a kindness, because if you knew the prices, you might choose water, and if you chose water, your sensibilities would not be sufficiently anesthetized by meal's end to tolerate the shock of the tariff.

This is a handsome restaurant, with putty-colored cloth on the walls and a ceiling of rough plaster in the same color. The kitchen is visible through large pink windows at the back of the room, and in the evening, when the restaurant itself is dimly lit, there is a dreamlike quality about the rosy view because you can see the men at work, but you can't hear them. (At lunchtime the dining room itself is more brightly lighted than it is in the evening, and you hardly notice the kitchen.) Under the pink windows there are four large fish tanks, populated by luckless trout. The tables are fairly large, there are fresh flowers on all of them, and each one sports its own pepper mill. Handsomely framed paintings and prints are on every wall and pillar. And just to ruin the effect, around most of the room, on the ledge just above the banquettes, there are bottles of wine, standing up (well, it's only Italian wine), and copies of the Romeo Salta Italian cookbook, which the author will autograph for you if you purchase it at $6.95.

But before you do, for several times that amount you can find out whether Mr.

Romeo is an authority on food, or an expert at seeming to be an expert. One of the dishes he names after himself and describes for you, you should know what you're getting. It is called Scampi alla Griglia ROMEO, and it is eulogized as "Broiled Giant Shrimps." One wonders why, if the size is given as "Giant," the number is not also given as "Four." (Or, similarly, why we are not told that the celery and olives are Economy size, the smoked salmon Small Family size, and the caviar Travel size.) Whatever the answer to these mysteries, the Giant Shrimp are not gigantic, but they are split, which makes them look big, they are breaded and broiled, and they are served with a perfectly nice sauce of oil, vinegar and minced anchovies. There isn't anything wrong with it, and if Romeo wants to call it after himself, perhaps he should be praised for not calling it after someone else.

You're better off if you start your dinner with Mozzarella in Carrozza, which is breaded cheese on bread, fried in olive oil. It is soft, pleasantly gooey, crisp outside, and it can be nicely improved with a few drops of lemon; this is a simple dish that is elegant even though it is slightly heavy. Or you may have roasted peppers and anchovies —soft, oily peppers; strong, salty anchovies; capers; all in oil, and all very nice. There are the usual soups—this in broth, that in broth—and the broth is rather dead. If it is escarole and beans you choose to have in it, you'll find that the escarole has lost its strength, and you'll discover, too, that some cheese has been added to the combination for you, but you will find it by looking, not by tasting, for it is virtually tasteless. The beans, thank heaven, are crunchy and satisfying.

The little potato dumplings called gnocchi are incomparable here. They are tender, light, smooth (almost creamy), and delicately but clearly flavored of potato. They are so eminently edible that they are almost friendly. And if you have the good fortune to order them in a sauce Bolognese, you will have flattered them almost to the extent of their merit, for this sauce is made long and slowly, and the meat, tomatoes and seasonings are blended into an earthy perfume. The gnocchi are coated with a tasty and oily film that makes their consumption a little easier than breathing. Or you can order Paglia e Fieno Papalina, a mixture of white noodles, thin as wire, and green ones, flat, and a little larger than linguine. The two kinds of pasta are cooked separately, and each to its own point of firm tenderness, so that the contrasting textures of the two noodles are clearly discernible in the creamy sauce accented with slivers of smoky ham. (The menu announces peas as another ingredient, but in the kitchen they are too busy to study the menu.)

You want fish? There is something called Zuppa di Pesce—Myra Waldo. (Myra loves Romeo.) It requires a wait of at least thirty-five minutes from the time you order it, you are warned, and this is a good sign because fish stews cannot sit around waiting for customers and be anything but disastrous when finally consumed. Sure enough, the individual elements of this mélange are good—flaky bass, firm, and slightly fibrous scallops, tender mussels and clams with their flavors intact, fresh-tasting shrimp, slightly chewy squid, and unfortunately, a frozen crayfish of some kind, probably included because the customers expect something from the lobster family in a dish like this, and a live lobster would bite off all the profits. The broth itself is thick, oily, spicy, loaded with tomato, and not subtle.

You order Scaloppine Chic Martini because it is described as sautéed in "Butter, Lemon & Parmesan Cheese," and you get something that tastes as if it were dipped in powdered American cheese and deep-fried—the only detectable lemon is a slice of it on the plate. You order Cotoletta Colombo because it is explained as "Stuffed Veal Chop with Prosciutto and Cheese," and it is OK, stuffed with breading and onions as well as the listed ingredients, and flavored with lots of sage, but the dish is heavy, and there is nothing sharp or sparkling in it to offset the leaden quality. They use perfectly decent veal here, but they don't seem to know what to do with it. And they don't do much better with chicken. The Spezzato di Pollo Scarpariello consists of chicken and chicken livers sautéed in oil, with parsley and lemon; the chicken is not browned, the liver is not pink, the sauce is salted rather than flavored and the whole thing is a minuscule fiasco.

Every restaurant in Little Italy makes deep-fried zucchini better than this place— the clumpy strands of deep-fried batter, a needle of zucchini inside, taste like Coney Island French fries. The salads are good, of fresh ingredients, but the desserts are merely sweets.

Customers are of a certain kind. Says one bronzed blonde to her similarly coiffed luncheon companion, "Why do you keep bringing me Italians? I *have* Italians. What I need now are Hungarians, or possibly Swiss." Later: "I think I'll just have a steak. Waiter, would you cut it up for me?" Later still: "I'm not interested in having my name in his will. I just collected a will. I can wait awhile for the next one."

★★ SAN MARCO

36 West 52nd Street
LUNCH, MONDAY TO FRIDAY; DINNER, MONDAY TO SATURDAY.
Closed Sunday.
Reservations, CI 6–5340.
Credit cards: AE, CB, DC.
Expensive.

This new 52nd Street San Marco is to the old place on 55th as a carefully selected second spouse to an impulsively taken first—perfectly suitable and all that, but lacking a certain capacity, recalled with some nostalgia, to infuriate. At the old you suffered a bit of crush at the bar for the thirty minutes between the hour of your reservation and the time you were actually inserted into your tiny allotted space; you endured your neighbors' loud camaraderie, the staff's conflicts; you longed for escape from intimate bedlam, dreamed of a comfortable and civilized setting for the vigorous food and sturdy Italian wines.

Well, you got what you thought you wanted. "Never pray for a new king," said the wise man, "he will be worse than the old one." How we miss that old despotism. The new San Marco is benevolent, like a well-run clinic.

The place is long, wide and airy, the large tables in well-spaced rows across the generous spread, the lofty ivory walls made less bare by numerous paintings that have no other purpose. As in the previous San Marco, the ledge above the banquette that rims the room is strung with bottles of wine; and tall étagères of dark polished wood, open front and back, one-wine-bottle-deep, display hundreds of bottles more, and serve as "room dividers," to break up the cavernous volume. But these displays, for all they ought to suggest of alcoholic abandon, are coolly architected and, therefore, sterile. Maybe the place would feel OK if it weren't an *Italian* restaurant, but the assertive food of Italy in these spare surroundings is like a hot pastrami on Arnold Brick Oven White.

Accordingly the customers, particularly at lunchtime—here or there the token beard, there or here a woman with men, and beyond those, little but pairs and quartets of suited executives, discussing, with studied squinted eyes, the games of corporate business as if they were the conflicts of states. At night, however, things loosen up, and the signs of life San Marco needs are provided by New Yorkers who can afford the restaurant and enjoy their prosperity—you see colorful duds on fetching folk, hear smart talk and tipsy laughter. But it is a rare night when there are quite enough customers to transform the place.

The menu is very much the old menu, at prices that are no less immodest, including, as a dinnertime appetizer, a little $4.75 number called Spedino Romana—a row of alternating layers of mozzarella cheese and bread, grilled until the bread is toasted and the cheese strong and pully, served in an oily and salty anchovy sauce. It is a terrific dish, at once coarse and well-balanced, the sharp flavors offsetting the solid weight of the food. One ordinarily avoids liver pâté in Italian restaurants, because it is usually imported. The lunchtime menu at San Marco, however, informs you that the pâté is "homemade," and you investigate by placing an order for same. Well, you should have figured that an Italian pâté will be oily where a French one will be buttery, and you might have anticipated that the difference, to a predisposed palate, will be off-putting. This may be an acceptable dish, it is herby and far from flat, but you will have to approach it with a wide-open mind.

Cappelletti in Brodo means chicken dumplings in chicken broth—little pasta pouches stuffed with ground chicken and herbs, in a broth which has the gamy quality of chicken fat and plenty of seasoning; the tender dumplings are just right in the sharp soup.

Good noodles, with a strong egg flavor, cooked to order so they are firm but tender, and in Fettuccine alla Veneziana they are moistened with a vibrant sweet-and-sour tomato sauce in which peas and bits of ham are apparent, the flavor of rosemary very subtle.

Veal dishes do not seem to be San Marco's strength. You can actually get a Veal Scaloppine al Limone in which it is difficult to detect either the flavor of lemon or that of sautéed veal. The obscurity of the lemon is miscalculation, that of the veal indolence —it is barely browned, only on one side (the side that is "up" on your plate), and permitted to stew for a while in bubbling butter. This is ruination of a good ingredient. The veal birds (Involtini di Vitello) are somewhat better—hefty loaves formed of veal around a strongly herbed and spiced stuffing of cheese and ham, served in a winy mushroom gravy. At lunchtime the serving is augmented with a dozen or so gnocchi —firm little potato loaves that make a better match for the gravy than the birds themselves.

Sausages and Peppers (billed as "farmers style") is the kind of dish one thinks of in those Italian restaurants with checkered tablecloths and waiters in shirt sleeves. The San Marco version is no less vigorous than what you get in neighborhood places, succulent and spicy, but there are touches of class—an admixture, in the sausages themselves, of an exceptionally fragrant black pepper which, despite its abundance, does not overpower the dish but adds an unexpected piquancy. The meat is garnished with sautéed red peppers and fresh mushrooms.

For perfect, elegant simplicity, have Branzino alla Pescatora—a great slice of immaculately fresh striped bass, moistened with a delicate tomato sauce that is lightly garlicked. Purists who insist that fish should be no more than buttered and lemoned are the losers.

San Marco has always made a lovely event of the simple act of serving up a dish of zabaglione. To begin with, your captain prepares the dish in the dining room, with much grand stirring over the flame; and the result is hot, sweet and winy. Moreover, it is served up in a handsome porcelain goblet, the thick golden foam mounded high above the rim, some of the excess coursing down the sides and stem. Don't worry, your fingers will not be made sticky. You eat it with a spoon. The cheese cake has a smooth, custardlike quality; it is heavy and moist, laden with chopped fruits—very nice.

★★SAN REMO EAST

33 East 61st Street
LUNCH AND DINNER.
Closed Sunday.
Reservations, 759–6684.
Credit cards: AE, DC, MC.
Medium-priced.

Comfortable, attractive, reasonably priced. And the food is good. This is a branch of the San Remo on lower Eighth Avenue, without, however, the accordionist, who fortunately cannot manage to be in two places at one time. San Remo East is not a particularly small place, but it is cozy, turns in the shape of the room making nooks and corners here and there. There is a nice little bar just inside the entrance, the walls are of rough-finished plaster, and they are hung with harmless oils. There are crisp white linen and fresh flowers on the tables, the floor is carpeted, and the ceiling, of dark wooden slats, suggests the interior of a snug little boat. This is a restaurant that suggests itself for relaxed eating rather than for "going out." The comforts are without pretense. And that seems to be the way the place has been taken by the following it has developed. What you see here is eating and drinking rather than wining and dining. No one is snowing a customer. You can get a complete dinner here at the price of a plate of pasta at Romeo Salta. Which is not to demean Romeo's noodles, but to praise San Remo's value.

You can (often) judge a restaurant by its menu, and the printed and folded sheet you are handed here is prepossessing for being hopelessly artless. We are told, for the thousandth time, "A meal without wine is like a day without sunshine"; that San Remo East is "A new concept in fine italian [*sic*] dining"; and that a number of the dishes are "From our family Recipies [*sic* again]." And the whole thing is written in a kind of broken-arm copperplate script, with tortuous, hand-inscribed dotted lines that trail from the names of the dishes across the page to the price (though sometimes that space is occupied, instead, by a helpful description of the food). You will learn, for example, that Breast of Chicken Parmigiana is "An Italian stand by." Stand by. Filetto alla Piemontese is "Sauted in Vermough, Stuffed Mushroo." Best of all, Eggplant Parmigiana is "And old Favorite." The ancient dispute about whether the little cup of coffee is espresso or expresso is here solved. It is "exspresso."

For an unimpeachable first course, begin with the Insalata de Mare, which, the menu explains, is "Seafood salad." Lots of crunchy little shrimps, tender slices of squid, soft mussels (perfectly fresh), circles of raw Bermuda onion, all in a sparkling and garlicky dressing—quite terrific. There are stuffed mushrooms, filled with minced chicken, onions and herbs, and moistened with lots of oil—the mushrooms are fresh but a bit oil-soaked, and the stuffing is just OK.

This is not a pasta house, which is not to say that there is anything wrong with the pasta dishes, rather that very few are available, and those the most familiar. What you get, however, is pretty good stuff, including straightforward manicotti (a tender pasta envelope filled with mellifluous cheese, the whole thing in a simple and piquant tomato sauce) or cannelloni (the pasta stuffed with a tender meat filling, the sauce thick with coarser ground meat).

One of the curioser entries on the menu is "Red Snaper.—Cooked in a Green Sauce, excellent." Snaper is similar to snapper, you will discover, in fact indistinguishable from it. The snaper is fresh, tender and flaky, and it comes in a rich, thick sauce of butter and parsley. You will find nothing to complain about in this simple dish. Nor, for that matter, in the Veal Piccatta—the meat is pale and tender, and the flavor of the lemon and the additional flavor of quite a lot of black pepper permeate the meat thoroughly. There are very good little salads, made of fresh greens and circles of raw onions, in a tart dressing.

A limited selection of desserts, including a rum cake that is in very large measure rum, though you can't miss the plain cake that carries the heavy soaking of the liquor, or the meringue on top. The cannoli is good in the way that it is odd. As a rule Italian custard has the consistency of warm lead, but this stuff is light and airy, studded with candied fruit and wrapped in a crisp pastry that is sprinkled with sugar.

★★ IL VALLETTO

133 East 61st Street
LUNCH, MONDAY TO FRIDAY; DINNER, MONDAY TO SATURDAY.
Closed Sunday.
Reservations, 838–3939.
Credit cards: AE, BA, DC, MC.
Expensive.

This is not Nanni's North, though Il Valletto is, in fact, the recent undertaking of Mr. Nanni, proprietor of the very popular Nanni's, of East 46th Street. But here (on the premises of the blessedly defunct Running Footman) Nanni has invested some of his midtown cash in uptown posh. If you dread this address for memories of the stuffy old Footman, be assured that no trace of that dreary mortuary remains. The Italian warmth has been transfused into the premises until the entire place glows pink and brown and gold. From the moment you become hooked on the mixed nuts (no peanuts) which accompany your apéritif at the massive polished bar, you grasp that Nanni is here expressing a side of himself that was never in evidence in the travel-poster-adorned little place downtown. Through the bar to the first room—small, softly lit, the walls covered with casually striped, glowing velvet, a handful of tables, a grouping of special places. Through that to the main dining room, forty pink-linened tables under chandeliers of lights in red shades hanging from a plum-colored ceiling a couple of stories over your head. There are heavy Italian murals set into the ivory walls—you need not look up at them. One thing in common with Nanni's: the place is an amplifier—a bit of conversation hits you from across the room, and a few minutes later, still bouncing around these hard walls, it hits you again. It makes everyone, even your host, cheerful, and he calls your companion *"Cara bambina,"* though she is well past weaning.

Another thing in common with Nanni's: much is made of what is not on the menu, and much of what is not on the menu is the best food in the house. As it is not on the menu, it may not have an official title, so the waiter suggests, with technical correctness, a hot antipasto which, on description, turns out to be a hot seafood salad—dozens of tiny scallops and a lesser number of shrimps, lightly floured, sautéed, with a bit of garlic, in oil and wine which have been simmered down to a smooth and oceanic broth. The little scallops are sweet and rich, the shrimps crisp, the dish just about perfect. Also not on the menu, but on display at the entrance to the large room, the cold antipasto —the principal attraction here is the *cold* seafood salad, a sparkling intermingled collection of chunks of lobster (!), tiny mussels, shrimps and onions, all in a limpid vinaigrette—the impeccable ingredients make this an extremely refreshing and stimulating appetizer. In nearby trays there are marinated artichokes and roasted peppers, good food, the artichoke leaves cured to the point where they have lost all their fibrousness, the peppers firm and sweet.

If you are granted one dish in this restaurant before you are added to the unemployed and consigned to your own kitchen, choose yet another that is not on the menu— gnocchi, with what the waiters have been trained to call "Nanni's special sauce." These plump potato dumplings are, miraculously, at once firm and ephemeral. The lightest pressure of your tongue and palate against the pale shells effects instantaneous disappearance. But the flavor of the sauce lingers, a slightly sour and yet creamy tomato sauce, with slivers of ham, tiny peas and herbs. The dish is sprinkled with cheese and very briefly put under the broiler before it is served, creating a lightly browned, gauzelike veil which adds a sharp, heady flavor to the otherwise gentle dish.

Your standard restaurant freak is, of course, frustrated by the almost universal "ordering off the menu" practiced at Il Valletto. Where is the inside-dopester appeal of ordering off the menu if everyone is doing it? Has been discovered, to fill this gaping gap, the practice of ordering *directly from the menu,* which has a return-to-innocence snob appeal, like the Mickey Mouse watch or forties musicals at 2 A.M. What you do is read the menu, select food you think you will like and instruct the waiter to bring those dishes. It's fun, and anyone can learn to do it. Start by ordering Trenette al Pesto. (Trenette is like linguine, but even more slender; pesto is a buttery green sauce of fresh basil and two or three cheeses.) This version is weighted toward cheese—crumbly nuggets and fine grains in among the fragrant green stuff—and it is served on just-cooked noodles that are tender but firm. You will require a spoon for the pool of flavored butter that remains at the bottom of your dish.

More from the menu: Zuppa di Clams—little clams, in their shells, steamed in wine and oil and garlic until they are warmed but not the least toughened, sprinkled abundantly with parsley and served mounded up over a deep plate of the briny broth they were steamed in. Sea Bass Marechiaro—a substantial length of fresh, resilient fish, lightly floured and then sautéed, to form a thin crust, moistened with a modest sauce of wine and tomatoes, with a little garlic and a bit of parsley, and garnished (nice note) with a few steamed mussels and a mound of crunchy spinach that is soaked in oil and garlic. Scaloppine alla Francese is a better than average version of this dish. The veal is pale, tender, crusted with a batter of eggs and flour, sautéed in butter and moistened with lemon—but despite the unusual sprinkling of strands of prosciutto ham, this is less than exciting. Pollo Scarpariello—chunks of chicken that are well-crisped but rendered a bit oily in the process; the dish is redeemed, however, by the flavors of fresh garlic and parsley. The chicken and the veal are served with artichoke hearts that are filled with buttered sweet peas and bits of bacon.

Il Valletto may well be the only restaurant in New York that makes available half a dozen or more imported Italian cheeses at room temperature: Gorgonzola, ivory veined with blue, smooth, creamy and sharp; Parmesan, hard and crumbly, with a strong bite and a scent that clears the head; Romano; Fontina; etc. The sweet desserts are a varying assortment of unabashedly rich cakes, including a Zuppa Inglese that consists of layers of moist white cake and pastry cream, all wrapped in a lightly browned, pully meringue.

Steak

The steakhouse appeals to he-men, and to women who like that kind of man. You start with a martini. Then you have a shrimp cocktail or some clams. Then you have a steak or, especially along so-called Steak Row, around East 45th Street, a broiled lobster. Then cheese cake and coffee. During dinner you either stick to martinis or you drink beer. If you drink wine instead, you are suspect. Anyone who closes his eyes while tasting his wine is queer, or "a" queer. Many of these places actually serve good food. And you do get a lot to eat.

★ BILLY'S

948 First Avenue (near 52nd Street)
LUNCH, MONDAY TO SATURDAY; DINNER, DAILY.
Reservations, 355–8920.
Credit cards: AE, CB, DC, MC.
Medium-priced.

Billy's is like P. J. Clarke's, but without the drunks. Also without the juke box, preserved decay, bouncer and ice blocks in the urinals, for which blessings you pay through the trunk, for the prices here are an object lesson to P. J.'s of what you can get away with if you don't have to fill three large rooms to pay the real estate taxes.

You come here for your shrimp cocktail, for your sirloin steak, for your hamburger steak for the lady, for your lamb chops, for your Irish coffee. And you eat and drink these ingestibles amid furnishings and fixtures that graced Billy's at the old spot four blocks from here, for doth not the sign read "Established by Michael Condron Way Back in 1870," and is that not Michael's bar, the same one as was in the old place, and are not these the old gas lamps wired up for electric, and don't the wooden doors and panels with the brass knobs and hinges seem to be the same ones as Michael knew? Sure. And isn't there a bottle of ketchup on the red-checkered tablecloth, same as in the old place? Sure. And isn't that Michael's own begotten son, Billy, behind the bar? You bet it is. And even if the place does look like a saloon, the waiters wear those little long-sleeved vests so you can tell them from the customers, and the only loud talking is from the kiddies some folks don't mind bringing here because this is a family-type restaurant, even if it did forget to close during Prohibition.

The menu is painted on a slate, and occasional daily specials are indicated by little signs tacked on the wall. Tomato juice is half a dollar, the onion soup is pretty ordinary, and the shrimp cocktail consists of four carefully cooked shrimp and cocktail sauce (you can add horseradish).

Eschew the pork chops (cooked to the point where you not only will not get trichinosis, but anything else either). Pass up the lobster tails (either for political reasons—they are from South Africa—or for personal ones—they had a tough trip). Do not order the broiled filet of sole (it may be broiled, but it is gently broiled, so it tastes as if it has been stewed in butter; the coloration is paprika, not natural browning by fire). Whatever you order, do not order the sautéed onions. They are limp (as such onions should be), but they lack the accent of burnt grease that can make this dish a kind of sinful pleasure.

Do order the steak. It is thick, cooked exactly the way you ordered it, tender and tasty. Or order the chopped steak—large, made of freshly ground meat, and excellent with the steak sauce that is a companion to the ketchup on your table. Or order the steak tartare—the meat is freshly ground, and you can ask for the pepper mill or whatever if you want to adjust the seasoning. The broiled chicken seems to be of a fresh bird, and the lamb chops are as carefully made as the steaks. Fair French fries (they are the kind you put ketchup on, not the kind you put salt on), baked potatoes that seem to be made in a slow oven, so the skin, instead of being flaky and slightly blackened, is merely a tired container.

The apple pie is a fair commercial variety, but the cheese cake is dreadful.

★★BROADWAY JOE STEAK HOUSE

315 West 46th Street
DINNER.
Closed Sunday.
Reservations, CI 6–6513.
Credit cards: AE.
Expensive.

One is greeted at table by a bored, formally attired gentleman who puts down a basket of bread, twenty to forty pats of butter, and immediately poises his pen at his pad.

"May we have a menu?" (Innocently.)

"Ova here we got no menu." (Bored.)

"What do you have?" (Expectantly.)

"We got pâté, shrimp cocktail, herring, tomato juice, lamb chops, steak, chopped steak, French fries, baked, cottage fries, hashed browns. Salad comes." (Bored.)

Not bad. He omitted only the onion soup and the chicken.

"Is there a wine card?" (Excitedly.)

"We got Valpolicella, Soave, Beaujolais, St. Julien." (Very bored.)

Steak is all. The first courses range from bad (pâté and onion soup) to fair (a shrimp cocktail consisting of half a dozen shrimp, sometimes overcooked, and a good cocktail sauce that contains plenty of strong horseradish) to very decent (pickled herring, with onions that are not wilted and retain their bite, in fresh sour cream and chives, served on fresh iceberg lettuce).

But that's not what we came here for, right? Right. We came here for steak. Thick, bloody, tender sirloin, blackened, with potatoes: baked potatoes are included, and they have crisp skins, and firm but thoroughly cooked interiors, into which you may insert a fistful of that butter the man brought, or some sour cream (still in its half-pint container, with chives stirred in); or cottage fries—two-inch, golden-brown, crunchy discs; or French fries—a bit limp, it must be admitted; or best of all, hashed browns that are of the brown-through-and-through school, with tiny flecks of almost blackened potato throughout, like a built-in zest. The steaks are cooked accurately, and the servings of potatoes are more than ample. There are also lamb chops, about three ribs thick; giant chopped steaks of good meat; and broiled chicken, which is often overcooked.

You get a huge salad, but you don't have to eat it. If you wish to eat it, be sure to specify the noninclusion of the house dressing (which is made with what tastes like a garlic substitute) and the substitution of oil and vinegar. Or you may have that most barbarous of salad creations—alternating half-inch slabs of tomato and raw onion—which is not recommended for before the theater unless you have a box of your own.

Nothing special for dessert—tortoni, spumoni, canned stewed fruit or, oddity, cookies.

"Are there any cookies left?"

"Sure. Why not?" (Still bored.)

There are lots of waiters at Broadway Joe, and though the service is cursory, it is never rude, and always available and prompt.

Broadway Joe is one of the two or three places on this restaurant block that do any business after show time, for the simple reason that many people eat here because they like it here, theaters nearby or not. At seven-thirty or so the ladies in creations and the men with pinky rings and pointed shoes are replaced by a more traditionally dressed set, to whom any dinner worthy of the trouble is by its nature too substantial to be a mere prelude to the theater. Such dinners, if they are preparatory at all, prepare one for pursuits more languorous than forced attention in an auditorium full of burpers.

Broadway Joe is a simple and comfortable restaurant—a barroom in front, with a huge mural of Broadway and Hollywood caricatures; a center room that is pointlessly but harmlessly papered in scenes of Colonial America; and a rear room of plain walls and beamed ceiling

★★★ CHRIST CELLA

160 East 46th Street
LUNCH, MONDAY TO FRIDAY; DINNER, MONDAY TO SATURDAY.
Closed Sunday.
Reservations, OX 7–2479.
Credit cards: AE, BA, CB, DC, MC.
Very expensive.

You are greeted by a host who, when you reject the first couple of tables he shows you to, does not, directly or by suggestion or by gesture, imply that Christ Cella can do without fussy customers. This is remarkable because Christ Cella *can* do without fussy customers. It has plenty of all kinds, and they pay more than liberally for the pleasure of eating in this establishment. But your host listens to your objections carefully, no sooner does he grasp them than you are escorted to the bar, and as soon as a table is available that meets your specifications (not in the traffic, not near the door), he comes to get you. The amazing policy of this restaurant is: you pay your money and you take *your* choice.

That bar where you waited for your table is very much of the place. The downstairs of this two-story restaurant is made up of many small rooms, and one of them is the handsome wood-paneled barroom, the bar the length of one wall, the three tables opposite spaced well apart. There are no stools at the bar (this is not primarily a drinking place), and the polished walls and the mounted antelope head notwithstanding, the room is not clubbily masculine, just comfortable. Then there are all the other rooms, with their pale-green walls hung with prints and photographs. At the back is the immaculate kitchen, open to view, with accommodations for a handful of regular customers who find that eating in the kitchen at an unlinened table, under the clamor of the pots and pans and kitchen patter, is a fillip that spices the simple pleasures this restaurant provides. Upstairs the rooms are large, bare and forbidding—a good place for big parties, where your companions are also your scenery.

Christ Cella has an Old New York feel to it, like a restaurant born in the Depression; it is Spartan in its appointments and lavish of quality, as if it knew and remembered the value of a customer and never learned the show-biz side of the food biz.

The customers have more than a touch of class—conservative but not stuffy, people who do not brandish their individuality, who are not dazed by their own success. The clothes worn here are neither uniforms nor political statements. (Of course, that is at dinner. At lunchtime the restaurant is just another place in the midtown business district, and the place is loaded with guys who seem more important outside their offices than at their programmed tasks performed at standard desks.)

There is no printed menu. The waiter tells you what there is, all of which is simple food. The crabmeat cocktail is copious, tender, fresh, with a brightly flavored cocktail sauce—not inherently a great dish, but as good as it can be for what it is. Shrimp and lobster cocktails of comparable quality, but no clams or oysters.

Perfectly broiled fish is available, on occasion roast beef, good liver. But the standard dishes here, making up probably 90 percent of the main-course orders, are steaks and lobsters, and they are more consistently excellent than in any other steak/lobster house in this Steak Row neighborhood, or, for that matter, in New York. The steaks are fibrous, tender, seared (but not burnt), so the juice of the meat is sealed into the center of the steak. The filet mignon is at least three inches thick, adorned with a few fresh mushrooms; the sirloin is not that deep, but it is substantial enough to be cooked for more than a moment and still come out rare. By and large, the degree of doneness of your steak is as you request it in this restaurant, and deviations are slight. The steaks are sprinkled abundantly with fresh parsley.

The lobsters are big but not huge, they are broiled, and they are fresh, unbelievably moist, faintly imbued with the taste of the charred shell. Unrequested, your waiter separates most of the lobster from its shell, so that even a child can eat it with a knife and fork; the meat from the claws is brought to you extricated from its housing and served up in a little bowl. Still, grown diners are up to their elbows in drawn butter by the time they have worked their way through one of these things, their wineglasses coated with the stuff, as if it wouldn't be a lobster without the mess. The hashed brown potatoes are lightly blackened and crunchy outside, soft within. The baked potatoes are done perfectly. The salads are of fresh, unblemished greens in a tart, limpid dressing —the arugula, for example, has a full, strong fragrance, as if it were just picked.

Excessive desserts, but good of their kind. The cheese cake at this restaurant is not what it was a few years back, but it is one of the best of its type in town—extremely rich and creamy, very heavily lemoned. The napoleon is made up, elementally, of thick layers of custard between very flaky layers of pastry. If all of that sounds like too much, which it should be if you have eaten well to this point, there is a more than decent raspberry sherbet served in more than indecent quantity.

• GALLAGHER'S

228 West 52nd Street
LUNCH, MONDAY TO SATURDAY; DINNER, DAILY.
Reservations, CI 5–5336.
Credit cards: AE, BA, CB, DC, MC.
Expensive.

The mahogany walls of this famous masculine Mecca, where fame is all and how you got it little, are crowded with sporting engravings and paintings, caricatures of jockeys in brightly colored silks, pen-and-ink sketches of lovable Broadway characters, and hundreds of photographs of pugilists and ballplayers, pols of the past (derbied, smiling thinly), race horses (head and shoulders, in brown or chestnut, against very blue skies), their owners (proudly holding the reins in the winner's circle), actors (in full dress) and actresses (in a little less). No epicures, however, are so honored, no gastronomes, no gourmets or famous gluttons, no chefs, no brewers or distillers even— the closest we come is a picture of the H. M. Stevens family.

Men come here, where the famous have been, to indulge their manly fantasies—pairs of men, groups of men, men alone—to read the paper and have clams, steak and beer. Ladies do not come here; ladies are brought here. And they wear skirts, mind you, *skirts*. Pants are rare. Men wear pants. The drinks are big and strong, and the food is big and (sometimes) tough.

Insular, speak-easy ethics govern. Not to suggest in any way that this is a violent establishment, but when one clown gets off his bar stool to knock another off his, the disputants are merely separated and the more flagrant offender asked to leave. "No police" is an ancient rule in these places, not always unspoken. (The mysterious explanation: "We don't want any trouble.") The house comes first, and men in dark-blue uniforms make certain regular customers uncomfortable.

You can predict 90 percent of the menu, but you can't predict the conversation.

"Microcosms are boring as hell," he explains to her, as he poisons his perfectly good oyster with a jigger of cocktail sauce. She lowers her eyes in respect, simultaneously forking a lump of tasteless chopped liver.

"I *never* make love to a woman I don't like," he remonstrates a bit later on, finding it difficult to handle her sudden insight while attempting to carve the resilient London broil (here peddled as Sliced Beefsteak on Toast and served with a sauce of watered Bahamian mustard). He by-passes that obstacle by changing the subject, and she learns that "Opera is Italian, orchestra is German" while learning, too, that the fried shrimp in beer batter are delicious—done in hot fat, crisp, moist, huge, tender. He's really fielding them now, and he does not notice that the French fried onion rings are coarse, greasy and wilted, because he is explaining, "Sure you're married. But you're married in Brooklyn. This is Manhattan."

They have a good laugh over that one, and she, happily surrendering to his good-humored but irresistible flow of virile logic, polishes off 75 percent of their delicious lyonnaise potatoes, and then makes the serious mistake of ordering Apple Pie Mel Ott. She errs again by not returning the tasteless mess to the outfield. He orders Kid Chocolate Pie on the assumption, presumably, that—like the Kid—it will be featherweight, when, in fact, it is overweight, dried out and past its prime. He doesn't care, because they are relaxing into a comfortable interlude of reviews of common acquaintances. "Martin? He reads a lot, goes to the track, and has a medium-sized circle of intellectual friends. Still, he's not a bad guy." She rinses out with coffee that arrives in a hospital carafe (Gallagher's Special Coffee), and he, now confident, and with the gracious generosity that comes of impending success, buys a couple of drinks for the yokels at the next table, who giggle and sip as he makes Mr. feel comfortable by settling with him into a discussion of grain futures ("I know for an absolute fact you're crazy not to buy corn tomorrow") while she enlightens Mother, complete with addresses written on matchbooks, about upstairs places where the "finest furs" are "less than wholesale."

That main course of fried shrimp makes an excellent appetizer for two. Good clams, oysters, herring, steaks, chops and roast beef; the grilled bass is reliable, but the accompanying stewed tomatoes come from an institutional container. The salad is nourishing. Michelob beer on tap. Bad desserts, though the strawberries are sometimes in good condition; they can be seen in the same glass-walled refrigerator near the front door in which the beef is aged and displayed.

Gallagher's is a comfortable restaurant: a handsome, commodious bar; large-enough tables, spaced well apart; captain's chairs and red-leather banquettes; and soft lighting from hanging fixtures of crossed logs and copper cones. At one time the logs were real, but the bark began to shed into the food.

The service is available, mechanical and bored. The waiters are at their best when no questions are asked.

★★ JOE & ROSE

745 Third Avenue (near 46th Street)
LUNCH, MONDAY TO FRIDAY; DINNER, MONDAY TO SATURDAY.
Closed Sunday.
Reservations, 355–8874.
Credit cards: AE, DC.
Expensive.

This is Old New York. The customers, some of them, are out of thirties movies, the ones about newspapermen and underworld figures and men about town in the days when such types didn't know any better and wore their hair short and slicked down, had their suits made with narrow lapels, wore stick pins in their ties, bought corsages for their ladies, who, in turn, spoke only when spoken to, and then adoringly, unless they were Rosalind Russell.

A series of homey little rooms, one of them with a bar, the others with tables and chairs and booths. The walls are a dusky tan, and they are hung with an assortment of prints, etchings, oils, watercolors, a few of them plumb. Above all that, of course, is the stamped-tin ceiling.

The place has a hustle-bustle air about it, within which the calm, competent waiters seem doubly self-composed, their tasks well in hand. You ask one of them for a bottle of good Chianti, and he offers an Antinori—he *does* know what he is about.

Joe & Rose is one of a type—the Italian steakhouse. It is generally not thought of as one of the Steak Row restaurants, though it is no farther from the Row than, say, the Palm. But there is something so relaxed about the place, and there is so little of the studied masculinity affected by the other Steak Row restaurants and their customers that this seems a place apart. Joe & Rose is superior to most of the Row restaurants, second only to Christ Cella in the quality of its food and almost equal to that place in the cordial professionalism of its service.

"First we'll split a manicotti." "Good," answers the waiter, and you get the impression that you are in fact being favored with an expert opinion and that favorable opinions are not the only ones he delivers. The manicotti is immense, a simple thing of pasta stuffed with creamy ricotta cheese and covered with a rich and oily meat sauce —this is hearty food, perfectly and freshly prepared. You can get excellent clams and oysters and shrimp here, but to give the Italian side of the place its due, a little pasta is recommended.

The steaks are of perfect beef, accurately broiled—lightly blackened outside; fibrous, tender and bloody within. During soft-shell season you get a different notion of soft-shell crabs when you eat them here. They are sautéed in olive oil rather than in butter, which gives them a distinctly Italian quality without sacrificing any of the delicacy of the crabs themselves, which are tender, fresh and sweet.

A good side-order house: lyonnaise potatoes that are almost spectacularly variegated, within the limits of lyonnaise potatoes—there are butter-soaked and soft slices of potato, slices that are leathery and brown, slices that are crisp, and in among these are the onions, limp and juicy, some almost burnt, some barely at the translucent stage; French fried onions that are crunchy and salty, made in a clean batter, so that the coating seems to crackle on the crisp onions. The orders are mammoth.

The desserts are pretty bad, but you won't want them if you didn't fight with yourself over whether to finish your potatoes. The rum cake simply lacks breed—a layer of chocolate between two layers of white cake, the whole thing awash in liquor. Commercial pies, ice creams, and little else.

★ MR. MIKE'S

345 West 46th Street
LUNCH, MONDAY TO FRIDAY; DINNER, TUESDAY TO SATURDAY.
Closed Sunday.
Reservations, 246–4220.
Credit cards: AE, BA, CB, DC, MC.
Expensive.

This is one of the more recently founded enterprises along this self-styled Restaurant Row, and unlike the other well-worn shops on this block that feed the before- and after-theater crowds, Mr. Mike's lacks a flavor of tradition, the quality of having arrived at its present over a period of changing times. This is not entirely a function of the restaurant's youth. This is a formula restaurant, derived not so much from Mr. Mike Macario's notion of the kind of place he would like to eat in, but from his estimate (apparently an accurate one) of what is likely to succeed. The wood paneling is very Motel; the walls of little framed "RESERVED" signs, each one with the name of one of the restaurant's regulars written in (the appropriate sign is taken from the wall and placed on a table when a reservation is made), are as contrived a "custom" as the clay pipes on the ceiling of Keen's; and the blackboard menu of steaks, a few veal items, a few seafood dishes, is obviously designed for popularity and low risk on the food inventory, rather than for interesting eating. Dozens of pictures of wild cats and domesticated dogs all over the place are supremely irrelevant. Even the fresh flowers on the table look calculated; it seems inconceivable that anyone around here *likes flowers*. It's just that there's a budget for flowers. There is also a budget for candles, but trimmed—the budget, that is, not the candles. So instead of candles we get those little battery-charged lamps that look so much like candles within glass that people who sit down to unlit ones, noting with envy the faint glow at other tables, sometimes lift off the glass and light theirs. As the things are made of a waxlike composition, they commence to burn. If this is permitted to go on, they can explode, and on occasion waiters are seen hustling ignited ones, at arm's length, into the kitchen.

You are greeted by Mr. Mike's missus, a brisk babe with the strut of a London cop and the determined cheer of a social director at a nursing home. On being asked by her if one would like a drink, one has the unmistakable impression that to say no would be to show insufficient cooperativeness, or enthusiasm, or community spirit. You order drinks and you get *big* drinks, as befits a sturdy steakhouse kind of place, and the food is pretty good too, as suits its immodest price.

A shrimp cocktail of big shrimp and strong sauce; ripe melon and good prosciutto ham; Italian roasted peppers made to look like a gigantic portion by being served as a blanket over a mound of lettuce. But one way to make the most of this restaurant's limited menu is to pass up the conventional appetizers and begin with an order of scallops divvied up as an appetizer. These are not tiny bay scallops, but they are so fresh and tender, so delicately breaded, so elegantly deep-fried in hot oil, their crusts so receptive to the squeezing on of lemon that it is difficult to imagine them more perfectly rendered. Even the tartar sauce that accompanies them, which they assuredly do not need, is creamy and tart.

Nor can you fault the steak; perfectly seared to seal in the juices, the excellent aged beef is on a par with what you get in the city's better steakhouses. Mr. Mike's makes much of its veal—plume de veau and all that, the whitest, tenderest, youngest veal going, etc. But what is the point if the ultimate preparation of it is lackluster, the subtle quality of the meat obscured by a Marsala sauce that tastes like candy? The meat itself, by the way, is poorly sautéed, and instead of being lightly browned in a hot greased pan, seems to be simmered in tepid butter. With your main course you are likely to get poorly fried potatoes, a bit greasy, lacking crispness; but the string beans, startlingly, are fresh, barely simmered, crunchy.

With all its flaws, there is one undeniable virtue about this restaurant: the veal, beef and seafood that they start out with are just about perfect. They don't know what to do with the veal, but their preparations of the beef and seafood are simple and pure, and for that kind of dinner, this is a good spot.

For dessert there is little choice. Ripe melon is available, or a rum cake that is not like many other rum cakes—a thoroughly rum-soaked mound of meringue, white cake and mocca cream. It should calm the appestat.

On your way out, you bid good night to Madame and her bulldog.

• PALM

837 Second Avenue (near 45th Street)
LUNCH, MONDAY TO FRIDAY; DINNER, MONDAY TO SATURDAY.
Closed Sunday.
Reservations for lunch only, 687–2953.
Credit cards: AE, BA, DC, MC.
Very expensive.

This venerable institution is certainly one of the most unusual-*looking* restaurants in New York. The narrow downstairs rooms and the more commodious upstairs dining area are painted a pale-coffee stain, and the walls and some of the ceilings are adorned, if that is the correct word, with painted caricatures, some forty years old. There is sawdust on the brown floor, the lights are bright, and from the choice window seats, there is a spectacular view of Second Avenue.

The Palm is one of those places in which there is no printed or written menu—the waiter recites the available dishes. There are about half a dozen things wrong with this idiotic system. To begin with, one makes his choice under the more or less impatient or bored gaze of the waiter, as he stands now on one foot, now on the other. Here at the Palm, where the listing is brief, some of the waiters recite less than all of it, anyway, and only initiates (who remember meals past) are in fact choosing from the complete selection. At places like Giordano's, on the other hand, the complete recitation takes about ten minutes even when delivered at an incomprehensible clip, and choosing one's food is not so much an act of selection as it is a feat of memory. Naturally, when there is no menu, there is no posted list of prices; your waiter at the Palm may inform you of the prices, and then again he may not; and of course there is no document against which to check the accuracy of the bill.

Fully 99 percent of the customers here have lobster, sirloin steak or filet mignon, preceded by shrimp cocktail or clams, accompanied by some fried potatoes, and followed by cheese cake and coffee. Deviates cause some of the waiters to lift their eyes heavenward.

A sample encounter:

Waiter: "What can I do for you?"

Customer: "What do you have?"

W: "Anything your little heart desires, my little lady." He pats her arm.

C: (Innocently) "Do you have steak?"

W: "You want filet or sirloin? How do you want it?"

C: "Just a minute. Do you have anything else?"

W: "We got lobster."

C: "That's all? Steak and lobster?"

W: "Anything your little heart desires, my little lady." He pats her arm again.

(Pause, while the waiter greets two customers, kissing the woman, shaking hands with the gent, happily getting *that* straight.)

C: "Could you tell us everything you have?"

W: "Sure. We got steak, lobster, chop steak, lamb chops, pork chops, roast beef."

C: "No fish?"

W: "We got sole."

It takes an additional five minutes to determine that there are two kinds of potatoes: cottage fries (good when they are pale; tasteless and pointless when they are dark) and home fries (a huge platter of deliciously fried and browned spuds, made without tossing, so that there are gradations of brownness and crispness through the dish); three kinds of salad dressings: Russian, Roquefort (made with the real thing) and oil-and-vinegar; that there is wine, but that there is no wine card to choose from, and so on.

The steaks and chops are good, though not invariably cooked as ordered. The lobsters are an achievement—they appear to weigh about four pounds and completely disprove the notion that large lobsters are tough or tasteless. They are broiled to perfection, tender and juicy, and the meat picks up an interesting flavor from the charred shell. Desserts are good, though undistinguished: cheese cake, ice cream and melon.

Strictly speaking, this is not a restaurant. It's a club for people who like it—people who like to wait for tables in the middle of a cramped dining room, since the house refuses to take dinner reservations (officially) because that would sacrifice a little business for customer convenience, and customers can wait; people who like to talk at the tops of their voices, or at least don't mind when people at nearby tables do; people who like to swagger and be recognized at a place where people swagger; people who don't like to be greeted by a host but prefer to be fought over by finger-snapping waiters when the place is not full; people who don't mind an occasional rotten tomato in their salad. These people come here by the thousands, and presumably there is something positive that they like about the place other than the food, which is not peerless. It's so casual, you can almost remove your shoes. Maybe that's it.

This is a very expensive restaurant, not worth the price. Try it. If you like it, you'll love it.

• PETER LUGER

178 Broadway (Brooklyn)
LUNCH AND DINNER.
Reservations accepted for three or more, EV 7-7400.
No credit cards.
Expensive.

Some of the legends that have developed about the New York restaurant scene are all-pervasive and indestructible. Ask a hundred people to name the six or eight best steak restaurants in New York, and 90 percent of them will include Peter Luger on their list. Most of them have never been to the place, because it is under the Brooklyn end of the Williamsburg Bridge, if that means anything to you. But nevertheless, they are correct. It is one of the six or eight best steak restaurants in New York, but what of it?

A wine expert, on the remote subject of vermouth, writes that "Vermouth-making is a complicated but not a great art." It can be said that steak-making is a simple but not a great art. The steak may be great, but the art is not. So for a steak place to be a fine restaurant, we look elsewhere for its art, and there is little to be found at Peter Luger. The art, or rather the imagination, is supplied by the customers, who attribute great value to such appurtenances as the simple, bare wooden tables—the honest color of unstained oak; and to the simple, bare wooden floor—a somewhat grayer but equally honest color. How much value can be found in the simple, rather tasteless home fried potatoes; or in the unstained and also uncooked pie crust under the apple pie; or in the simple wine list which is also almost bare; or in the simple cheese cake, which is simply insipid and barely worthy of a stand-in-line cafeteria?

But now for the good (well, better) news. The shrimp cocktail comes with a good, tangy sauce, and the shrimp have a fresh taste and they are firm. The other appetizer consists of a plate of alternating slabs of tomatoes and raw onions. The tomatoes are good for these days, red and fairly juicy, instead of the usual items of pulp and dry seeds; and the onions are freshly sliced, moist and strong. There is a pitcher of red stuff on the table—the famous house dressing—and it is sweet and spicy, and very good on the tomatoes and onions.

Peter Luger serves the best steaks in Brooklyn—huge porterhouses, the equal of any steak in Manhattan. But they tend to cook them rarer than you want, unless you ask for them rare, and you can't very well send them back for more cooking because they arrive at your table already sliced, and to broil or grill a sliced steak is to drive all the moisture out of it. You have to demand a new steak, and you can imagine what kind of reaction that generates.

Sometimes there is roast beef, and sometimes there is not, and sometimes there are lamb chops, but not always. These items are competently prepared, but you can't be sure of the availability of anything but porterhouse steak.

The place is certainly unpretentious and comfortable—when you arrive you hang your coat on one of the coat hooks that are all along the walls. And when you sit down you are promptly brought a basket of rolls and good rye bread and a plate of cool butter by one of the corps of waiters, who are almost invariably courteous, friendly and alert. And if what you want is a dinner of shrimp cocktail, steak and ice cream, you will have difficulty faulting this restaurant.

★★ PIETRO'S

201 East 45th Street
LUNCH, MONDAY TO FRIDAY; DINNER, MONDAY TO SATURDAY.
Closed Sunday.
Reservations, MU 2–9760.
No credit cards.
Very expensive.

You go up a flight of stairs to a tiny staging area with a four-stool bar. Here the waiters pass from the kitchen to the dining room, and here you wait, among the culturally deprived rich. In this place, women without make-up are taken to be in mourning, and men in mere woolen suits are assumed to be detectives working on the earie. What they hear is that "the languini is great."

This is one restaurant that always lives up to at least one aspect of its reputation: your reservation is courteously accepted, but your table is never ready at the appointed hour. If you arrive on time, you get an apology. But if you come ten minutes late, the host is hurt: he shakes his head and mutters that he doesn't know what he's going to do with these customers who should realize that they can't hold tables all night when there are other people waiting who know that eight o'clock is eight o'clock not eight-ten and *maybe* there will be a table in half an hour but that's not a promise so don't say it was a promise it was a maybe.

When he's not weeping, he's teaching the passing waiters some of the fine points of dining-room management: "Hey, Table 26 got dere coffee awready—givem da check." The waiters, however, know better—they are working for tips, not turnover, so they don't rush you. And the food is good. So once you get seated in the dining room you're OK, if you brought a shoe full of money—the prices here are wondrous.

Pietro's is a Steak Row restaurant that is also a little Italian, so the usual steakhouse appetizer listing has been deprived of oysters and clams to make room for minestrone ($3.50!) and prosciutto with melon (only $3.25), which are both fine, as is the shrimp cocktail (whoops, $3.50 again).

If you figure you can save money by sharing a pasta as a first course, you are mathematically correct, but admit it, you had in mind saving more than 25 or 50 cents, right? The pasta is cooked to order, and the sauces are good, but spaghetti and meatballs at $6.50 has to be a New York record, if for no other reason than that the more expensive Italian restaurants in New York usually don't list the item. And spaghetti with white clam sauce—fresh clams, abundance of garlic, crisp parsley, and added fillip of lemon notwithstanding—is really something at $6.

Pietro's has not heard about the $10 steak, so they charge only $9.50, even though the steak is huge, perfectly seared outside (sealing in the blood) and cooked to specifications. If your wife whispers that she forgot to bring her mad money, switch to the chopped steak.

Of course, if you're simply stingy, you can have the broiled shrimp, and you'll get what your parsimony deserves—decent enough shrimp, inundated under oily bread crumbs, all of which adds up to something tasting like a shrimp sandwich with oleo. For those who are shrewd as well as stingy, there is broiled chicken at a frugal $7.25 —a perfectly cooked bird, young and thin, so eat slowly to get your money's worth.

Also in the merely outrageous price range is a dish that indicates there is someone in the kitchen who can cook not only simple dishes but dishes that have to be tasted as their cooking goes along. The Veal Cacciatore is of tender sautéed veal in a splendid sauce of wine, mushrooms, carrots, tomatoes and celery, and lots of Italian parsley, which gives off a vibrant aroma—you won't get a much better version of this dish anywhere in New York.

À la carte means à la carte, of course, so if you want some potatoes with your meat, the beautifully browned and crusted platter of hashed browns will be $1.75 please, and if it's some onions you want, the French fried ones are the same price; they are crinkly, skinny little things—a huge mound of them—and have a good, sharp taste.

Four tomato discs under four discs of red onion is the combination favored as salad here, and the vegetables are in fresh-from–New Jersey condition. The blue-cheese dressing you can have with the green salad is superb.

Aside from a perfectly good but unspectacular zabaglione, the desserts are without interest—spumoni, tortoni, rum cake, etc. Just have a cup of espresso—it is strong and thick, and it will set you up for the check.

The menu provides a little light reading which is an exercise in smartspeak, the language of the intellectual automation: "Here, at Pietro's, all meals are prepared directly upon order and we ask your indulgence in giving us sufficient time. Our famed chef, Nat, will make anything you suggest not seen on the menu." And: "Your host, Pietro, will be glad to offer his suggestions in the selection of a fine wine to complement your particular choice of entrée."

One flight up, there are about twenty tables crowded into a small room. Another flight up, and there are twelve more, in an even smaller room. The place is clean, neat and popular. With few exceptions the food is solid and good—always of fresh ingredients in sparkling condition.

Fish

This is a thin chapter, not for lack of seafood houses, but for lack of interesting ones. A couple of places (Sweets, Gage & Tollner) that could appear under this heading are listed elsewhere in the book.

Gloucester House is the best fish restaurant in New York, but it has its faults; for one thing, it is spectacularly expensive. Its good points were once enumerated in an article I wrote in a national magazine. The proprietor of Gloucester House sent me a letter of copious thanks, with a request that I introduce myself the next time I visit the restaurant. I responded in writing, cautioned against hasty gratitude and included a fuller version of my views, as they appeared in *The Restaurant Reporter*. The owner was not heard from again.

More and more in New York restaurants, the fish seems fresh but tasteless and mushy—no smell, but no anything else either. In fact, the fish is frozen, which eliminates spoilage but also taste. The city is set at the edge of the Atlantic, but a can of Bumble Bee Chinook is a known quantity that is superior to what you get in most places.

★★★ LE COLISÉE

36 East 60th Street
LUNCH AND DINNER.
Reservations, 421–8151.
Credit cards: AE, BA, DC, MC.
Very expensive.

Le Colisée's singularity is in the provenance of some of the food it serves. Each day an Air France flight from Paris brings fresh seafood of France to New York for this establishment. Unfortunately, whatever the restaurant may have ordered, the exact make-up of the shipment is unknown until it arrives, or so the management would have you believe when, as often happens, many items on the section of the menu headed "Arrivages de France" are not available.

In an effort to give the place an oceanic air, the rooms have been fitted out like the interior of a high-class yacht, the walls covered in a subtle paper that looks like pale rectangles of end-wood, or sections of cork; walnut columns break the walls into large square sections, each with its print of a sailing ship or an ancient navigation map, framed and behind glass. Here there is an island of greenery, there the lobster tank, and rimming the room a banquette of real brown leather. The effect is a bit stuffy; you expect that the captain, in gray flannels, navy-blue blazer and captain's cap over his closely tonsured silver hair and pink complexion, may wander through at any moment, reacting huffily if anything is out of place or style. And yet the whole restaurant is (but for the colorful china and wild flowers, which come nowhere near making this place gay). True, it is not required of a restaurant that it be cheerful, and many do well to be somber, but there is something inherently light, gay, almost festive about this kind of menu. To think of seafood is to think of holidays at the shore, of boating under brilliant sun, of eating lobster on a wharf at water's edge, of escape from the confining walls of executive offices and book-lined drawing rooms, which are what this place smacks of. But the food is often exceptional here, so wear your rose-colored glasses or your parti-colored goggles or, best of all, your kaleidoscopic contact lenses, and make your table your oasis on this solemn shore.

On occasion your captain (the one who works in the restaurant, not the one who owns the yacht) takes great care to explain to you that the Saumon Cru aux Deux Poivres is not of smoked salmon, nor of cooked salmon chilled, but, rather, of *raw* salmon. He is perhaps unaware that in New York, where Japanese restaurants have been serving raw fish for a couple of decades, uncooked seafood has become almost a commonplace. So humor his protestations, assure him of your understanding and get yourself a little plate of this excellent stuff. Raw salmon is slick and shiny, sweet and moist, almost bland. To serve it under heavy grindings of black and green peppercorns seems like a sure way to obscure what flavor the fish does have, and the pepper does have that effect. Yet this is a wonderful dish, one in which the unalloyed flavors of pepper stand out from a delicate carrier, the way a sauce is revealed by its contrast with pasta. Salmon, you say, is expensive and should not be used as a backdrop? If you eat in places like this, you should not be concerned with the cost. Remember, the world of food is a repertory company, in which the star performers occasionally take minor roles. And the heady fragrance and flavor of freshly ground pepper deserve their brief moments in the limelight.

Clams au Thym (pronounced *clam oh tam*) is a simple dish whose character derives from the generous use of fresh thyme, one of the most useful of all herbs, particularly with seafood. Even during the seasons when fresh thyme is available, most cooks in restaurants (as well as most at home) habitually reach for dried thyme, which is better than nothing, but not much more. These clams are steamed in a peppery and milky broth that fills the air with the smoky flavor of the fresh herb, perfect flavors for the plump little clams. And the steaming is not overdone, so the clams reach you approximately as tender as they were the moment they were dredged from the sea.

One of the best first courses in the place can be lifted from the main-course listing. The Langoustines à la Nage (one of the dishes the makings of which arrive from overseas) are those hefty prawns often served cold in France, with mayonnaise or other thick, cool sauce. But they are often eaten hot, as here, served up in the broth in which they were cooked. The flavors of the langoustines and of the broth are very much oceanic, without being sea-gamy—they are at once sweet and strong. And they are best enjoyed eaten with the hands, tearing the thin shell away from the firm white bodies. Naturally, you drink a cold white Burgundy with this dish, and naturally, the outside of your glass looks like a milky finger painting before long.

Order fresh glasses after you have cleaned up with the aid of finger bowls, and proceed to Sole Normande, another of the "Arrivages de France," served as half a dozen folded filets, laid out in the design of an asterisk under a creamy fish-stock sauce and a handful of local mussels. The international combo plays just fine together. That sole is also available as Goujon de Sole, an inelegant but satisfying dish in which short lengths of fish are sautéed until they are very much like nockerl, plump and shapeless noodles, here used to good advantage to show off a thick sauce flavored principally with fennel, and flamed in vodka. There have always been a couple of places around town that received fresh turbot from France each day. Le Colisée is now added to the list. The delicate yet firm fish is served simply, with a thick and lemony hollandaise. If you passed up the raw salmon on any grounds at all, you may have it as Saumon Poellé à l'Oseille, which is to say, pan-fried salmon served with sorrel. Well, the fresh salmon is lightly browned in the frying, and a creamy little sauce is provided to moisten and lighten it, but that so-called sorrel tastes like very good spinach, made with much nutmeg. International license.

Le Colisée serves a great cheese, which they refer to as St. Hubert. Whatever or whoever that may be, this is an irresistibly rich and pungent cheese, served in copious quantity, excellent with the crusty bread. For something sweet, the blueberry tart has its excellences—principally that the berries are just barely cooked. You are eating plump, firm berries, a creamy and polished custard, and browned and flaky pastry, all at the same time! Very clever, these French.

★★GLOUCESTER HOUSE

37 East 50th Street
LUNCH AND DINNER.
Reservations, PL 5–7394.
Credit cards: AE, BA, CB, DC, MC.
Very expensive.

Gloucester House does what it can to perpetuate Puritan propriety, economic stratification, racial separation and bluenose privacy. To keep the riffraff out, gentlemen are required to arrive with coats and ties and about a pound of bank notes—the à la carte prices are insane.

The room itself is rather severe, though not unattractive or uncomfortable. There are sanded tabletops on the main level and finished ones on the level above, all unclothed; there are comfortable captain's chairs just like the ones on the customers' boats; an interior window display of ship models; and a plaque of sailor's knots. To this Northern severity is added a plantation note: the serving staff is almost exclusively of color, and their supervisors uniformly pink.

You're greeted at the door (and inspected) by a type who carefully checks your name against a list and turns you over to one of the handwringing floorwalkers. (They say "Ahem" a great deal, and look back every few steps as they lead you to your table.)

And yet, unfortunately, this is probably the best seafood restaurant in New York— in part because Gloucester House serves some superb food, and in part because the other fish restaurants in New York are terrible, or OK, or even, on occasion, good— but only on occasion. Gloucester House has a variety of foods and of preparations, and this breadth is found among the listings of first courses, shellfish stews, curries, broiled fish, Newburgs and au gratins, salads, vegetables and even (astonishing in fish restaurants) desserts.

Many New York restaurants list a number of oyster varieties in addition to local ones (usually bluepoints), but Gloucester House sometimes goes so far as to actually sell them. These oysters are not superior to New York oysters, just different. Cape Cods, for example, are clearer-tasting, less metallic, less oily, rather stimulating. Chincoteagues (from Virginia) are also available on occasion. The menu says: "Please state your choice: large or small oysters." Ask for large ones—unlike large clams, large oysters are as good as little ones, and they are bigger. Eat them with lemon juice and a few grains from a pepper mill; if you're going to bury them in cocktail sauce, they might as well be pickled onions. The alternate sauce Mignonette served here lacks shallots and parsley, and simply has no sense to it.

The crabmeat at Gloucester House is *fresh*. You can have it straight, in a cocktail, or wrapped in bacon and broiled—a nice dish, though only four morsels, each the size of a child's thumb. The littlenecks (8) are, happily, minuscule; the steamers are sandy, though the hot clam broth is hearty and lightly celeried; the roasted shrimp in garlic butter are tender and just lightly garlicked; the "Freshly opened Clam Juice" is from freshly opened clams, not bottles; and if nothing else will serve, half a cold lobster is an elegant first course. There are good chowders and shellfish stews, and while all this is getting under way, superb, fluffy hot biscuits, just out of the oven, are brought to your table when you ask for them, and sometimes even when you do not.

There are about thirty varieties of fish listed on the menu, and on a given day about a dozen prices are written in, indicating that those kinds are available, or at least that they were at the beginning of the day. They are fresh, and broiled carefully, so that each variety maintains its character—dark, succulent bluefish, flaky snapper; strong, oily halibut; nutlike flounder, and so on. The shad roe, as in most places, is a little overcooked unless you specify that you want it rare. The overcooking is a gesture to those who want the luxury of eating shad roe but don't actually like the stuff—it is moist and jellylike when it is cooked properly, but it tastes much better that way. After all, fish eggs—what did you expect? The roe is served, bizarrely, with a poor hollandaise sauce, presumably to offset the overcooking. A better solution is melted butter and lemon. The best solution is not to overcook it in the first place.

The broiled and steamed lobsters are done perfectly, and each arrives with a numbered tag on a plastic pole, like the ducks at Tour d'Argent. God knows why. The lobster bibs are of nice soft linen.

Terrific vegetables: thin, thin, delicious, crisp, deep-fried onion rings; delicate, fluffy discs of fried zucchini; good charcoal-broiled eggplant. The French fried potatoes are called "Raw French Fried Potatoes," which means they are not parboiled early in the day for future frying, which is the right approach, but the eventual frying is not hot enough to make a really crispy potato. Fresh corn on the cob is available.

At least one of the desserts is a peerless masterpiece, called Gloucester House Special. It is an airy froth of fresh orange juice and whipped cream, garnished with a tangy marmalade made on the premises. Blueberry Slump is stewed blueberries with whipped cream—in winter, when scrawny Mexican blueberries are used, it is just so-so; much better in summer, when large local berries are available. The delicate strawberry mousse is uncompromising in its purity—nothing is done to emphasize the strawberry flavor, which is naturally thinned out a little in the preparation. The strawberry shortcake is authentic—fresh berries on a light biscuit, covered with unsweetened whipped cream. The apple pie is fairly good.

Next to a number of items on the Gloucester House menu are the words "When Available," which is fairly uninformative, as none of the items can be had when they are not available. But the clear implication is that everything else is almost always available (setting aside the unpriced fish varieties). Which brings up a problem here. Take, for example, the soused shrimp, mussels in curry sauce, billi-bi, turtle soup, various desserts, twenty of thirty wines, and four of six listed beers, most of which were not available at three of three lunches and dinners. When engaged in conversation on the subject, the plump, close-cropped, narrow-lapelled proctor smiled tolerantly and explained that late in the day certain items run out. At lunch the same authority attributed shortages to the weather. He mumbled and became a little hesitant when challenged about the wines, but recovered his poise at once when asked about the chronic unavailability of guilfords (listed in three places on the menu). He stood up even straighter than before and won that one with "We had those last Tuesday!," emphasized with an orator's index finger pointed heavenward.

The proprietor is a white-haired patrician giant who concerns himself primarily with the placement of nautical paintings on the walls. On occasion he takes a seat in the dining room and gazes, over the heads of the diners, out to sea.

The service is unsupervised, and varies from cursory to gracious. A number of the waiters know the menu inside and out, and enjoy talking about the food. Others are short-answer specialists. At these prices the place should be staffed with professional captains.

At lunchtime the place is packed, which tends to dim the austere atmosphere somewhat. The same menu serves at lunch and dinner.

★ OSCAR'S SALT OF THE SEA

1155 Third Avenue (near 68th Street)
LUNCH AND DINNER.
No reservations (TR 9–1199).
No credit cards.
Medium-priced.

Oscar's is a three-room restaurant with such a heavy volume of business that fully a third of the store space is given over to the amenities and mechanics of handling the flow of customers. The center one of the three large rooms in series (the shape-up area) includes the entrance to the restaurant; a booth at which a comely thing takes names for future seating in order of arrival (the wait can be an hour); the mechanized coat-check apparatus; rows of seats, movie style, in which the patient sit and stare so blankly and intently that one turns and looks automatically for the television set that isn't there; and a giant square bar which holds forty comfortably, seventy-five usually, behind which shirt-sleeved mixer-pourers stir and make change like plugged-in automatons. Through it all a wanderer with a clipboard (he has Miss Comely's list of names now) traipses and calls "Mr. Brllumpy. Mr. Brllumpy? Mr. Brllumpy!" as tables become available.

Today's Oscar's is a modernization and expansion of a smaller place that did business at this site when the El shaded Third Avenue. Today the place looks almost Scandinavian—walls of polished wood or white brick, rows of white globes in the dining-room ceilings, ranks of polished wooden tables. The food, however, is old-fashioned, and there are few surprises on the menu except the prices, which are among the lowest of any decent fish restaurant in New York.

There are the usual raw clams and bluepoints, and as you would expect in a place this busy, they are always fresh. The fish chowder has lots of fish, dill and pepper in it, but it is a dull soup, rather leaden; the New England chowder, though light on clams, has a nice smoky pork taste, and cubes of potatoes that are added shortly before serving, so that they are just done. The mussels with garlic broth are a much more interesting matter. The mountain of mussels (imperfectly scrubbed, it's true, many still wearing beards) has been steamed with great quantities of onions, carrots and celery, and immense branches of fresh dill (a favored Oscar's herb). It is served with the cooking liquid thickened with butter and strongly flavored with garlic—a splendid solution to the problem of what to do with the billions of mussels that line local shores. There are baked oysters (whole); baked clams (minced) in which bread crumbs and paprika play major roles; and steamers, shellfish cocktails, and so forth. But the mussels take the prize.

At Oscar's you can have your fish broiled, deep-fried or steamed plain, or steamed with the same mixture of vegetables and dill used in the mussel dish. The broiling cannot be faulted. Many of the unaccompanied middle-aged men who take a lot of their meals here get their daily ration of cosseting at the same time. The motherly waitresses lean over them solicitously and record in detail the instructions for the exact broiling procedure: leave the fish whole and make the skin crisp; split it and remove the skin; bone it and split it; remove the tail but leave the head (imagine). Deep-frying should be reserved for fish and chips, and steaming removes the oil from a fish—it's a bad preparation for, say, bluefish (with or without the vegetables), but it works out pretty well for salmon. There are sixteen varieties of fish on the menu, and blackboards in the shape-up room list the ones that are out (not many) and the extra varieties available on a given day.

The Clam Fry is delicious if you like fried clams, the Shrimp Fry not quite so successful—but these are gestures to the Howard Johnson crowd, served with a shiny bottle of Heinz ketchup. There is something called Shrimp with Clam Sauce, which only sounds Cantonese—the shrimp arrive in a flour-thickened, oregano-flavored clam soup. It's a bad thing to do to shrimp, and the clams come off no better.

It's astonishing how many people believe that lobster tails are lobsters without claws. ("Just give me lobster tails—the claws are too much work; let the kitchen use them in salad.") Lobster tails are quite another animal. They usually come from South Africa, aren't as good as American lobsters to begin with, and by the time they arrive here, they taste and feel like rubber. Real lobsters can be had at Oscar's, broiled, boiled or baked, and they are sensibly priced.

The desserts are a good reason to make the most of the earlier sections of the menu. Good American wine is available by the liter and half-gallon. Drink up.

This is a no-nonsense restaurant, and if you linger at your table during the busy hours, the busboy will quietly pick up everything but your cigarette lighter, to let you know your time has come. Go.

★★OYSTER BAR & RESTAURANT

Grand Central Station, lower level
LUNCH AND DINNER.
Closed Saturday and Sunday.
Reservations, 532–3888.
Credit cards: AE, BA, CB, DC, MC.
Medium-priced.

The refreshed Oyster Bar is an affectionate restoration of a bit of Old New York, a rediscovered underground cave much like an abandoned subway station, long and cavernous, its vaulted ceilings of tan tiles newly polished and glinting as if half a century of accumulated grime had preserved their sheen for us; the installation of simple and cheerful appointments has converted these potentially somber halls (for the last few decades they *have* been dreary) into a subterranean surprise, picnic grounds in a grotto.

The familiar winding counter at one end of the longish premises has been resurfaced in white. The long bar that adjoins is topped with the old red marble, gleaming stainless-steel appliances behind, including the familiar hemispherical pots the shellfish stews are made in. At the eastern end the terrazzo and red-tile floor has been sprinkled with tables that are gaily linened with blue-and-white gingham. At the center, just inside the glass-and-ironwork entrance doors are the lobster tanks. And at either end, high up on the varnished wooden walls, there are railroad clocks, complete with the correct time—long ago, before it was an OTB office, Grand Central was a railroad station, and in those days the Oyster Bar never closed. Offer up a fervent word of fervent thanks: this may be the only seafood restaurant in New York that has eschewed the usual hanging junk—no stuffed fish, no buoys or watercolor seascapes, nary a seine. This is a straight restaurant, peddling little more than honest food in comfortable surroundings. And the casually uniformed young people in navy blue (light-blue vests on the waiters, light-blue aprons on the waitresses) handle the service cheerfully and efficiently.

For all these virtues New York has turned out, madly at lunchtime, and with just enough enthusiasm to keep the place busy but not booming at night. Solitary late-working commuters have a fish *cum* newspaper before training home for two hours of TV and then bed. Brave city people come by subway, eat, go home by subway, setting foot on city streets only at the beginning and end of their evenings out. Others arrive by cab at the Vanderbilt Avenue entrance—no chichi, at least not of the day, but there have been some dignified-looking arrivals who appear to have ventured from their apartments for the first time since the war (WW II) on the rumor that a piece of the lost city has been located.

You will like the menu, that is, the physical thing itself: a sheet of paper, the size of a small pillowcase on which are listed about 125 items of food, 100 or so with prices alongside; no price means not available, and new menus are printed daily, with revisions.

Six kinds of oysters is a big deal these days, when most restaurants merely list "oysters," and you take what they have. But there was a time when a mere six varieties would have been the stock in trade of a street vendor, when respectable seafood restaurants had listings that read like the complete roster of an Eastern milk train. Take, for example, this collection, reported by Joseph Mitchell, in 1945, as an old man's memories of the good old days: Shrewsburys, Maurice River Coves, Narragansetts, Wickfords, Cotuits, Buzzards Bays, Cape Cods, Chincoteagues, Lynnhavens, Poko-mokes, Mobjacks, Horn Harbors, York Rivers, Hampton Bars, Rappahannocks, Goose Creeks—the list goes on and on. With overdredged and polluted waters, that romance is over, and we are well off with this restaurant's six, plus the usual clams, herring, chowders, over thirty varieties of fish (with more than half of them available on any given day), live lobsters, five preparations of shrimp, several cold fish dishes, a dozen different stews and pan roasts, and a handful of international seafood preparations.

OK, very nice. But it must be told that all is not exactly delicious—nothing actually bad (or less than fresh), you understand, but you can be disappointed by a gross cooking one time, a careless one another.

Those raw clams and oysters are fresh, but the most interesting items in the mollusk category are the cooked oysters. The trick in cooking oysters is to preserve all the qualities of the raw oyster—that tender and oily sweetness, the briny, almost gamy edge —heighten them by the addition of heat, that is, give them the quality of actually being *cooked,* and surround them with flavors and textures that enhance but do not obscure the oysters themselves. And the trickiest part of the trick is to not toughen the oysters in the process. Very tricky, this Oyster Bar. You can get some extraordinary oysters broiled in anchovy butter. The deep bluepoint shells are filled to the brim with hot melted butter that is brown and sharp with its admixture of ground anchovies, and at the center of each shell sits a plump oyster, tender and rich, with, actually, a broiled (emphasized) taste to it, and nothing of its freshness lost. And you can get an impeccably prepared oyster stew—a simple dish of oysters that are gently poached in their own liquid, milk and cream, butter and seasonings. This is a rich bowl of food, well-populated with oysters, distinctly American cooking in its warmth and simplicity.

Rhode Island is represented by Point Judith Herring, and the Oyster Bar by the dill sauce served with it. The silvery cutlet of fish is at once sweet and tart, firm and tender without any of the mushiness you find in commercial herring; and the dill sauce is a simple thing of sour cream and fresh dill. Happily, the sauce is not made in big batches in advance of mealtimes, but apparently to order, for the dill has all its delicate springiness and pungent flavor.

There is another herringlike entry on the menu, inappropriately listed under "Today's Catch." This is Lake Winnipeg goldeye, a flaky reddish-gold fish that is salted and smoked before shipping and steamed to your order. The meat is almost buttery and because it is salted it seems like a rich herring—a terrific plate of fish.

If you have wondered why all the sturgeon you run across is smoked, the reason is not merely that smoked sturgeon tastes good, but that fresh sturgeon does not. Fresh sturgeon is on the menu here, broiled, and it is a dry and stringy thing. You are safe with familiar fish—bluefish, striped bass, shad—they are fresh and usually accurately broiled, in butter. On occasion fried whitebait is available, but the little sliverlike bodies are rather heavily battered and deep-fried overly long—their flavor is too near that of the heavy and far-from-crisp French fries that accompany the dish.

The lobsters are live, and at $5.75 per pound they are not outrageously priced for these days. But a broiled lobster with a moist body but dried-out claws is no bargain at any price, and they manage to overbroil the lobster without charring the shell—too bad, for a charred shell can add a lovely taste to the meat itself. Have yours steamed.

Desserts include a couple of decent pies, ice cream and sundaes, a "strawberry shortcake" that is not strawberry shortcake, but nice sponge cake with strawberries and whipped cream.

With its flaws, a welcome addition to the scene—now that it is here, indispensable.

★★SEA FARE OF THE AEGEAN

25 West 56th Street
LUNCH AND DINNER.
Reservations, 581–0540.
Credit cards: AE, BA, CB, DC, MC.
Expensive.

The décor says: Bring on the conventioneers. You can also bring your out-of-town in-laws, your secretary on her birthday (if you don't take her anywhere at other times), and visiting diplomats from Jackson Heights. The art on the walls will make the mail-order print collectors feel right at home, as will the furnishings—the statuary, idle pillars and stuffed chairs appear to have been abducted from a seraglio.

All this attracts a lot of people. It also frightens away the more knowing crowd, who understandably consider tasteless appointments an omen of bad-tasting food. This time they are wrong. Put on your dark glasses and see for yourself. The food—all seafood, except for a couple of chicken dishes and the desserts—is very good, and the service is cordial, helpful and quick.

Though this is a Greek seafood restaurant, most of the dishes are not Greek. Only four of the twenty-two appetizers and soups are Greek, but the four are authentic and well made. There is a splendid red snapper soup, flavored with lemon and a little celery. It has a distinct taste of the sea and is clearly a broth of red snapper, not the canned clam juice that is the base of most fish soups served in local restaurants. The tarama (the well-known paste of fish roe and moistened bread, with onion, oil and lemon) is very delicate, understating the roe and seasonings. There is a good Aegean salad, with greens in perfect condition, feta cheese, strong ripe olives, anchovies, and a lemon dressing made with a very light oil. (With anchovies omitted, it would make a much better house salad than the sorry one with a cream dressing that is served with the main courses.) The clams casino, though hardly Greek, are among the best in town. Lightly flavored with pimentos and green peppers, they happily lack the quality of bread crumbs made sodden with oil. The other first courses—raw clams and oysters, shrimp, chowders, and so forth—are fine, but available anywhere, and here one should order the Greek specialties.

There are more than sixty main courses, and eight of them are interesting and authentic Greek dishes. Of necessity the fish is American but only the better varieties, including striped bass and red snapper. The baked bass with clams, in wine sauce, is very nice. Fresh clams are used, in their shells, and the dish has a wonderfully hearty ocean flavor. The casserole of baked shrimp, with feta cheese, is a very earthy concoction. Feta cheese becomes very loud when it is cooked, so if you like strong, gamy food, you'll probably enjoy this dish. There is no compromise here for the institutional palate.

This restaurant offers an abundant variety of simple broiled fish—about twenty kinds are available in season. There is no special trick to broiling a fish (get a fresh fish, butter it, broil until done), yet Sea Fare of the Aegean is one of the few places where broiled fish is prepared properly.

Plan on having no dessert; the dessert menu is long but of no interest.

★★ SLOPPY LOUIE'S

92 South Street (near John Street)
LUNCH AND DINNER.
Closed Saturday and Sunday.
No reservations (952–9657).
No credit cards.
No liquor.
Inexpensive.

In appearance Sloppy Louie's is about as primitive a restaurant as you will find. In the dining room there are two rows of long wooden tables, one row along each side, six chairs at each table. The kitchen is behind the dining room, partially hidden from view by a mirrored partition. At one back corner there are coffee urns, and at the other there is a steel cabinet that holds glasses and silverware. In front there is a cash register, and near the door, a cigarette machine with a few extra chairs inverted on it. Three frosted-glass lamps hang from the wavy, stamped-tin ceiling. This is a seafood restaurant, and along the walls hand-lettered signs announce the varieties of fresh fish that are in season and available. There is also a printed menu. When the place is crowded, a rough line forms at the front just inside the door. The long tables are shared by strangers. This causes no problems.

On each table there is a bottle of ketchup, a bottle of Worcestershire sauce, and a bottle of Red Devil. The place is patrolled by waiters in assorted uniforms—this short, thin man in a neat blue linen jacket, that giant in a limp short-sleeved white shirt and a white apron down to his ankles. They are diligent and intelligent, and compared to the clowns at Sweets, around the corner, they are courtly, gallant, empathic, clairvoyant. The customers are diverse—respectably suited men come here from the financial district, second-generation Chinese walk over from Chinatown, people from SoHo come here, as do people from the low- and middle-income high-rise housing projects that are within walking distance of South Street. This restaurant is in the neighborhood of the old Fulton Street fish market, and here you can still get fish and shellfish that are as sweet and fresh as any in the city.

The thing to know about Sloppy Louie's is that you should order the simple dishes. Avoid the chowders, which are rather thick. The bouillabaisse is an artless and not particularly satisfying soup; the squid (or whatever) sautéed in garlic sauce is toughened in the process, though the sauce itself is very tasty. This leaves you with a lengthy assortment of shellfish and fish, raw, broiled or deep-fried, and you get them in perfect condition nearly every time.

If you start off with a shellfish "cocktail," you'll find, not surprisingly, that the oysters or clams are sweet and juicy. But the shrimp and crabmeat taste just as fresh, and that is rare. You can also have your oysters fried, and the dish is something of a miracle—true, the batter is dull, but it is perfectly crisped, and the frying is done so rapidly that the oysters are warmed without being the least bit toughened. When shad roe is in season, this is a good place to get it. The roe is carefully handled, so that the membrane that surrounds it is not broken; this keeps the moisture of the roe inside, where it belongs, and you get moist roe in a crisp, browned skin. The broiled fish at this restaurant is as good as any in New York. You can prove this five times at once by ordering the Seafood Combination Broiled. You will get lemon sole, striped bass, snapper, halibut and salmon, or, sometimes, another fish that is in season substituted for one of the listed ones. If all fish tastes the same to you, try this dish—each fish is so carefully prepared that its character is preserved, vividly clear, and after a few bites you will be a minor expert on the flavors of certain Eastern fish.

Little dishes of salad are served when you sit down: sometimes good cole slaw; sometimes cold beets that are pretty good; sometimes lettuce, in vinegar and paprika, which is bad. This is not, as they say, a dessert house—the strawberry shortcake, for example, is made with frozen strawberries. There is ice cream.

Customers continue to arrive right up until closing time. At seven fifty-eight you may order and be served and not be rushed. At eight the front door is firmly locked, and no more orders are taken.

In the middle of the afternoon this is a sleepy restaurant. The waiters, cooks and dishwashers nurse mugs of coffee at the back tables. A few regular customers sit down with them and gossip. A handful of people with no afternoon obligations let their lunches spin out, talking or reading. At first glance Sloppy Louie's looks like an end-of-the-line place, but in recollection it is shining clean.

Iberian/Latin

This little collection of restaurants, under the umbrella of the Iberian languages, proves, if it proves anything, that there exists among these cuisines of common ancestry more diversity than likeness.

Restaurants that serve the food of Spanish- and Portuguese-speaking countries have never caught on in fancy dress; the appeal has always been food-of-a-poor-country for the unrich citizens of this one. Restaurant Associates, for example, never made a go of La Fonda del Sol, their essay in South American chic, and after a couple of transformations gave up. The Spanish Pavilion was something of an exception for a number of years—both posh and popular—but it is now defunct.

The best Latin meal in New York is discussed in another chapter. It is the feijoada, the national dish of Brazil, served at Casa Brasil on Wednesday nights only.

Clue: sangría, the Spanish drink of sweetened wine and fruit, is a method of selling inferior wine at superior prices, and few places make a decent version of it; the brandy, for example, is almost always omitted. The best drink with Mexican and Cuban food is beer; with Spanish food, Spanish wine.

★ BRAZILIAN PAVILION

141 East 52nd Street
LUNCH AND DINNER.
Closed Sunday.
Reservations accepted for dinner only, PL 8–8129.
Credit cards: BA, MC.
Medium-priced.

A pretty restaurant, smallish, made to seem larger by mirrored walls. There are colorful murals of Rio, simple caned chairs at the tables, much green and yellow, the colors of the Brazilian flag. The menu is extensive and authentic, the prices reasonable for a good restaurant in midtown Manhattan; and the place has become very popular. At lunchtime it gets a substantial share of the traffic from the nearby office buildings, and in the evening New York's casual and experimental young keep coming from all over town and help to keep the place busy. The Pavilion is a little noisy, a soothing hum, and part of the sound is the gentle, singsong sibilance of the Portuguese language, for the place is also frequented by members of New York's growing Brazilian population.

The assorted appetizer platters include a number of simple things (canned sardines, hearts of palm and olives), but also a terrific Portuguese sausage that is oily, spicy and fibrous, and best of all, shrimps that have been cooked in their shells, in oil—they are warm, crisp, strongly flavored (leaving the shell on does that) and satisfying.

None of the main courses here is what you would call a delicacy. Brazilian food is vigorous and full of contrasts, and this place, like the other Brazilian restaurants in New York, puts plenty of food on your plate. When you have eaten, you know that you have eaten.

Churrasco Gaucho is a delicious steak, marinated and accurately broiled. The meat, which is tender, has been marinated thoroughly (with onions, peppers and tomatoes), so that the flavor of the marinade has permeated the meat; and it is served in a thin sauce of the marinade itself, with rice and a mound of manioc meal, the zesty flour ground from the yuca root, which is a common starch in Latin America.

On Fridays there is Cod Fish "a Gomes de Sa," a heavy and hearty dish of cod fish, baked with potato salad and slices of hard-cooked egg—oily, salty, loud. It is sprinkled with parsley, which is something like garnishing a side of beef with a cherry tomato.

Virado a Paulista is a dish of pork chops that have been peppered and blackened, served with substantial discs of grilled sausage and black beans that are winey and thick, all surmounted by a fried egg, and served with kale and the manioc flour. This is about as vigorous a plate of food as you can imagine.

Marmelada com Queijo, as you probably guessed, is quince paste and cheese—a cool, hard block of sweet preserves served with a Brazilian cheese that is not likely to develop a substantial following outside Brazil. The caramel custard here is cool and jellylike, covered with shredded coconut. Powerful coffee that is very good.

★ CABANA CARIOCA

123 West 45th Street
LUNCH AND DINNER.
Reservations, 582–8510.
No credit cards.
Inexpensive.

Cabana Carioca is a center for Portuguese-speaking people in New York, though a rather humble one. Brazilian magazines and newspapers are sold here; notices of lectures, concerts and meetings are posted; and though the front room of this second-story establishment is a restaurant open to all, complete with linen-covered tables, many of the Brazilian regulars, to whom this is a second home, eat at the bare tables and counter in the back room, where, even when voices are amplified in argument, the soft notes of Portuguese fill the room with music.

The dining room proper, though absolutely devoid of splendor, has a certain charm. One wall is papered in the famous waved pattern of mosaic of certain sidewalks of Rio; elsewhere there is a juke box, a cigarette machine, two dream paintings of Rio, stacks of beer cartons, and a poster of American Presidents; and if one is bored, a seat at the large front window decorated with credit-card imprimaturs and beer signs affords a view of West 45th Street, including the Hotel Peerless (you can imagine), and other human zoos of constantly changing management. With all that, the place is comfortable, and the food is reliable.

The menu is in Portuguese and English, and the translations from the former to the latter are sometimes approximate. Caldo Verde (literally "green broth," which is in itself hardly descriptive) is translated as Mashed Potatoes Soup, which is perhaps closer but rather off-putting. The delicious soup is a purée of potatoes strongly flavored with finely shredded collard greens, a little garlic, salt and olive oil. The black-bean soup is less interesting, the usual thing plus rice. The other first courses are sardines or fruit.

Feijoada, the national dish of Brazil, is served here on Thursdays and Saturdays, and a portion served one day may well hold you until the other. One receives a huge pot of the hearty stuff, with the very peasanty and peppery sausage, stringy dried beef, tender beef ribs and strong dried pork buried in an abundance of dark moist beans. It is served with rice and slices of fresh orange, and if you order it, the thoughtful waiters here will warn you away from preceding it with a heavy first course.

On Fridays, according to the English-language menu, bluefish is served. In fact, the fish is not necessarily bluefish, but simply fresh fish baked with tomatoes and onions. On the same day there is served a very satisfying dish of tripe, white beans and sausages, stewed in tomatoes, herbs, garlic and onions—cold-weather food.

Among the dishes served throughout the week there is an interesting one of boiled shrimp flavored with tomatoes, and in the style of Bahia, a heavy dosage of coconut. Most of the food is served with black beans and rice; and a harmless-looking little plastic dispenser is usually placed on the table which contains piri-piri, a superb essence of hot pepper in olive oil—a couple of drops will suffice.

Beer is recommended, or maté, the favored drink of Brazil's poorer classes. To describe it is to undersell it. It is made from dried ilex leaves, has a strong, smoky taste and is drunk either hot or cold. Some people like it, and some don't.

Avoid the rice pudding. The custard and guava desserts are OK. Best is the intensely sweet, heavy, honey-textured milk caramel, and a cup of the strong, delicious coffee.

Green-and-yellow printed paper napkins, rolled up, wait in the drinking glasses at each set place. There are a few wine bottles on the walls. In midafternoon the proprietor sits at one of the tables in the front room. Visitors come and go, interrupting him with gossip.

★ FRINI

271 Amsterdam Avenue (near 72nd Street)
LUNCH AND DINNER.
Closed Monday.
Reservations accepted, TR 4–8950.
Credit cards: AE, BA, CB, DC, MC.
Beer and wine.
Medium-priced.

Everyone is a convert to plastic ornamentation after one visit to this garish and gay gallery of gauds. To show off the baubles we have walls and ceilings of brite-white plaster, from which are hung golden autumn leaves that were never green, and geometrically perfect conical clusters of purple grapes (seedless), all interspersed with leetle lights. Also we have these ropes of red onions, these guitars, these hats of the matador, these depictions of the red-dressed flamenco dancer dancing, presumably, the flamenco, and naturally, bullfight posters. Nestled among the flowers and greenery in one corner, a brass maiden forever pours from her jug into a little pool—a thin stream that makes a familiar sound and an unexpected light mist (you may prefer a table once removed —it is only water, but still . . .). There is live Muzak—most nights a "Paraguayan harpist" plinks pleasantly on his Paraguayan harp. Your suave black-shirted host is unbuttoned almost to the waist. On a chain that depends from his belt, where you wear your Phi Beta Kappa key, he displays the Playboy rabbit. Red napkins form diamonds on the white-clothed tables. The waitresses wear skimpy red dresses and speak just a bit of English, but good and willing translators are usually available at neighboring tables—the customers are mostly from the neighborhood, and this neighborhood is now in large part Spanish-speaking.

They come for the food of Mexico, Cuba, and Central and South America. Cuban and Mexican dishes, of sorts, are available in many places around town, but right now this is the restaurant that offers the widest variety of dishes from countries farther to the south.

Seviche is a dish that is generally associated with Peru, but it is made all over the (Latin) place. Usually it is made of fish—marinated, raw, in lemon and/or lime juice, with hot red peppers and onions, until the fish is "cooked" and turned white by the citric acid in the fruit juice. In addition to the usual fish seviche, Frini sells a seviche made of shrimp, and though it does not have the odd sweet-and-briny quality of raw fish, it has virtues of its own. The marinated shrimp are perfectly crisp (never been cooked), and behind the hot-and-sour flavors of the marinade they taste elegantly, elementally shrimpy, loud and clear. The raw onions are nice too, and the whole dish is served still in its marinade, which will, if you drink it, take care of your Vitamin C requirements for the day.

Good guacamole, a huge bowl of it, studded with fritos, like little sails. It is made of ripe avocado, bits of tomato, green pepper and onion, and plenty of hot pepper. It does suffer a bit from being cool rather than at room temperature.

A couple of interesting Argentine first courses: Matambre is a dish of flat, marinated beef, rolled around vegetables and hard-cooked eggs, poached and served either hot or cold with a spicy sauce in which the strong, dominant ingredient is the loud form of parsley called cilantro; here it is served cold, as an appetizer, cross sections of the loaf, so you can analyze the insides, the fairly loud beef quite delicious with the sour, herby sauce. Empanada Argentina, a turnover stuffed with ground beef, hard-cooked eggs, olives, and unexpectedly, sweet dark raisins—heavy going, but good.

Admittedly, the Calamares Rellenos en Caserol is a dish that is more Spanish than Latin American, but this should not prevent you from ordering it. In this version the little squid bodies, instead of being sliced into circlets, are left whole and stuffed with the tentacles, which is, don't deny it, clever. They are sautéed with garlic and herbs and onions, stewed in their own ink and served in a little pot. The squid are slightly rubbery, as they should be, the inky sauce the consistency of heavy oil. Very good stuff.

Most of the food here is complex. The Bistec Palomilla is not. It is a slab of marinated beef, just the tender side of tough, actually of a very pleasing and slightly chewy consistency, served under lightly sautéed crisp onions. Watch out for the Venezuela Hallaca, beloved, undoubtedly, by the natives and obviously a vivid evocation of the earthiest kind of cave-in-the-side-of-the-hill cooking; it will probably horrify you. The menu description is gripping enough ("made with corn meal stuffed with chicken, pork, raisins, olives, capers, onions, bacon, sweet red pimientos, served with rice and black beans $4.50"), but you may have trouble coming to grips with what it is—heavy, wet corn bread studded, here and there in the morass, with the listed solids. Even the heavy flavoring with bay leaf fails to give an edge to this end-of-a-long-cold-day-in-the-freezing-mountains dish. Next to it the accompanying black beans (with bits of meat) and rice are a light relish, something to liven it up. Not to criticize. Recommend it to a friend and taste it while you order the Carne Mechada for yourself, which is potted meat dotted with stuffed olives, and served in a peppery but not excessively hot tomato sauce.

The common flan and guava shells are available. But you will want something more musical, like Pudin de Coco Loco, a very sweet custardlike pudding, in caramel, sprinkled with grated coconut, or Dulce de Leche Casero, a slightly pebbly pudding made with sour milk, brown sugar and coconut—terrific with the good coffee served here.

★★ GRANADOS

125 MacDougal Street (at 3rd Street)
LUNCH, MONDAY TO FRIDAY; DINNER, DAILY.
Reservations, OR 3–5576.
Credit cards: AE, CB, DC, MC.
Medium-priced.

Granados is not an immediately engaging place. Though firmly established in a section of Greenwich Village which has always been Greenwich Village, its stained stucco exterior looks like a broken-down roadhouse outside a depressed factory town.

Things do not improve much in the front room (where one enters). "Check your coats for the dining room," you are commanded, and in this slightly frightening atmosphere, which somehow seems to be composed of electrified purple-and-black air, you obey. The people at the bar are not invariably waiting for tables in the dining room, and it is difficult even to speculate on what they *are* waiting for. There is a cigarette machine, juke box (with those forties teardrop-shaped Seeburg loudspeakers spotted here and there), television set, and over the bar, a mock chandelier of sangría pitchers.

And yet, as soon as you enter the back room, it's immediately clear that this is an honest restaurant. The impression is certainly not caused by the décor. Three of the walls are of pale rough plaster, cracking in places; electric conduit is visible, leading to the wall-mounted space heaters used on the coldest nights; the ceiling is an aged red, with wooden beams; and the fourth wall is the showpiece—a bit of red-flocked wallpaper and rickety, red Venetian blinds. There are hideous paintings here and there, and a mysterious sign reads: "Paintings on Display are for sale. Inquire Within." (There are also dozens of Goya etchings—not for sale.) But there is something about the simple arrangement, albeit rather crowded, of the tables that suggests a straightforward establishment. They are in three rows, some of them covered with white cloths, and others are of exposed Spanish tiles. And there is something about the customers that suggests a satisfied clientele—they have been eating here for many years, they know the menu and order easily, and they look as comfortable as they could possibly be in their own living rooms.

There are only two first courses on the menu—a good, strong garlic soup and, served in the summer, an unusual gazpacho with raw fruit. Regular customers usually order several main dishes, make appetizers of one or two, and then eat the others by helping themselves from communal plates placed in the center of the table. Fish and seafood are generally eaten first, game and meat afterward.

There is a rather complex salmagundi of octopus served here, made with green olives, onions and red peppers, in a dark oily sauce flavored with bay. The octopus is well-cooked, so that it is not rubbery, and the tentacles are bespangled with their rows of the little suckers that cause some people to rise slowly for a breath of air. Wonderful stuff—the octopus, not the air.

The Zarzuela de Mariscos (literally a "light opera of seafood") is, rather, a tragedy. The whole thing is apparently cooked at once, the shrimp without their shells, so they are tasteless, and the clams right from the beginning of the process, so they are hard. The lobster tails, scallops and mussels can take it, and they are OK, but the whole thing is in something called egg sauce and tastes like a preparation designed for a delicate stomach. But the Shrimp Rebozados—breaded, fried and covered with a strong cooking sauce of oil, pimentos, parsley and wine—is what you should have ordered in the first place; care must be taken not to consume all the bread in the effort to soak up all the sauce. Use a spoon.

Five items are listed under Game, but this is a mistranslation of Aves, which means birds, and three are chicken. The other two are partridge, called quail, and mallard duck, called mallard duck. The partridge is splendidly browned over a fire and served in a limpid sauce of oil, sweet wine and rosemary, and happily garnished with slices of fresh orange.

Pork marinated in garlic and wine, roasted and served in huge slices with a roasting-pan glaze made with almonds and pine nuts is understandably one of the most popular dishes here. Years ago only almonds were used, but they are expensive. Presumably, in the not distant future, only pine nuts will be used, which will be the ruination of this succulent and very satisfying dish—there is an edge to the flavor of almonds that is simply not present in pine nuts, and that quality keeps the dish from being simply heavy.

The salad and desserts are the usual stuff found in New York's Spanish restaurants: the former consists of greens and tomatoes in a dressing fortified with red pepper—a take-home bottle of the stuff is $1. The desserts are flan, ice cream, fresh fruit, and so on.

In warm weather a few outdoor tables are set up, but table-side encounters with MacDougal street passers-by are more education than one wants during dinner.

• EL PARADOR CAFÉ

325 East 34th Street
DINNER.
Closed Sunday.
No reservations (679–6812).
No credit cards.
Medium-priced.

Its proponents claim that what distinguishes El Parador from the myriad of mediocre Mexican restaurants that are beginning to line Manhattan's avenues in the middle-income neighborhoods is not the food based on the tortilla—no, the tacos, tamales and tostadas at El Parador, they admit, are just junk food, sound excuses for an evening of beer drinking. It is, they claim, the more pretentious specialties that make this quite pretentious establishment. It is true, they are better than the junk food.

El Parador is a busy restaurant, but it is not the mob scene it once was. Nevertheless, when you arrive and there are tables empty and ready (and they cannot be ready for anyone in particular, because the house does not accept reservations), you are told that there will be a wait at the bar, you are assured that it will not exceed thirty minutes, and the scene has been set—here on 'way-East 34th Street, what can you head for and be sure to be seated in much less than thirty minutes? So you hit the bar, order the two drinks the whole charade is designed to sell, and as soon as that transaction is completed you are seated at one of the several available tables. And your host is so gracious! Shame, *shame,* Señor Jacott. Just to sell a couple of your excellent Margueritas?

You are led to your table by a waiter carrying your barely sipped drinks, lambs from the slaughter.

Seviche is a marvelous dish of raw fish that has been "cooked" by marination in lemon or lime juice and any of several other ingredients, depending on which Latin country is the source of the recipe. If we may take it that the seviche at El Parador is typical of the Mexican method of preparing this dish, then we may conclude that Peruvians, Bolivians, Cubans, etc., enjoy it more. They start out with a nice fish here —red snapper—and they marinate it in lemon juice, but somehow some of the fish becomes chewy in the process. Then they garnish it with a couple of slices of avocado whose quite brown, loud overripeness could not have been concealed in a guacamole, and serve it on a pile of shredded iceberg lettuce that becomes limp in the drained-off marinade from the fish. The production is strewn with fresh peas. Unusual. The latest sampling of guacamole at El Parador is superior to the bland stuff this restaurant used to serve—it is garlicky and sharp, almost winy, and it would be first rate if it were not served at refrigerator temperature.

You were warned when seated that your Chicken a El Parado would take thirty minutes. You should have been warned twice. Eventually it arrives, a giant serving of crusty, garlicked fried chicken, garnished with a huge poached onion and a scattering of fresh peas. This is good fried chicken, albeit a bit heavy, but its reputation is not on its merit, but on its comparison with most Mexican food in New York. It may be the best dish in the place, but that is not a particularly exalted position. There is a pretty fair dish of shrimps in green sauce served here—good shrimps in a sauce that has a loud, clear flavor of fresh parsley. Unfortunately, the sauce is watery and if you spoon it over the excellent rice that is served with the main courses, you ruin the rice.

Slightly better than average Mexican-restaurant desserts, including nice guava shells, grainy and tart, with a creamy cheese and crisp saltine crackers—homey but good.

El Parador is a dim, sexy place, but avoid the downstairs room—Grand Rapids brick and ornate mirrors, and every time the kitchen door opens, the glaring white light jars.

★★PUERTA REAL

243 East 58th Street
LUNCH, MONDAY TO FRIDAY; DINNER, MONDAY TO SATURDAY.
Closed Sunday.
Reservations, 758–4756.
Credit cards: AE, CB, DC.
Medium-priced.

Eleven tables in a cozy room, most of them occupied by Spanish Abe Beames and Mrs. Beames, also priests, also prosperous East Siders who have discovered the place. None of these is noisy, but in this setting of low ceiling and close walls of rough, chalky plaster, the softest sounds are converted into a minor din. If the place were not so dimly lit, it would be cutesy, but by this starlight one only vaguely senses the dark beams, shelves of folk crockery, false windows over painted country scenes. The tiny bar at the front is often rather crammed with waiting customers. In the dining room the service is of a certain kind—the waiters move very quickly, but they shift into a very polite "Park" when they are at your table; you sense, however, that the engine is idling fast, and sure enough, when the at-table service is done, they are off on their sprints. To support a restaurant on East 58th Street, particularly with reasonable prices, eleven tables must be well served—efficiently but not hastily.

To begin, have the Salpicon de Mariscos—a vibrant seafood salad of chunks of lobster, shrimps and mussels, with capers and minced hard-cooked eggs, in a tart dressing that rouses the flavors; the lobster and shrimps are firm and tasty, the mussels tender and vividly fresh. The specialty of the casa is Caracoles en Cazuela Puerta Real —plump, tender, salty snails in mushroom caps, in a deep pool of spicy oil; the dish is not brilliant, but the ingredients are so impeccable, the snails so soft and meaty, the mushrooms so fresh, crisp and browned, the oil so smooth and fiery that the food achieves elegance from simple perfection. There is a black-bean soup, Crema de Alubias Pintas—a thick purée, winy, enriched with cream and sharpened with red pepper.

There is a touch of hokum in the serving of the main courses, a bit of the passing of the pans of food over a flame before it is spooned onto plates, but it is more a gesture to a tradition than a pretense that any actual cooking is taking place on the serving stand, and the food is finally handled with such respect, it is so deftly spooned or speared, so artfully arranged on the dishes that one is not offended. The menu is like that of many Spanish restaurants in New York, but a few dishes are listed separately under "Our Specialties." Pollo en Cazuela del Jefe, for example, is a chicken dish with mushrooms, *lots* of chicken and *lots* of good mushrooms, but for some wholly inexplicable reason, there is an admixture therein of the kinds of little onions that come in jars to displace some of your Gibson. The chicken is fine, hot and moist, and like many of the dishes here, salty, though not beyond reason—but oh, those onions! You are better off with another of the specialties, Zarzuela de Mariscos del Jefe Antonio—tiny, tender little clams in their shells; fresh mussels in theirs; a good portion of lobster in its; all moistened with a superior sauce of sherry that has been laced with the licorice flavor of fennel; the extra sauce is fine on the delicious rice.

A flan that is different! Even in shape. This custard is cut from a loaf, and it is firm and moistened with caramel, as most are, but it is also studded with nuts and additionally flavored with a citrus liqueur—very nice. A dessert that is different! A pine-nut cake, light, liquored, with lots of crunchy nuts in the moist loaf.

★★ TORREMOLINOS

230 East 51st Street
LUNCH, MONDAY TO FRIDAY; DINNER, MONDAY TO SATURDAY.
Closed Sunday.
Reservations, 755–1862.
Credit cards: AE, CB, DC, MC.
Medium-priced.

White stucco walls, bare brick, high beamed ceilings, lofty archways between rooms, old iron street lanterns, a fireplace, hanging hams and sausages and cheese and onions, shelves of crockery, a few copper pans, an old-city setting, suggesting a Spanish street café under a portico. The tables before you sound an elegant note in the earthy setting—white cloths set with brilliant-red napkins, tall red candles, long-stemmed red carnations in slender vases.

In the kitchen they start with good ingredients; they do not misuse them, sometimes they even improve them—never brilliantly, but often artfully.

If you come once, the appetizer to begin with is Gambas al Ajillo. In a little earthenware pot you get about ten little shrimps, crunchy morsels, in a thick sauce of oil, red pepper and minced fresh garlic, all very loud and lovely. You tilt the pot so that when the sauce forms a deep pool on one side, you can completely immerse each shrimp before you eat it. Since there will be a good bit of the pungent liquid left over after you have finished the shrimps, you polish that off with bread—the bread itself is terrible, but its tastelessness is utterly overwhelmed by the pepper and garlic. The Mejillones Salsa Verde are no match for the shrimps, but these mussels in a so-called green sauce are pretty good. The mussels are fresh, clear-tasting, tender; the sauce, however, is bland—not much sherry, not much parsley—and it tastes better straight than over the mussels because the mussel flavor obscures the sauce. Nevertheless, a pretty good dish. Strong black-bean soup, creamy and winy and well-flavored with pepper, thick and satisfying.

Nice service of the main courses. The food is wheeled to your table on a cart; there it is, attractively laid out on serving platters or in gleaming pans. It is dished out onto hot plates and served. There is no pretense that anything is being done to the food beyond what was done in the kitchen—this is not an imitation of so-called French service. But there is something slightly coarse in service that consists of merely carrying dished-out food from the kitchen to you, and there is something distinctly gracious about arranging it attractively and serving it at the table.

Mignonette de Ternera Riojana is veal sautéed with Rioja wine. The veal is thick, pale, tender, nicely browned in the sautéeing. It is bedecked with lengths of Spanish ham and garnished with white asparagus, a vegetable the canned version of which is not bad, and an artichoke heart, the canned version of which is. The good sauce is winy and herbed.

Filetes de Lenguado Granada is described on the menu as "Filets of Sole Sautéed with Banana and topped with Hollandaise Sauce." The sauce is not hollandaise, but the dish is good anyway, the fish fresh and fluffy. The mild white sauce and the sweet ripe bananas cover the fish and are browned under the broiler. The main courses are accompanied by good vegetables—crisp string beans, fresh sweet peas.

All the standard Spanish desserts, of course, but also a few others: a rich, wet chocolate cake that is liquored and covered with crisp almonds and powdered sugar —very good; and strawberries in a sweet sherry sauce—the sauce is a bit icky, but the strawberries are ripe and juicy.

As the evening wears on, the guitarist switches from his soulful flamenco repertoire to the requests he receives at the bar and at the tables. He does an unfortunate Guantanamera, but it brings in the tips. Sometimes (not often) he takes a break, because one of those trios of Spanish "students"—mandolin, guitar and tambourine—stop here on their rounds and fill the place with their healthy baritone voices in renditions of what are purported to be Spanish student songs. Are Spanish students allowed to *have* student songs? At any rate, it seems the students never return to their studies, because they are doing too well financing them with their nightly tours of New York's Spanish restaurants.

A happy place.

Chinatown and Beyond

The Chinese restaurant scene is seething and has been since the first Szechuan restaurant opened in the mid-sixties. Every time things begin to settle down, someone comes up with a new province. To Americans who have a casual knowledge of Chinese food, developed, perhaps, from eating in Chinese restaurants and reading restaurant reviews, there are thought to be four major regional categories of Chinese cuisine, named for the province where each style of cooking was developed, or for the principal city of the province: Cantonese, Szechuan, Peking, Shanghai. The distinctions among these styles of cooking are valid if not invariably clear, and things get even fuzzier when the food of the other Chinese provinces is considered; these places may border on a couple of the Big Four regions, and the typical food of these areas may influence, be influenced by and, perforce, resemble the food of its neighbors. Such a place is the province of Hunan, which is hard by Szechuan and Kwangtung (of which Canton is the capital city). Hunan shook 'em up when reactions to the first injections of Szechuan blood were subsiding. Yunnan has just arrived. The first Mongolian restaurant is yet to be opened—be not the first on whom the new is tried. A Chinese-restaurant watcher perceives a movement for Reformation emerging from within the midst of the peppery excesses of the day; there will be a return to traditional values; just below the horizon, *Cantonese* food (which is what everyone was talking about in the thirties, forties and fifties, when they said, "Let's eat Chinks tonight") is ascending.

Some Chinese-restaurant mythology is true. The chefs *do* move around from restaurant to restaurant. You get great pig's liver with mushrooms one night, so you bring a circle of your friends (for one of the big, circular tables) a week later. The stuff is tasted by the assemblage, and everyone offers a silent prayer that the others will make a respectable dent in the communal dish. New chef. And you have a reputation to rebuild.

General rules about eating in Chinese restaurants: (1) the best alcohol with Chinese food is beer or whiskey (though champagne can be not bad, Western still wine is ridiculous); (2) if you order a dish and the waiter tries to talk you out of having it, insist; it's probably one of the better items in the place, but with an assertive individuality which, the waiter has found, is generally not acceptable to non-Chinese palates; (3) have dessert somewhere else.

★★ CHEF MA'S

10 Pell Street (near the Bowery)
LUNCH AND DINNER.
Reservations, 964–5842.
No credit cards.
Beer.
Inexpensive.

By Chinatown standards this is a good-size restaurant, and much of the floor space is given over to large round tables that can accommodate the multi-generation Chinese family parties that make up a good portion of this restaurant's business (bottles of Johnnie Walker Black Label on the tables for once-in-a-lifetime events, Red Label for annuals). There are booths along the side, walls of tan and white patterned tiles, walnut paneling, mirrors. It is all rather smooth for Chinatown, and the effect is only slightly undone by the hand-lettered sheets of pink paper, Scotchtaped here and there to the walls, announcing, in Chinese and in English, or in Chinese only, specialties of the house that are not printed on the menu.

The service is casual and sweet, even intelligent and informative if you are taken care of by the gentleman with the gold tooth. But the principal appeal of this place is Mr. Ma's cooking, and you can just about select from the menu blindfolded. The food arrives at your table in sparkling condition, just prepared of fresh ingredients (to the extent that that is possible with Chinese food in New York), and the preparation and flavoring are almost invariably artful and appetizing, often startling.

Not everyone will want to start his dinner with Spiced Kidneys. Kidneys, face it, taste funny, and feel funny. At least they usually do, because they are rarely thoroughly rinsed free of their acids, and because they are not cut free of their tough membranes. Kidneys, as they are served at Chef Ma's, are delicate, almost sweet, and utterly free of gristle. They are sautéed very rapidly, so they do not toughen, and they are flavored with little nuggets of excellent black pepper and served steaming in a perfumed brown broth.

A dish that may be more immediately appealing to American tastes is Beef with Whole Baby Corn. This simple dish consists of tender slices of beef that have been briefly sautéed, so that there are still traces of blood at the center of each piece of meat; crisp green snow peas; and tiny ears of corn, the size of your large finger—you don't attempt to eat just the kernels, you eat the entire thing, and it tastes slightly of that sweet juice you suck out of an adult corn when you have bitten off all the kernels. This dish is served in a fairly thick sauce that is dominated by the juice of the meat. The dish called Pork with Scallions is actually pork with garlic chives, and it is not an exact replication of the original Chinese dish, which is made with a chivelike shoot grown in China which is yellow because it is never exposed to sunlight. Authenticity aside, this approximation will do. The dish is made of shredded pork, the chives and fried strips of bean curd. You get a huge spicy mound of the mixture, and the glistening succulent meat, crisp greens and pliant, browned bean curd are a perfect balance of flavors and textures.

It is assumed you will make several visits. And when you have satisfied yourself with the aforementioned, you may wish to sample the chicken or seafood dishes. Among the former is Chicken with Chestnuts (not on the menu). The startling thing about this dish is the fresh, yet smoky quality, almost like bacon, of the whole chestnuts. They do tend to overwhelm the mild chicken, but the dish, accented with chopped scallion greens, is delicious nevertheless. Also not on the menu is Fish with Asparagus. The asparagus makes this dish. The vegetable is cooked to that perfect point where it is still crisp, brilliantly green, tender and moist. The sautéed fish (lightly browned), which one might expect to play a leading role, is actually more like the spaghetti to the sauce. The fish is *al dente,* and good in itself, but the asparagus is perfect. The two elements are combined in a barely flavored, velvety, almost limpid sauce. If you are not hungry, but want something delicious, the Steamed Crabs are steamed with ginger and served with a bowl of soy sauce and scallion greens, to dip the crabmeat in—but this is a dish for a mouse milker. The trouble it takes to separate a bit of pleasure and sustenance from the crab shell will seem excessive to any self-respecting glutton, the delicious taste of the dish notwithstanding.

The Ma Poo Bean Curd is a delicious and very spicy accompaniment to any of the dishes here—cubes of bean curd in ground pork, quite fiery. The Hot Cabbage is actually cool, but it is heavily flavored with Szechuan peppers; many Chinese restaurants in New York serve versions of this dish of marinated cabbage with sugar and strong seasoning, but this quite oily one, only slightly sweetened, is very likely the best around.

★★ CHI MER

12 Chatham Square (near Pell Street)
LUNCH AND DINNER.
Reservations, 267-4565.
Credit cards: AE, BA, CB, DC, MC.
Inexpensive.

Once inside Chi Mer, it's hard to believe you are in Chinatown. The place is spacious, clean, almost antiseptic, though not unpleasant. An exposed brick wall in a Chinese restaurant? Decorator colors, like deep-mustard and Mediterranean-blue? Why doesn't this place look like a renovated movie house, or a converted brothel, or a whitewashed furnace room? We must relieve ourselves of our preconceptions.

The kitchen of this restaurant is one of the most reliable in Chinatown, and they are always working with good ingredients. It is virtually impossible to have a bad meal here. But if you are looking for local color, the best this place has to offer is the casual, amused, head-scratching carrying-on that goes for service.

The cold dish called Aromatic Smoked Fish (which, inscrutably, is not actually smoked) is composed of fish that has been marinated in soy sauce and wine, deep-fried until it is almost black and served cold, flavored with anise. The version here is tender, crisp outside, and very moist. The cold Roast Shrimp are, unfortunately, served in their shells, which means that you (1) eat the shells with the shrimp, which is not bad, or (2) tear the shells off with your fingers, which is messy, but you can get one of those little foil-wrapped wet paper towels for after this course and before the next one, or (3) bring your own knife, and perform the de-shelling with that and a house fork, for house knives are not available. The dish is worth the trouble, however, because the shrimp are perfectly cooked, and they are served in a sweet, thick sauce flavored with ginger and anise.

The Chi Mer Soup is a strong chicken broth, populated by such contrasting delicacies as fish and shrimp balls (mild and tender), pork balls (stronger, meaty, just as tender), chicken, black mushrooms (smoky and pleasantly rubbery), snow peas (bright green, sweet, crunchy), fresh spinach, and for good looks and a slippery texture, strands of cellophane noodles (firm and glistening).

Chi Mer manages to get the food to your table looking as good as it tastes. The Crab Meat with Vegetable Hearts is a large platter of pale cabbage hearts, a few mustard greens, an ample portion of red-flecked crabmeat, all in a pale sauce with heavy globules of chicken fat.

The Crisp Fried Chicken with Special Sauce is in a sauce that has a strong flavor of caramelized sugar; and the Crisp Duckling with Butterfly Roll is just as moist and crisp as the chicken, served with steamed bread and seasoned salt. Something called Three Taste Sizzling Rice is a mélange of spicy ham, chicken balls, shrimp balls and pork balls, green vegetables, glutinous sea cucumbers, and mushrooms, in a thick sauce, served over crackling, sizzling rice.

★★ CUISINE OF SZECHUAN

33 Irving Place (near 16th Street)
LUNCH AND DINNER.
Reservations, 982–5678.
No credit cards.
No liquor.
Inexpensive.

If the nation's shortage of resources engenders utilitarian chic, Cuisine of Szechuan will, to its astonishment and without so much as the flick of a warped chopstick, find itself aglitter with galaxies of awards of three- and four-star ratings for undécor. From the white plastic frame just inside the door, wherein the pay telephone once rested but which now serves as a resting place for your elbow when there is a wait for tables, to the twisted metal hangers waiting for your coat on the flaking, formerly chromed pipe rack, this little place is a hair-down, jeans-up, boots-on repair from the pretensions of Gramercy Park—plain white walls and strands of plain white air-conditioning duct across the dreary acoustical ceiling, an enameled red rear wall echoes the plastic red of the booths along the sides. (In recent years the paper place mats on Formica tabletops have been replaced by white linen—a dangerous trend.) Functional, and the shirt-sleeved waiters merely function—they record, deliver and bill. Consultants they are not. But as in many neighborhood Chinese restaurants around town where each copy of the printed menu serves its purpose through a full cycle of the four seasons, you get your advice from clients who have come before—they leave check marks next to recommended dishes (valuable restaurant lore: this is usually sound guidance), the urban equivalent of the Welcome Wagon.

One of your predecessors has checked Aromatic Sliced Beef, so you send for a platter of this cold dish while you and your companions determine the highest check-mark scores among four menus. You have plenty of time for the arithmetic, since the platter of cold beef is rather immense, which is nice because the dark slices of tender, fibrous meat are saturated with the flavor of peanut oil (though the meat is not oily) and accented with the sharpness of the chopped scallion greens that have been sprinkled over.

Three check marks out of a possible four to Smoked Duck with Camphor and Tea —the duck, in the Chinese manner, cross-sectionally slabbed through skin, fat, meat and bone, the outer layer crisped and dark-brown, plenty of fat just under it, the meat saturated with the smoky flavor of tea, some of the bones crumbly enough to eat, all served with a thick plum sauce and shafts of glistening scallion.

In a tie with the duck for the three-check-mark lead is the mis-Anglicized "Dried Sautéed String Beans." Fear not—the string beans are not dried but dry-sautéed, which means they are stirred about in a barely oiled and very hot pan. This process yields beans that are cooked, but as firm and bright-green as raw ones, at once crisp and chewy. They are served tossed with heavily seasoned ground pork, the earthy and oily meat a perfect garnish for the vibrant freshness of the beans.

Many, many two-check-mark entries, including Bean Curd, Szechuan Style—a fiery, weighty porridge, inexplicably not flagged with the red asterisk that denotes "Hot Spiced Flavor" (doubtless a typographer's oversight). It is like the rice, potatoes or noodles that are the starchy bulk of meals designed in other sections of the world. To a Szechuanite, of course, such stuff would be undetectable (if not unpalatable) in the context of this blazing cuisine. The ubiquitous scallions are present.

For $1.25 you get a giant bowl of two-check-mark Cold Noodle with Sesame Sauce. By the time the dish reaches your table, the sesame oil, peanut oil and soy sauce will have drained to the bottom—stir the noodles well in the liquid, even go so far as to obtain a spoon with which to ladle the salty mixture over the firm strands. The dish has an intensity of peanut flavor almost like that of peanut butter, and of course, this richness is offset with a sprinkling of, you guessed it, minced scallions.

Now you have grown confident. You are no longer dependent on and therefore shun the advice of the early pioneers who left their marks and went on. You hack out a path of your own—Hot Spiced Sautéed Kidney. Really have to credit those first settlers, don't you? Next time, it's back to the check-mark system, right? Nothing actually wrong with the food, what with its crisp water chestnuts, tender mushrooms and impeccably rinsed kidneys all in a spicy brown sauce, but nothing special.

Hurry to Cuisine of Szechuan before they lay in a supply of clean menus. Bring enough beer (it is not sold on the premises), which, with this food, is about a quart per person.

This is now one of the best Szechuan restaurants in New York, better than any of the places run by the Szechuan Taste chain, and offering a menu that is longer and more surprising than those of its competitors.

★★FOUR FIVE SIX

2 Bowery (near Doyers Street)
LUNCH AND DINNER.
Reservations, 964–5853.
No credit cards.
Beer.
Inexpensive.

Two floors, one dining room above the other, each as Chinatown-ugly as the other, garishly tiled and ornamented, glaringly lighted. But this place is the offspring of the very successful Say Eng Look across Chatham Square, and though little taste was invested in its conception, there were sufficient funds—these quarters are not cramped, there is plenty of ugly for everybody. Anyway, in this part of New York, pleasant surroundings would jar. You come to Chinatown for food, and Four Five Six is one of the best restaurants in the area. It serves an extensive array of Shanghai dishes (177 by actual numbered-on-the-menu count), and for your visiting relatives, chow mein and chop suey. There is, moreover, another part of the menu, a stapled-on yellow sheet, an unnumbered unpriced forest of "Special Dishes," listed in Chinese (we take it on faith) and English. You will spend handsomely if you order only from this group, but you will be eating singular food of exceptional quality.

If, however, you must begin with beginners, appetizers are listed only in the white pages. You can have all of them as part of the Imperial Plate, which comes in five sizes: Large, $17.95; Medium, Medium and Medium, at, respectively, $8.95, $7.95 and $6.50; or Small, $4.95. However much you want, you get an excellent Aromatic Smoked Fish —chunks of oily fish flavored with anise, the exterior blackened and toughened and pleasantly fibrous, the inside soft; good Cold Fried Shrimp in shells you can eat, with a pungent aroma of Chinese parsley; Sweet and Sour Cabbage, cool in temperature, hot, sweet and spicy in flavor; Aromatic Beef, braised in soy sauce, oil, wine, ginger and anise, and served cold, in extremely thin slices, even a small bite of which is distinctly fibrous and pungent.

One of the most remarkable dishes at this restaurant is the Fried Roll Fish with Bean Curd Sheet. Relatively bland, perfectly fresh fish is fried in a parchment-thin wrapping of bean-curd sheet until the fish is tender and the bean-curd crisp. This is served with seasoned salt. You dexterously lift a slice of the fish with your chopsticks, touch it to the little mound of salt and eat. The thing is spectacular, an amazing coming together of delicacy, crispness and high flavor, perfectly balanced.

If you learned to like shrimp shells in Cold Fried Shrimp, you will love them in Fresh Prawns in Hot Spiced Sauce. The prawns *are* fresh, and what with their being cooked in their shells, they have a strong flavor; and the sauce they are served in is spicy and thick with ground meat—very good stuff.

There is Pressed Duck—soft, moist chunks of duck, tender and succulent, cooked to the point where the little ribs are soft and edible, served with crisp scallion greens and huge smoky-tasting Chinese mushrooms. And there is Dried Beef Sautéed—hefty strands of beef and crunchy lengths of water chestnut in a loud brown sauce that will make your lips burn if you let it touch your lips. And there is Crab Meat and Abalone with Baby Corn—a very nice dish of sweet and tender crabmeat, firm abalone, crisp snow peas, and whole little ears of sugary corn, which, of course, you eat inside and out.

If there is to be a climactic dish here, it might well be the Fish Head Casserole. You get a giant pot of broth—it is thick, oily and gingered; meat has been cooked in it, along with the fish, so that it has depth; there are chunks of bean curd; and of course, slabs of fish that are strongly flavored of the broth. The thing will wake you up.

Four Five Six is an elemental restaurant. The service is perhaps a bit primitive, plates of food delivered and plunked down, beer served in cans (Budweiser only, in six-packs if you order that many). For no discernible reason, some of the tables are linened, some bare. The waiters may not be particularly helpful, but in Chinatown one may be grateful if they are not truculent.

★★ HUNAM

845 Second Avenue (near 45th Street)
LUNCH AND DINNER.
Reservations, MU 7-7471.
Credit cards: AE, DC.
Medium-priced.

When this place first appeared, the *Times* announced that heaven had opened a branch on Second Avenue. Anyone can make a mistake. But then, about a year later, the *Times* checked and *confirmed* that heaven was doing business on Second Avenue. People who know heaven when they eat at it pooh-poohed and entertained uncharitable Emersonian thoughts about the dimensions of minds that are foolishly consistent. This restaurant serves some paradisaic food, but also some that is quite mundane. This restaurant is to be thanked for introducing the food of Hunan to the citizens of New York. But much about the place is hell on earth. For instance, in heaven would a tray stand be set beside your table with an aluminum tray, so that used plates and silverware from various parts of the dining room can be noisily tossed thereon?

Hunam is a noisy madhouse of a restaurant. If you manage to overhear any conversation at the table that is one inch from your own, like as not what you hear will be "What did you say?"

So is it worth it? Well, yes. But try this restaurant in the off-hours, unless you dig aural and optical cacophony. And try to start your dinner with Turnip Cake—balls of moist ground turnip, crisp outside, only vaguely turnipy, sweet, light, appetizing. Do *not* start your dinner with Crisp Chicken with Peanuts—slabs of dry, puttylike chicken, crisped, and coated with stale-tasting peanuts. Proceed, most assuredly, to Hunam Preserved Duck, a singular dish (your captain may try to talk you out of it, explaining that most customers don't like it, but persist). The dish does have one off-putting characteristic—abundant duck fat, but when duck is steamed this way, with the fat in place, the meat remains astonishingly moist. It is steamed over ground pork, and the entire product tastes vaguely smoky and has a subtle citrus-fruit flavor—wondrous.

The dish here that has received a great deal of publicity is Hunam Beef. This is eminently edible food—the beef in a hot, clear, oily sauce made with red peppers and an intensity of garlic, the watercress a crisp, leafy garnish that sets it off perfectly. Beef is also served here in the form of Orange Flavor Beef, and unlike most of the orange-flavored dishes served in the Szechuan and Hunan restaurants around town, the flavoring in this dish is of the juicy inside of the orange, not the rind. The dish is hot and spicy, the beef is tender, there are bamboo shoots here and there, and to eat it is to decide that almost anything can be successfully cooked with almost anything. Who would have featured beef cooked with orange juice?

The Sliced Leg of Lamb, Hunam Style, is a very highly flavored as well as seasoned dish, so much so that the flavor of the meat is virtually obscured. It must be lamb, but it is hard to tell. In any event, the dish is made with an abundance of huge shiny mushrooms, crisp scallions, and onions, all in a thick fiery sauce that is densely flavored with garlic—good stuff.

Another good dish is something called Shrimp Puff in Ginger Sauce, and what is meant by "puff" nobody knows. The dish consists of a huge mound of good firm shrimp in a dark viscous sauce that is thoroughly gingered. Avoid, however, Fillet of Sea Bass with Shrimp Roe Sauce. Sounds interesting? Comes out flavorless fish with snow peas.

The Honey Crisp Bananas are dreadful, and you will not be surprised to learn that the *Stuffed* Honey Crisp Bananas are also dreadful.

This place has been shoveling in money so consistently since it opened that it has developed a few very bad traits. Waiters who barely nod when you order—you're never quite certain they have heard or understood. Captains who are eager to subdivide your dishes—to place them all in the center of the table is impossible for lack of room, and to serve them in series requires more planning than they want to undertake. They prefer to spend their time ceremoniously distributing shrimp toast to a circle of adventurers, picking up each slice with a pair of tongs and idiotically rotating it in a flame before placing it on a plate.

★★★ PHOENIX GARDEN

46 Bowery (in the arcade, near Elizabeth Street)
LUNCH AND DINNER.
Reservations, 233–6017.
No credit cards.
No liquor.
Inexpensive.

From the Bowery to Elizabeth Street a new street has been carved out, more storefronts for the commercially insatiable, retail-obsessed merchants of Chinatown. The arcade is a few years old now, and fully occupied. It's one of the places the locals go for pizza. There is a candy store that sells beer, for the patrons of the restaurants that don't. But the principal attractions along this chain of baubles are the Chinese restaurants, and no one can tell, just by appearances, which of these gilded boxes is worth looking into. This is the place.

The place looks like the inside of a refrigerator with the light on, all white polished surfaces, with here and there some hardware, ducks and chickens hanging at the front near the stainless-steel counter, a bustling little kitchen at the rear just beyond the stainless-steel coffee urns. The stainless-steel silverware is available on request; otherwise you get chopsticks. If you are not an Oriental, you may feel out of place here because most of the customers are Chinese, often in large groups around the large round tables, often every nose buried in a rice bowl, chopsticks shoveling—Phoenix Garden is a Cantonese restaurant, and eating rice is very much part of eating almost anything.

Cantonese cooking has, of recent years, been looked down the turned-up nose upon. The foods of the provinces to the north and west have been the local favorites and fads. Your Chinese-restaurant goer doesn't merely utter the word "Cantonese," he expletes it, a one-word dismissal of a restaurant. There is an explanation, of course: hundreds of dreadful Cantonese restaurants in New York. But no, the Cantonese are not to China what the Dutch and Germans are to Europe, that is, plain ignorant about food; it is we, rather, who are ignorant (those of us who are not Cantonese), though admittedly at the hands of unscrupulous restaurateurs who have for years purveyed slop as Cantonese food, to the miseducation of the locals. At its best, Cantonese food is simple and subtle and light (rice provides the weight), emphasizing the basic ingredients and textures more than the flavorings and seasonings, a relationship that is reversed as you move away from Canton. Please, exception us not with exceptions to the rule.

You receive two menus, a great big printed orange thing and a typed menu encased in celluloid. If your waiter is the young fellow with acne, you may set aside the reading matter and follow his advice; otherwise the best plan is to order from the typed menu the items listed as "Chef's Specials," or you may read on and bend to the vivid prose.

Begin with "Pepper & Salty Shrimp (in shell)," which is not what it says, being peppery, not pepper, and thereby a good introduction to the English served here. These remarkable shrimps are either fresh or so carefully frozen that virtually no damage has been done to the sweet flavor and crisp texture. They arrive pink, bursting from their crackling shells, lightly spotted with bits of black pepper and moistened with an oil which is flecked with slivers of scallion and fresh ginger—everything conspires to emphasize the pristine flavor of the shrimps themselves.

Fried Fresh Milk with Crab Meat will strike you as yet another typo, and there are perhaps better translations of whatever the Chinese name for this dish might be, but as the dish is singular, it might as well go by this unique title. What arrives looks like a giant mound of moist white soufflé; dig around under it and you find crabmeat and crisp rice noodles. The meat is moist and firm; the noodles, included for texture, are crisp and slightly chewy; and the "soufflé" is glistening white, light and airy, and only faintly flavored with the slightly burnt taste of cooked milk. You may not like it, but that is merely culture shock.

Steam Flounder is not a new kind of flounder, but a steamed flounder. Now, you may say to yourself, "Steamed flounder, big deal." Well, first of all, this flounder is *fresh,* almost sugary in its sweetness, so fluffy it is difficult to hold it in chopsticks. It should be eaten alone because it arrives at a point of steamy perfection from which it deteriorates, since it continues to cook in its own heat. Quickly now, while the glistening silver fish is still somewhat hidden in the hot rising water vapor, push away the bony edges of the fish, pluck the moist, snowy meat from the spine and large central bones, and swallow it down. When it is all gone (in about two minutes), you can concentrate on the mushrooms and scallions you left behind in the broth the flounder was steamed in.

Fried Stuffed Bean Curd is, you guessed it, bean-curd sheet stuffed with bean curd, crinkly layers of the sheet around bricks of the soft and mealy bean paste, in a brown sauce that is oily and just vaguely fishy. This is a mother's-milk kind of dish, warm and satisfying, like buttered noodles, or bread and jam, or grits, and neither a fine nose nor tuned palate is needed to appreciate the simple oral pleasure of gumming it down.

Another good transition dish (we are heading toward birds and beasts) is Mixed

Vegetables with Noodles, which is a party on a plate, here a carrot, orange and crisp and cut in the shape of a butterfly, and there one in the shape of a fish; ears of baby corn and brilliantly green snow peas; straw mushrooms and cloud ears, the mysteriously smoky fungi of your mysterious East; soft and buttery gingko nuts. The vegetables are not married, just joined in a gentle syrup, with rice noodles for a contrasting texture of dry crispness.

Head and all, here comes your Phoenix Special Roast Squab, much pushed by the waiters, advice that is much appreciated by first-time starters. The former bird arrives disjointed, skin browned but still soft, meat fibrous but still tender and moist, some of the little bones sufficiently crisped to be chewed down and appreciated for their salty oiliness. The bird is good as is, better when dipped in the seasoned salt that accompanies it, and utterly transformed when moistened with the lemon that is supplied. Enthusiasts eat the head.

Those birds hanging in the front window are not just for atmosphere. You can eat them. Recommended is the Roast Duck, listed under "Barbecue" on the white menu. Your relentlessly sensible waiter (the one who insisted you eat your flounder in a trice) suggests most seriously that you have the duck as is, at room temperature, not reheated and dried out. Sure enough, it is profoundly succulent, not to be tampered with, served, in a way that seems French, over white beans that are in a bit of peppery gravy. To make one bite a little different from another, you dip it in the little dish of sweet ginger sauce.

To prove that a Cantonese can inflame food good as a Szechuanese, you are offered a dish of pork and green peppers. The green peppers are searingly hot, the meat and vegetable combined in a succulent sauce, straw mushrooms present for gentleness—but this is not this restaurant's strength, just another not particularly harmonious assortment of ingredients to make a dish.

You get your beer across the arcade.

★★SHUN LEE DYNASTY

900 Second Avenue (at 48th Street)
LUNCH AND DINNER
Reservations, PL 5-3900.
Credit cards: AE, CB, DC.
Medium-priced.

It is possible to have a great dinner in this restaurant, equally possible to have a dreary one. One thing you won't get is *bad* food, so it's a safe showplace for visiting entertainees. Shun Lee Dynasty is affiliated with Hunam, the madhouse restaurant across the avenue. The most important thing to know about Shun Lee Dynasty is that it eliminates the need for Hunam—you never have to suffer the commotion of the garish inferno popularized by the *Times,* because equally good Hunan dishes are available here, though only main courses, and those in far less variety than you can get, if you are willing to suffer, at Hunam.

The Dynasty is, visually, a singular spot. If you wait for your table in the barroom, you will feel surrounded by tufted black leather and threatened by a twenty-foot paper lion over the length of the bar—the room is called the Lion's Den, but it is just a clubroom for the rows of guys in polo shirts, sitting on chairs, opposite rows of wives under blond soufflés, sitting on the massive banquette. The bartender, in civvies, slouches, drinks, chews peanuts, and wipes his hands on the glassware towel. Well, bring your own glassware. The dining room proper, however, is not just some more horsed-up New York bar. This is modern design, in spades: tall plastic wall panels, ceiling to floor, emblazoned with gay animal illustrations; booths made private by Mylar drapes; a ceiling centerpiece of hanging chains and chimes and pennants and dolls and fans, all in muted and softly lit golds and tans; and throughout the room massive enameled pillars. Carpeting, of course, the tables set with mustard-colored linen, sculptured napkins and ornate plates at each setting. The effect is blessedly somewhat diminished by restrained illumination.

You will not get better hacked chicken in New York, and you can order the dish in almost half the Chinese restaurants in town. This is the famous dish of cold, coarsely shredded chicken served in a peanut sauce; here the chicken carries the flavor of chicken, which is the flavor of chicken fat, and the sauce is spicy and heavy, almost mealy, somehow cocoa-like; the dish is sprinkled with bits of scallion and the almost overpoweringly fragrant Chinese parsley one must learn to like to like—its headiness is perfect against this rich dish.

The menu informs you that the Spicy Cucumber is "First Time Served in New York." This is a nice little number, cool and oily lengths of cucumber that have been marinated in sesame oil and spices, studded with bits of pepper and comingled with strands of carrot—a high-class pickle.

A couple of good Hunan dishes. Hunan Calf's Liver—thin, tender slivers of liver sautéed in a thickened oily sauce that is high on ginger and garlic, the sweet and sour elements combined into a kind of elegant relish; it is served with fresh, brilliantly clear-tasting, strong, metallic spinach, an audaciously right contrast. Hunan Smoked Duck—slabs of duck, skin, fat, meat, bone, served with a dish of salt, which diminishes quite perfectly the slightly excess oiliness of the bird and emphasizes the flavor of tea that the bird picked up in the smoking.

But the rest of the main-course menu is the compendium of OK cooking for which Shun Lee Dynasty has inexplicably always won the highest praise. Shrimp, Szechuan Style—prawns, crispy, in a thick sweet-and-sour sauce that is almost pebbly with bits of onion and scallion—is good food. Mandarin Beef—a meaningless though harmless mélange of beef, abalone, ham, chicken and vegetables; as the beef is overcooked and bloodless, you tend to eat around it. Slippery Chicken—strands of chicken browned in a honeylike sauce, served with a garnish of perfect spinach—more OK food.

Some find the service here overbearing, but it is really just a little dumb. You inform your waiter that you want the dishes served in series, one at a time; he announces that he will ask the captain's permission. Later, because of a change in the guard, your still-present waiter cannot accept any instructions and your yet-to-arrive waiter is yet to arrive. The folks love it.

• SZECHUAN EAST

1540 Second Avenue (near 80th Street)
LUNCH AND DINNER
Reservations, 535–4921.
Credit cards: AE, CB, DC.
Medium-priced.

Take the Szechuan Taste Restaurant in Chatham Square, increase the prices by from 10 to 60 percent, add lobster, honeyed bananas, almond cookies, a rug and a captain, and what have you got? Right. Szechuan East, which for some reason was not called Szechuan Dynasty or Szechuan Imperial or Szechuan Palace, in recognition, perhaps, that the interior, though pretentious, is neither dynastic, imperial nor palatial but, rather, Chelsea Byzantine, with sandstone-colored walls, arched portals, a garish blue ceiling, niches here and there, and, sorry, no belly dancers.

The ownership here is the same as that of Szechuan Taste in Chatham Square, but this location serves several dishes not on the menu downtown (and vice versa). Among these is a cold Aromatic Beef, a delicious preparation of beef which has been boiled with soy sauce, fresh ginger, sesame oil and the ingredient that dominates the dish, star anise—an aromatic, licorice-flavored spice. The beef is served as a seemingly endless train of thin slices of the slightly chewy, nutlike, sweet meat, on a huge platter. You may be served mustard, but don't use it.

Szechuan East's Sautéed Shrimp with Hot Pepper Sauce includes, unannounced by the given English title, whole peanuts, as well as hot fresh ginger in a fiery sauce. And the Bean Curd Szechuan Style, one of the best dishes on the menu, turns out to be a dish seemingly designed as a setting for the purest, most intense garlic flavor to be found in any dish anywhere. The slices of bean curd are mixed with chunks of good pork and shredded scallions, and the brown sauce in which they are combined has been so strongly flavored with garlic that it seems more concentrated than eating the straight stuff. But the pork and the bean curd act as a buffer, and it is entirely possible for a human being to consume the entire serving alone, though anyone with a companion should share it.

Presumably because it serves the supposedly delicate citizenry of New York's East Side, this restaurant, more than the other Szechuan places in New York, modifies its cuisine to what it takes to be the refined, moneyed palate. It goes so far as to misrepresent. A so-called Szechuan Roast Duck will arrive very much like a so-called Long Island Duck, as prepared by, say, a Little Necker. The bird is well cooked—crisp skin, moist meat, and all that—but as it is served here, it is not a Chinese dish.

In further deference to the notion that the East Side's prosperous clientele is less attuned than the rest of us to anything that happens to be actually of the region, this Szechuan restaurant offers honeyed apples and honeyed bananas for dessert. What is more, it offers a captain who not only takes your order to whisper it to the waiter, but who, if he has any inkling at all that this dish is for Mr. A, that one for Miss B, will spoon this stuff onto Mr. A's plate, and that onto Miss B's, which ruins the fun and ritual of having a little of this and a little of that. Stop him before he begins.

★ SZECHUAN TASTE

23 Chatham Square (near Mott Street)
LUNCH AND DINNER.
Reservations accepted for more than five, 267–0672.
Credit cards: AE, DC, MC.
Beer.
Inexpensive.

If you have a store, a few tables with chairs and a gas range, open a Szechuan restaurant. Szechuan food is not merely a fad or a craze, it's an addiction. If you stand still, for example, outside the entrance to the Szechuan restaurant at Broadway and 84th Street at, say, seven-thirty of an evening, you will be trampled. At another, on Second Avenue in the Eighties, the customers are more refined, and you will merely be shoved aside. What is it all about? It is in part about *Xanthoxylum piperatum,* a hot red pepper native to the Szechuan province of China, a spice of such overpowering delayed heat that it can weld the most divergent flavors into dishes that betray no imbalance.

Take, for example, Chicken in Orange Flavor, in which sautéed chicken (previously marinated in wine, soy sauce and onions) is combined with sautéed orange rind, the aforementioned hot peppers (also sautéed) and vinegar. It sounds crazy, but it tastes great. Many Szechuan dishes are of ingredients that seem just as uncongenial, but *X.p.* makes it all OK.

Among the cold dishes, something called Hacked Chicken in Assorted Flavor consists of slices of chicken (skin on) in a searing sesame sauce—the oiliness of the sauce makes the heat acceptable. (When properly prepared, all of these dishes are so constructed that there is a built-in protection against the heat of the pepper: heavy chunks of meat, a thick sauce, solid—almost coarse—vegetables, and so on.)

If you don't mind the oily quality of carp, you will probably object to its abundance of bones. If neither disturbs you, try the carp with hot bean sauce. You will receive a huge fish (longer than, and hanging over the ends of, its foot-long platter) drenched in fiery sauce with black beans. There are also good shrimp dishes, including prawns in hot spicy paste (with minced scallions—the second most common ingredient in Szechuan dishes), and excellent pork dishes, including, in a milder world, the familiar pork-and-egg dish usually called (in a very approximate transliteration) *moo shu* pork, here called sawdust pork.

Long before Szechuan restaurants were as common as saloons and churches, sour-and-hot soup, the national soup of the Szechuan province, ran a close second to egg drop in the Chinese Soup Popularity Sweepstakes. It is not a difficult dish to bring off, and variations in the-quantity-of-this-vs.-the-correct-amount-of-that do not defile it. Presumably the version served here is more authentic than most; it is more sour than hot, and rather thick. The vegetable dishes are good, particularly the slightly blackened Dried Sautéed Stringbeans, under a copious garnish of garlic, chopped salty pork and minced pickled cabbage. The noodles with sesame paste are at once delicate and strongly flavored, garnished with a crunchy accent of minced scallion greens.

This is a Chinatown restaurant that has been described as "less nondescript than most," which probably refers to the sidewalk section, from which there is an impressive view of several downtown housing projects, and at the back end of which there is a refrigerator, which contains your beer, in cans. The service is casual, by casually clothed young men. The portions they bring are huge.

★★★ UNCLE TAI'S HUNAN YUAN

1059 Third Avenue (near 63rd Street)
LUNCH AND DINNER
Reservations, TE 8–0850.
Credit cards: AE, DC.
Expensive.

The main room of this spacious Chinese restaurant manages to be at once cold and gaudy. The great expanses of blue and white filigreed wallpaper are illuminated by an invisible source of ice-blue light; the unspeakable chandeliers look like they are made of icicles; there are dark-blue enameled pillars; the wall-to-wall floor is covered with a blue carpeting of low saturation and low brilliance that shimmers nevertheless; and the rows upon rows of tables are surrounded by chairs that are upholstered with gleaming mock leather. But don't go away. The food is good, and there is a back room; true, the furnishings are of the same ilk (here it is a red rug that shimmers), but the back room is smaller, dimmer and cozier than the barn out front.

The food of Hunan has had a vogue of late, not because it is unique, though in some ways it is distinctive, but because some of the exponents of this new-to–New York cuisine are restaurants where the general quality of the cooking is very high. The immediately noticeable differences between the menu at Uncle Tai's and the menus one expects at Chinese restaurants is the presence of game—rabbit, pheasant, squab; a goodly number of ham and lamb dishes; and the stratospheric prices. Also, the servings here are not the giant mounds one has become accustomed to in Chinese restaurants, and the standard one hour may not be required before hunger is experienced again.

The dishes listed as appetizers include such surprise names as Diced Boneless Squab Packages. Packages? Packages. The contents of said packages are a delicious mixture of minced squab meat, red and green peppers, water chestnuts, black beans and ginger. The wrapping is the lettuce leaves the stuff is served on—you eat it by wrapping some of the squab mixture in the lettuce and biting off a piece of the bundle. Very good. The Honeyed Hunan Ham with Dates consists of a mound of hot dates (they are pitted and seem steamed) under an overlapping series of slices of ham. The edges of the ham are slightly hardened in the cooking, which adds a textural note, as does the soft fat here and there in the meat. There is also Hunan Preserved Steamed Poultry: Chicken and Duck. This odd dish is made up of quite salty and smoky chunks of duck flavored with cloves, and chunks of chicken that are milder and nutlike. The dish is served hot, the meat still attached to the bones.

There are soups, many like the soups you know, but an alternative to the usual hot-and-sour soup available here is Hot and Sour Fish Broth—spicy, slightly thickened, flavored with strong Chinese parsley, a green which, when eaten raw, is much too perfumed for people not accustomed to its high flavor, but in this soup it is a mild element that adds a tolerable but strong leafy quality. Leave behind the fish in the broth —it has been boiled to extinction.

There is a listing of seafood dishes, one of poultry and one of meat. But there is also a listing of Uncle Tai's Specialties. As is usual with such menu sections, the items therein are a leetle beet more expensive than the main courses listed elsewhere on the menu, but here, at least, the list really seems to consist of the most interesting dishes available. There is, for example, Minced Squab in Bamboo Container. This remarkable dish consists of two meatballs, in two bamboo containers, each of them up to their waist in a winy broth. The meat is clearly squab, ground fine and spiced, and it is almost unbelievably moist. The dish amounts to just a couple of morsels of food, but it is probably unlike anything you have ever eaten, and it is a perfect thing of its kind. The Chunked Rabbit with Orange Flavor is a combination of chunks of tender rabbit meat, sautéed orange peel, scallions, ginger and a flavoring of the hot red peppers that are used about as often in Hunan cooking as in Szechuan. The Hunan Fish Rolls are good, but the dish is very much like the sweet-and-sour fish available all over town, and the sweet-and-sour vegetable sauce does not seem to mix well with the other food here. If you do order it, have it as a separate course.

One of the best noodle dishes available in New York is Cold Hunan Noodles with Assorted Dipping Sauces. The noodles are green (made with spinach); they seem to be swung rather than machine-rolled and cut, because they have a nice irregular, though long-and-thin, shape. They taste vaguely pickled, oiled; they are interspersed with tiny bits of scallion green and seem to be served already dipped in a bit of soy sauce and vinegar; there is a subtle flavor of peanut. Perhaps the dish should properly be served with four dishes on the side, for dipping, as the name suggests, but as you get it, all dipped for you, it is pretty miraculous.

Most experienced Chinese-restaurant goers pass up the banal desserts offered in most Chinese restaurants. Here, however, even if you order numerous dishes, you may still want dessert. Fortunately they are made with more than cursory attention, and the Sesame Bananas in particular are good—ripe bananas, honeyed, lightly fried and buried in sugar and cinnamon.

The place has its idiocies. Captains, at least some of whom make no effort to part with their knowledge, if any, of the food. Their recommendations run to Assorted Special Appetizers (a circlet of banalities surmounted by a pointless fire—some customers have been seen warming their spring rolls in the flames), or steamed fish, or snow peas and water chestnuts. When your order is delivered to the side stand near your table, you can actually watch one of these gentlemen lean over the food as, by deft spooning, he transfers it from the serving plate to the eating plate, right before your eyes. It's a good idea to suggest that the food be placed on the table in its serving dishes. Much about the place suggests that it is geared to the assumption that all American customers want their Chinese food Westernized as much as possible. The dishes marked "hot and spicy" are not particularly, but, they add, "we can alter the spice according to your taste." What we want, Uncle Tai, is food according to *your* taste. But it's impossible to deny the excellence of the food here, just the way it is.

★ WO PING

24 Pell Street (near Mott Street)
LUNCH AND DINNER.
Reservations, RE 2–0847.
No credit cards.
No liquor.
Inexpensive.

Long before the city began to become sophisticated about its Chinese restaurants, there were some that were better than others. Wo Ping was one of those; accordingly, it thrived, and now it is well into its second life, its once seedy appointments veneered over with Formica, tiles, backlighted cityscapes of Hong Kong, plastic booths, background music, the Chinese works. There are the usual family dinners, with Groups A and B, Special House Dinners of "Special Real Cantonese Dishes Recommended by Our Skillfull Distinguished Chefs," all described in a style that one hopes is being preserved somewhere on magnetic tape for all time. How about "Long Island duck it tenderly fried leaving the skin crisp and melting under a thin coat of finely chopped almonds, it is then majestically placed over in a delicate sauce"? Or, "No change or exchange of order after it is given and being prepared in the Kitchen."

Har Hop consists of little nuggets of shrimp toast, oily crusts, a bit bland, minced shrimp and herbs between the little triangles of fried bread; you dip each morsel in hot mustard to give it an edge. Or begin with Dim Sum, balls of mildly flavored ground pork encased in a noodle envelope—unexciting, the kind of thing everyone ran from when Szechuan arrived, but quite nice with a shot of Scotch whiskey—soothing food.

You have ordered the famous Fresh Crab Cantonese Style, and you are brought little stainless steel bowls, little cocktail forks for the extraction of the crabmeat from its carapace, and little plastic-enclosed moistened paper towels for the degreasing of the hands when the operation is over. This is a challenging dish to eat, but worth it. So roll up your sleeves and come to slippery grips with a lot of work for a little meat. These are fresh hard-shelled crabs; if you know where to look, you know where the nuggets of meat are, but wherever you look there is the excellent eggy black-bean sauce, thick and pungent. For something easier to tackle there are Fresh Clams (Chinese Style), a simple dish of cherrystones burst open in a pool of red gelatinous sweet-and-sour sauce, at once sugary and sharp. But the winner is Lobster A La Canton Style (to reproduce exactly the menuese). The lobster is live (or was but a moment ago), and it is cooked with minced pork until it is just done, retaining all its flavor and moisture, and served in a rich egg sauce that is sharpened with slivers of scallion.

For your more traditional New York Chinese restaurant dish, try Four Seasons, which may be translated as something for everybody—the menu says it all: "Shredded roast duck, chicken, abalone and roast pork w. finely cut mixed vegetables, topped over with crisp rice noodles." Withal, it's pretty good.

Throughout, good ingredients and good preparation. The results, though clearly close to the kitchen's intention, are not close to today's tastes.

Broadway Bistros

In the West Forties and Fifties there are a couple of dozen French restaurants that serve good food at prices that are reasonable for New York. This cluster of eating places is one of the city's principal restaurant assets. Their menus are similar and familiar, mostly their wine cards are limited and they all have little bars at the front, where the French-speaking locals sit and jaw or read.

With all the competition these places have from one another, they have to maintain decent quality. The customers who come here are rarely rich (the well-to-do have their own cluster of French restaurants, in the *East* Forties and Fifties), they want value, and they bristle when things in their favorite places begin to slip—as well they may, for within a block or two there are several similar restaurants waiting to pick up the trade.

This is the theater district, and lots of customers flow out the doors a few minutes before curtain time; a few flow in for the after-theater suppers that were instituted in some spots in response to the early curtain. But most of the restaurants covered here do good business even while the shows are going on. Better-than-average food and/or lower-than-average prices account for it.

★★ LE BIARRITZ

325 West 57th Street
LUNCH, MONDAY TO FRIDAY; DINNER, MONDAY TO SATURDAY.
Closed Sunday.
Reservations, 245–9467.
Credit cards: BA, DC.
Medium-priced.

As the cost of rental living escalates along Central Park South, it becomes necessary to offset. You descend from your penthouse as grandly as ever, smiling benignly
to the elevator operator as he delivers you gently to the mirror-and-marble lobby at
Main, you favor the doorman with a pleasantry, automatically wondering, at the same
time, if you can possibly give him no more for Christmas this year than you gave him
last, and you slink down to a place like this for a little prix fixe, vowing to eschew the
extras, but a moment later rationalizing that the saving on cab fare would take care
of half a dozen snails and that the whiskeys-and-soda you had at home instead of at
Le Biarritz would permit your roommate (doing her best, the darling, to *enjoy* the
convenience of washing her own hair) the luxury of some Bayonne ham.

You have begun to discover a whole new world of nether vogue. For example, many
of the customers at Le Biarritz speak French; and this is a French restaurant. Now,
there is a romance somewhere in there; something about something called *authenticity.*
It seems, you have heard, that if people from a foreign country frequent a restaurant
that serves food from that country, it suggests that the restaurant prepares the food
correctly (whatever *that* means), and this is somehow *good.* Very interesting. And
apparently this interior, looking much like what the old homestead in the Bronx would
have looked like if Pa had let Ma let that skinny decorator have his head, is *charming.*
Something about all this shiny copper and pottery and gilded chandeliers and flowers
and plants and carpeting being, somehow, *innocent.* Very confusing. Moreover, there
is this proprietor, in maroon pants and a Hawaiian shirt, and a blazer. And a French
student's beard. And a voice like a frog's, a real frog. All night long he has little snacks
brought to him, and he eats them at the bar. Then when things slow down he has a
huge steak brought, and he does the same thing to that. The newfound virtue here is
that this is *eccentric.* And you thought the man just did not know his place. *Very*
confusing. Well, best not to think about it. Just let it soak in.

Meanwhile, soak in some of these hors d'oeuvres. There is salami, thin slices of the
redolent and oily stuff; a livery pâté that seems to be freshly made; crunchy celery
rémoulade. For that little extra payment you can have silky ham rimmed with pure
white fat, all nice and smoky, served over slices of ripe melon. For a cold night there
is, when it is the soup of the day, a lobster bisque that is actually made with plenty
of lobster—it is dark, thick, strong, sweet and winy.

The main courses are the usual West Side items, but they are all well-prepared. The
Gigot aux Flageolets is rare, and your plate is quite covered with thin slices of the pink
meat immersed in a thin, dark, bloody gravy; at the other end of the platter a mound
of firm beans, a warm and juicy grilled tomato, and a cluster of crisp watercress. Terrific
sweetbreads—thick slices of them, sautéed until they are crackling, the insides still oily

and soft, served with mushrooms that have been sautéed until they are chocolate-brown, little onions that have been cooked with sugar, and roasted potatoes, all in a meaty sauce. There is duck in a cherry sauce that looks like chocolate syrup and tastes like a powerful stock that has just been lightly sweetened and brandied. The bird itself is carefully roasted, and you get a crisp skin around the moist, pleasantly oily meat. The salad is fresh, and it is served in a clear oily dressing.

The cheeses are in the refrigerator, the St. Honoré has been recently, and the Crêpes Suzette, though well-made, are overpriced at $7 for two. Stick to the mousse au chocolat, a gigantic dollop of the airy stuff, and the decent fruit tarts.

On occasion this place gets its family trade, and children can shout as loudly in French as in English. There are a few tables up front, near the bar, if you do not mind the occasional noisy drunk. But these are just sometime annoyances, and the place is comfortable.

★ BRITTANY DU SOIR

800 Ninth Avenue (at 53rd Street)
LUNCH AND DINNER.
Closed Sunday.
Reservations, CO 5–4820.
No credit cards.
Medium-priced.

A dark wooden wall, four feet high, zigzags through the center of the dining-room floor, forming banquettes and booths. There are wall sconces, chandeliers on rough wooden wheels, tiny-paned glass-doored cabinets on the walls, sideboards with crockery, wine racks, plaques, rough beams, a frosted-glass front window with decals of costumed French provincials, and framed little prints of the same characters. A bit of wall space unoccupied?—stick in a mirror. Red gingham cloths form fringes under the white linen. Busy, busy, busy. And the help busy too. Hefty, energetic waitresses thump about, delivering and taking away, under the supervision of a softer, plump type who greets you, seats you, and presents you with a menu which defiantly catalogs the most familiar foods served in New York's French restaurants.

Fortunately this reliable establishment prepares most of these dishes well, and if in the search for the new you have been avoiding the traditional, this is a good place in which to be reminded of the elemental virtues of such simple dishes as mackerel in white wine, served with a disc of raw onion, carrots from the marinade, and little pickles; the fish is tender, tangy, vaguely sweet and delicate. You can also have such familiars as mussels in a nice warm buttery broth; a genuine country-style pâté, heavy and porky; and plump snails that are unabashedly garlicked, in a sauce that is thick and vividly green from the copious fresh parsley that goes into it. Naturally, the soups are onion and vichyssoise, but they are not bad.

The crisp sautéed frogs' legs are served with an excellent, spicy tomato purée—if you ask, you can have an extra dish of the rich stuff. Such items as Veal with Mushrooms are perhaps a little better than one expects in West Fifties French restaurants. The veal is pale and tender, and the mushrooms have been carefully but fully sautéed (they are dark brown), so that their strong flavor permeates the dish. The Beef Stroganoff is a large serving of extremely tender slices of beef, with a very thick and rich sauce of sour cream and a beefy stock.

An item called Médaillon de Boeuf Bordelaise is perhaps not informatively named, but it is good—the *médaillon* is a perfectly broiled filet mignon, and the "Bordelaise" is represented by sautéed mushroom caps that are filled with a superb stuffing flavored with garlic and oregano. The list of main courses also includes competent versions of Duck à l'Orange and Sole Amandine. These are adequately prepared, but they are dishes that require restraint rather than bluntness for their best execution, and this is not the place for subtleties.

Brittany du Soir actually names varieties of cheese on its menu, instead of the usual listing—*fromage*. Nevertheless, despite this apparent seriousness about cheeses, they are kept refrigerated, and if you order some anyway, it will take at least an hour for the stuff to warm up—one receives a slab the size of a brick.

The sweet desserts are as familiar as the other listings—pastries, crème caramel, berries, and a few ice cream things, including Cherries Jubilee that are rather overwhelmed by a liberal allotment of kirsch.

Despite the knickknacks, the place is comfortable, and you will rarely get bad food here.

★★ CHEZ NAPOLEON

365 West 50th Street
LUNCH, MONDAY TO FRIDAY; DINNER, MONDAY TO SATURDAY.
Closed Sunday.
Reservations, CO 5–6980.
Credit cards: AE, BA.
Medium-priced.

Of the twenty or so moderately priced French restaurants in the West Forties and Fifties near Eighth and Ninth avenues, not all are worth entering for any reason other than getting in out of the weather. But Chez Napoleon is one. Not only are there a couple of surprises on the menu, but the familiar dishes are carefully made of good ingredients. Moreover, the service has not deteriorated over the years, despite steady, good business—the waitresses are intelligent and good-humored, and except during the very busy weekend dinners and at the peak of the lunch hour, prompt.

Dinner begins with a plate of good-quality black and green olives to hold you while the menu is read. An experimentally inclined guest consumed them by the plateful to determine how frequently the house would refill the plate. The management's generosity outlasted the diner's taste for olives, but this may have had something to do with the customer's excellent native French, a useful passport to good treatment in all of these West Side bistros.

At any rate, don't eat too many olives, because the listed first courses (and subsequent courses) are far more interesting. The mackerel in white wine, which in many restaurants should be labeled "pickled fish," is here a tart, strong appetite builder, the fish marinade made of lemon juice as well as white wine, flavored with vegetables and slivers of pickle. The pâté maison is simple, coarse, strongly flavored with garlic and served with real French cornichons instead of the usual domestic gherkins. The snails are small and tender, but the preparation is rather bland. The Mussels Biarritz, on the other hand, are something else; served in addition to the run-of-restaurant Moules Ravigote, they are breaded, seasoned with garlic and parsley, moistened with butter and oil, and baked—much the way snails are usually prepared—and it is a pleasant change to have mussels this way.

Another surprise is the rabbit cooked in white wine. Rabbit is rarely found on New York menus, and here the meat is well browned before the stewing, the bones go into the pot, which helps to make for a thick, rich sauce, and sautéed onions and mushrooms add a perfect accent. The Coq au Vin is easy on the red wine, heavy on a strong chicken stock—a difficult preparation to bring off. The Duck à l'Orange is far better than one expects in this caliber of restaurant—the duck is moist, the skin crisp, and the sauce carefully built.

Chez Napoleon is best known for its bouillabaisse, available, unfortunately, only on Friday, a very crowded evening at this restaurant. (You may avoid the crowd by coming late, but by that time the bouillabaisse is frequently all gone.) This is an eccentric bouillabaisse, very heavily flavored with fennel, but it is made with a variety of good ingredients—red snapper, sea bass, eel, lobster, clams, mussels. The fish is cooked to flakiness, not mush; the shellfish to firmness, not leather; all in a fragrant, thick soup.

To most palates the salad dressing will seem far too oily—understandably, as it is almost pure oil. Ask to have it made with a bit more vinegar than usual, or if you prefer a Roquefort dressing, here it is made with real French Roquefort.

Of the desserts, the cheeses are refrigerated, and the Crêpes Suzette—well, this is not a Crêpes Suzette restaurant. They are flamed in a few droplets of Grand Marnier, which yields almost no sauce. They are much too dry. If you must have a flame, the Cherries Jubilee are good. The *café filtre* is superb.

★★CHEZ RAYMOND

240 West 56th Street
LUNCH, MONDAY TO FRIDAY; DINNER, MONDAY TO SATURDAY.
Closed Sunday.
Reservations, 245–3656.
Credit cards: AE, BA, DC.
Expensive.

Chez Raymond is a spotty restaurant, but for its best items it's worth knowing about. The place looks like dozens of French restaurants in New York—a small bar at the front, with a few tables around it along the wall; in the back room there are wood paneling, framed murals, a gold-colored banquette, fresh flowers on the white linen. It is ever so slightly gaudy, in an innocuous way, tasteless but inoffensive.

In this simple setting, devoid, as it is, of distractions, the food is the thing, and you can have it with some quite nice wine.

Don't begin with the Moules Ravigote—the mussels, if they are not canned, might as well be. But there are any number of good things you *can* begin with. The stuffed oysters, for one, are sweet, briny and tender. They are not really stuffed, but sprinkled with chopped shallots and parsley, and covered with a small slice of bacon. The oysters are put in the broiler very close to the fire so that the bacon becomes slightly charred before the oyster has a chance to toughen. A dish like this requires careful timing, and when it is properly made, the warm but still raw-tasting oyster is perfectly accented by the sharp, slightly smoky bacon.

Or you can begin with saucisson chaud—the warm, spicy sausage always served with potatoes in oil. You get two thick slices of the sturdy sausage here, and the potatoes are firm but thoroughly cooked. The problem with this dish is that after an hour you will not yet be hungry. There are also such standard first courses as marinated mushrooms—they are fresh and strongly perfumed with spices and herbs; and céleri rémoulade—the root is crisp and radishy, and the rémoulade sauce is slightly tart and lemony. All in all, this is a better version of this dish than you get in most French restaurants of this class.

If you want soup, the onion soup is sweet, hot, admittedly made with a rather weak stock, but topped with excellent Swiss cheese, nicely browned. The special soups of the day include a watercress soup, which is principally potatoes, butter and fresh watercress, and a fairly similar hot leek-and-potato soup, in which the chicken and the strong flavor of leeks blend very nicely with the sharp taste of cooked cream and the succulent one of chicken fat—a really first-rate dish.

The outstanding dish of the house is Le Pintadeau en Croûte aux Chanterelles Monbazillac, which, in case you are wondering, is guinea hen and the delicious wild mushrooms called chanterelles, baked in stock, wine and herbs under a glazed crust. The pot arrives at your place with the crown of pastry intact, and when you break it, an extraordinarily sweet and earthy fragrance fills the air. Guinea hen is a rather delicately flavored bird, like pheasant, but it is the preparation rather than the bird that makes this spectacular dish. If you come to this restaurant once, this is the dish to have.

There is a very good poached striped bass, moist and flaky, served with a thick and lemony hollandaise, and the broiled beef and lamb dishes are good. One dish that is good but could often be better is the Filet de Boeuf, Sauce Périgourdine. The whole filet is roasted at the start of dinner, and when you order the dish, a couple of slices are cut for you and served in the thick, sweet sauce that was deglazed from the roasting pan. This is all to the good, but because the meat was prepared early in the evening, it may be too well done by, say, nine o'clock, and the house is not above dabbing the slices of meat with that bloody-looking liquid sometimes called "paint" that some restaurants keep around to convert well-done meat to "rare."

The salad course is taken seriously here. You get good ingredients, like watercress, endive, Boston lettuce, and an oily vinaigrette made sharp and vibrant with plenty of strong mustard. There is usually Brie in good condition.

For some reason many of the regular customers here order soufflés for dessert. There is no special oven for them in the kitchen, and during the busiest part of the dinner hour they are baked at the temperatures demanded by the other dishes with which they must share the oven space. Even late at night, when they can be treated a little better, the results are heavy and improperly flavored. You are better off with the pastries— the napoleon is made with a sweet, rich custard and a very flaky pastry. The fruit tarts are good too.

Occasionally the rather officious proprietor dresses down a waiter in the dining room, which he should do in the kitchen. And occasionally it seems as if the floor is understaffed, so this may not be the place for a quick dinner before the theater or before a concert at nearby Carnegie Hall. But those are minor shortcomings, and you can have an excellent dinner here if you order carefully.

★★ L'ESCARGOT

47 West 55th Street
LUNCH AND DINNER.
Closed Sunday.
Reservations, 245–4266.
Credit cards: AE.
Medium-priced.

First there were La Potinière du Soir and Le Gourmet. Then La Potinière swallowed up Le Gourmet, its next-door neighbor. Then L'Escargot supplanted the enlarged Potinière. All to the good, for this is a better restaurant than either of its predecessors. In fact it is one of the most reliable and least expensive of the West Side bistros.

But for a couple of model snails mounted over the portal between the two dining rooms, hardly a stick has been changed. The front room is still ivory, the back room still dominated by large murals framed by dark-red walls. Some of the plates still carry the Potinière insignia.

There is no shortage of tables, and they are as close together as blades of grass. No matter, for this is not an intimate getaway but a bustling eatery, straightforward and convivial, where the solid bourgeois cooking is answered with lusty feeding and tippling.

One assumes that a restaurant called L'Escargot makes a specialty of its snails. In fact, there is nothing singular about them. They are simply tender, well-flavored by good stock, and served in a buttery combination of abundant garlic and parsley. Barring some of the more exotic preparations of snails, these are among the best in town.

One hesitates to praise a restaurant too highly for serving good foods that require little or no attention from the kitchen. But it would be unfair to dismiss this restaurant's excellent ham and melon, when other places fill orders for this dish with second-rate meat and unripe fruit. It is at least *something* of an accomplishment to provide perfectly ripe melon that is not the least bit over the hill, and thin slices of well-fatted ham which is pale-pink, smoky and salty, retaining some of its slightly fibrous texture. You can get a pretty disastrously overcooked artichoke here, so pass it up for the Saucisson-chaud, Pommes à l'huile, which consists of three thick slices of strong, moist sausage garnished with a mound of warm sliced potatoes in oil and parsley—all very good.

Included in the modest price of your dinner is a soup course between the appetizer and main course. The vichyssoise is a rather thin blenderized version of this cool soup, lacking the texture that is part of its enjoyment, but the flavor is good, and the soup is refreshing. An occasional soup of the day is Purée Mongol, the thick hot soup of split peas and tomatoes—the version served here is thick and spicy and, fortunately, not ruined with the admixture of canned curry powder that is often included in restaurant soups of this name.

In restaurants like L'Escargot you do not look for brilliant preparations of refined dishes. You expect, instead, solid and honest food. You expect, for example, that the Tripes à la mode de Caen will be thick of the gravy, tender and gummy of the tripe, with plenty of good spice. You will not be disappointed. The waiter brings a steaming pot to your table, spoons half the contents onto your dinner plate and places the pot within easy reach if you want more. The smoothness of the stew is set off by the tender boiled potatoes and crisp discs of carrot that accompany it.

If your idea of Frogs' Legs Provençale suggests tomato as well as garlic in the sauce, you should so specify, because that is not the way the house looks at it, though they will accommodate your wishes. However you order them, the legs are plump and tender, and you get lots of them, with sauce that is heavily laden with fresh garlic and onions. The legs are served with a hot ratatouille, the flavor of which is dominated by eggplant and oil, and with boiled potatoes.

The rack of lamb, served only for two, is the most expensive dinner in the place. It is worth the extra money. This is true baby lamb, the eyes of each rib hardly more than an inch across; before it is cut down to its individual ribs, the rack is coated with bread crumbs, garlic and parsley. When the little roast is ready, a sauce is created in the roasting pan—it is thick with the flavored bread crumbs that dropped to the bottom of the pan, and the meat of the rack is juicy and tender. The lamb is served with chunks of roasted potato.

A salad is included, and there is nothing remarkable about the mixed greens you are served here except for the simple fact that the leaves of the lettuce and cress are crisp and spotless. The simple dressing cannot be faulted.

Several good cheeses at room temperature, including, sometimes, powerful goat cheese, or creamy and strong French Roquefort. The sweeter desserts include a light and airy chocolate mousse that is flavored with orange, more-than-decent tarts and pastries.

★★ THE FRENCH SHACK

65 West 55th Street
LUNCH, MONDAY TO SATURDAY; DINNER, DAILY.
Reservations, CI 6–5126.
Credit cards: AE, BA, DC.
Medium-priced.

If you can overlook the absurdity of the interior, you'll find that this is a restaurant worth knowing. Far from being a shack, this is an excessively decorated place, with bizarre columns, primitive carvings, plush banquettes, carpeting and pink illumination. The place has, on the whole, an ambience appropriate to the lobby of a small but pretentious Miami Beach hotel.

You can have several meals here, never repeat a course, and eat nothing but dishes you have never had before. To begin with, the Oysters Bourguignonne are baked with butter, garlic and parsley, and they are baked so carefully that the oysters remain soft and tangy. Or you can have a delicious Cold Bass Antiboise—a firm slice of flaky fish in a sparkling sweet and acid sauce of tomato, celery, carrots, green and red peppers, and onions. Of course there is a pâté, but this one is in a crust of bread surrounded by cubes of a powerful broth-and-wine jelly, and it is composed of such raw-tasting gamy meats that to eat it seems slightly atavistic. Among the more refined appetizers are the creamy cheese croquettes in a brown tomato sauce.

Your waiter may explain, if you innocently ask, that the Roast Duck Poivrade is made in a "little brown sauce with a touch of cognac." This explanation has perhaps served him well and raised no objections for many years. But the chef knows how to make it, and the excellent bird is served with wild rice and a sauce that is dominated by black pepper and vinegar. The beans in the cassoulet are crunchy, the mutton tender, the oily sausage lyonnaise strongly flavored with fennel, the dry sausage hot and spicy, and the whole thing covered with seasoned browned bread crumbs. This is not the greatest cassoulet in town—the diverse flavors are not perfectly brought together, and it is idiotically served with mundane potato croquettes—but when you're very hungry there is nothing quite like even a passable cassoulet. The Emince de Veau Normandie is the usual thing, in a creamy sauce, with mushrooms, served on rice, but it is pleasant. And the Trout Rôtie au Vermouth is a well-prepared fish, with crisp skin, lightly flavored with the wine.

The salad (listed as an appetizer) is good—watercress, Bibb lettuce and tomatoes in an oily dressing. The cheese is second-rate.

Mangoes and papaya in tequila are not French, but this simple dessert, made with very ripe fruit, is extremely fresh and stimulating. The Beignets Soufflés Abricotines are just out of the oven—an eggy cream puff with warm apricot sauce.

The real shortcoming of this restaurant is the exhibitionistic behavior of the dining-room staff: one waiter, in tossing a salad at the side stand, tosses part of it out of the bowl, and another points and jeers; a $1 tip is cursed audibly; the maître, to alibi his own blunders, excoriates the chef; the cashier carefully checks a credit-card number against the blacklist, and the impatient waiter marches up and down before her and explains to the customers at the bar that she even checks the cards of customers who eat in the place five times a week. It is possible to take amusement from all this.

★★ LES PYRÉNÉES

251 West 51st Street
LUNCH AND DINNER.
Closed Sunday.
Reservations, CI 6–0044.
Credit cards: AE, CB, DC.
Medium-priced.

Of the couple of dozen French restaurants in and near the theater district, Les Pyrénées is one of the better ones. It is also one of the few which keep their doors open late enough to serve post- as well as pre-theater customers.

The look of the place is corny in the French country manner, with copper pots and pans, a fireplace, pretty little plates hung on wood-paneled walls. There are cutesy slogans painted on wooden plaques—"A lunch without wine is like a woman without temperament," we are informed.

The food here is straight country cooking, with a few pretentious dishes on the menu that you will have the good sense to pass by. Stick to such appetizers as the pâté—it is wet, garlicked and spicy, delicious with bread and butter, and you get a portion the size of Monsieur's hand. Or have the Onion and Custard Pie, actually an onion quiche, and you get a slice the size of Monsieur's other hand, and a lot thicker. It has the sweet taste of sautéed onions, a touch of nutmeg and more than a touch of black pepper;

though it is coarse, it is not heavy. Sometimes there is cold poached bass, and when there is, you can order it as an appetizer or as a main course. Either way, the fish is fresh and flaky, and it is served with a mellifluous mayonnaise that is made on the premises.

Of course there is Gigot aux Flageolets—roast leg of lamb with white beans—and the lamb is rare, slightly gamy and tender, and served in a thick gravy with beans that are thoroughly cooked but still firm. The braised capon is good—it is made with tarragon, and when it is brought to your table, or when a portion of it passes by, you will note an almost overpowering aroma of the mysterious herb. The sauce the bird was braised in is white and thick, streaked with the tarragon, and the dish is very sensibly served with rice, which is well suited to the task of soaking up the sauce. As in virtually all French restaurants of this class in New York, tripe is available, but here—shades of pretension!—they don't admit it at dinner, and you must get your tripe some day when you are in the neighborhood for a matinée. The tripe is slightly gummy, as it should be, and it is served in a fatty broth that is strongly flavored of bay and thyme. The rather sour flavor of the wet food is offset nicely by the firm boiled potato that arrives immersed in it. Even the side orders of vegetables are good here, particularly the oily, hot ratatouille, which is sometimes the vegetable of the day.

Your salad is dressed just before it is served, the greens are fresh and the vinaigrette is well balanced.

Why, in the peach season, is the peach tart made with canned peaches, when, in the simultaneous strawberry season, the strawberry tart is made with fresh berries? Hard to say, but the former suffers and the latter benefits, though not enough—the pastry is a little pasty. By evening the St. Honoré is also flat. The best desserts here are the caramel custard and the ice cream items. As to the cheeses, if you look like you know what you are doing, the waiter discourages you from that experiment.

This place has one of the most extensive wine cellars of any West Side French restaurant, both Burgundies and Bordeaux. Of the twenty or so Bordeaux offered, some go back to 1955; of course those run up to $60.

The place is garish (orange banquettes, grandfather's clock, everything they could fit in) and garishly lighted, but it's comfortable. Busier at noontime than in the evening, it is never packed. And at night, when business is sometimes sparse, the place never feels desolate.

★★RENÉ PUJOL

321 West 51st Street
LUNCH AND DINNER.
Closed Sunday.
Reservations, 246–3023.
Credit cards: AE.
Medium-priced.

Of the numerous French restaurants in the West Forties and Fifties, several of which are operated by members of the Pujol family, the one that sports the family name is among the most attractive (in a kitschy way), comfortable and reliable.

The kitsch—rustic-looking rough plaster walls, dark beams, exposed brick to either side of the large fireplace, copper pots and pans, pottery, a stately grandfather's clock —does not seem to disturb the French workingmen who hang around the bar nursing their apértifs and reading French-language newspapers. To them the frippery is an accepted necessity, to lure *les Américains,* and the irrelevant trappings do not unmake their neighborhood café or distract from the business of reading, talking and drinking (any more than the icons and pageantry in the church up the block move the minds of the religious from their prayerful thoughts). For the more occasional visitor the *déjà vu* quality of the place is immediately hospitable. This is *the* French restaurant, the familiar place around the corner, the place you go to instead of suffering through Act II at the Circle in the Square—a medal is earned by the one who says first, "The hell with it. Let's get something to eat."

If you're lucky, you get something to eat before you order. A little pot of pork rillettes is sometimes brought to the table to occupy you while you consider the menu—the pounded meat is dark-brown, pleasantly fatty and spicy, and one can easily make a pig of himself with this and the good bread. This is, after all, the general idea, so if they don't bring it, point out how much you enjoyed it the last time, which is one way of letting them know you know it's available.

After rillettes, the pâté may seem redundant, but, just for the record, you get a substantial slab of the stuff (about the size of a slice of Wonder bread). It is coarse, and there are nodules of jelly in it, bits of unabashed fat, chunks of meat, a few of which are almost cartilaginous, and plenty of garlic—the rich stuff is garnished with crisp and tart little pickles. There is an odd appetizer on the menu called Les Little Necks aux Amandes—it would be disastrous if it were not so carefully made, with wine, butter and lightly browned slivered almonds; the clams themselves are small, sweet and tender, the nuts are crisp, and the juice of the clams, the butter and the wine make a lovely sauce, but the whole thing is a bit queer. Snail shells are dispensed with, in favor of a deep, six-socket porcelain pan—one snail per socket, all very tender, lots of garlic, butter and parsley; you use the handle to pass the snails around the table, and at a table for four you can be a big loser. The quiche is fluffy, steamy, browned and studded with chunks of good ham. And there is a Coquille St. Jacques made with fresh scallops that are soft and fibrous, in a strong, dark sauce. The onion soup is stout, almost black, and thick with cheese.

None of the main courses is bad, but a few are merely good. To get those out of the way first, there is a chicken dish invitingly entitled Le Poulet Sauté au Calvados—nice bird, well-browned skin, moist meat, in a creamy sauce that was merely introduced to the Calvados. The combination of apple brandy and cream is typical of Normandy cooking, but the brandy should not be wasted unless you're going to use enough of it to contribute to the flavor. There are kidneys in mustard sauce—the kidneys are given a hearty quality by being browned to a crust, which is nice, and the sauce is thick and satisfying but barely flavored with mustard. The frog's legs Provençale are sautéed to the perfect point, plump and moist, but the word "Provençale" suggests more garlic than the chef ventures to use.

So, instead, have the duck—it's not every restaurant in New York that produces an orange sauce that is dark, edgy with the taste of slightly sour orange, and faintly liquored, to be poured over a moist, well-roasted bird. This is also a good place for Steak au Poivre—the beef is not perfectly aged, but it is excellent meat, fibrous and bloody, and the deglazing sauce, of brandy, cream and pepper is syrupy and strong, just right for beef. The poached salmon is flaky and fresh, and it is served with a mellifluous hollandaise sauce that is loaded with egg yolks and lots of fresh lemon.

You may want cheese, and the waiter may look over one shoulder and then over the other and then inform you that the Port-Salut is domestic and terrible and that the blue is Danish and tolerable. There is mousse, of course; it is light and syrupy, with the flavor of milk chocolate rather than of good, dark chocolate, but it's pretty nice anyway. And there are fruit tarts made with fresh fruit—berries, apricots, etc.—and they have a flaky pastry with a layer of custard. The captain shudders at the request of Crêpes Suzette, but he brings himself around to the task and does OK. The pancakes themselves are not particularly thin, but they are delicate just the same, and the captain's sauce, rather abundantly of orange and lemon juice, and only slightly of butter, is good, tart and strong, but a bit thin. Good coffee.

Madison Avenue French

On the other side of Fifth Avenue, in the *East* Forties and Fifties, there is a heavy sprinkling of French restaurants that are the gilded mirror images of the Broadway bistros.

Draw a line from the United Nations to The Plaza; it's the diagonal of a rectangle on which hundreds of thousands of office workers descend each day, from Monday to Friday. Most of their lunch requirements are filled by sandwich shops and fast-food chains, but for the business lunches among board chairmen, vice-presidents and the middle managers who come along to take notes, those places will not do. A little cosseting is required, thank you, a little midday reinforcement of importance, if the afternoon's decisions are to be made decisively.

The food in these restaurants is certainly just as good as it is nearer Manhattan's West Coast, but the amenities are always fancier—murals instead of travel posters, captains to take your order and flame your duck—and the prices are higher.

Herewith a sampling that includes the best of these and the best-known.

★★ LE BISTRO

827 Third Avenue (near 50th Street)
LUNCH, MONDAY TO FRIDAY; DINNER, MONDAY TO SATURDAY.
Closed Sunday.
Reservations, EL 5–8766.
Credit cards: AE, CB, MC.
Medium-priced.

The place is well-named, for this *is* very much a bistro, with its simple, square-room layout with a little bar at the front—tan walls, heavy hanging lamps, travel posters (behind glass!), a comfortable red banquette all around. The neatly set tables are covered with white linen, fringes of red gingham showing at the edges. Le Bistro is a cheerful place, everything about it is hearty, you enter and judge at once (correctly) that the food will be sturdy stuff. The surest clues are these waiters, barrel-chested, one and all, in aprons over shirt sleeves (the cuffs rolled up). They are gruffly polite, intelligent, on the job. They make suggestions. Take them.

Take, for example, the saucisson chaud. The sausages themselves are not the moist fatty ones that usually go by this name; they are, instead, rather dry and firm, but they are spicy almost to the point of hotness. They are served with superb warm potato salad —the potatoes are salty, they are covered with an oily dressing that is thick with mustard, and they are sprinkled with plenty of chopped fresh parsley. Or take the quiche—well above average, the custard light and fluffy, the bits of ham abundant, smoky and salty, the crust carefully made, so that it is crunchy and browned on the bottom as well as along the exposed edge.

You may get an undercooked artichoke here, hard-hearted, the leaves resistant to scraping by all but the sharpest teeth—good vinaigrette and all that, but too much work. You are better off with the mussels; do not be deceived by their not being in their shells—they are perfectly fresh, and the huge mound of them is in a good thick dressing that is highly flavored with bay.

Definitely a soup house. Sometimes there is a hot leek-and-potato soup; it is thick and slightly grainy, with lots of butter and sharp taste of boiled milk. And sometimes there is a cream of lentil soup, which is an elemental thing, thick, studded with discs of fairly uninteresting sausage, but the sum of it very satisfying. Of course there is onion soup—made with a good beefy stock and onions that have been cooked until they are dark-brown and sweet.

An oddity: Pieds de Porc Grillés—pig's feet, and very good, if not what the doctor ordered. You end up eating pig fat, cartilege, gelatine and an oily browned breading, which is all very succulent and sinful. You are left with a plate of glistening bones. The dish comes with some of the best French fries in town, crisp, thin, perfectly browned, tasty. This is one of the minority of French restaurants in New York where, when you order duck bigarade, you get duck *bigarade,* which is to say that the sauce is not a candied consommé but a flavored stock. This is not the best version of this dish in town, but it is the real thing—a good bird, with plenty of fat and moisture left behind in a judicious roasting, a more than decent sweet-and-tart sauce, and a nice garnish of sliced oranges.

On Fridays there is bouillabaisse—not a gargantuan bowl of it, which is surprising in this place, but the soup is thick and vibrant; the fish is flaky (albeit bony); and—surprise!—the lobster is fresh, you get a good bit of it, and it is cooked to the proper point.

The Boeuf Bordelaise is of good beef, accurately sautéed, but the sauce lacks balance—too strong a flavor of raw wine, which is not offset by the presence of good fresh mushrooms.

Some sturdy desserts, like Gâteau de Riz, a moist, heavy and extremely satisfying rice cake with a vanilla sauce. The chocolate mousse is intensely flavored of dark chocolate, fresh, and served with good whipped cream. Most restaurant parfaits are just ice cream and syrup, but the coffee parfait here is much better than that—the ice cream is of a strong coffee flavor, and the sauce is made with rum and caramel. Avoid the pears in wine—they taste as if they should be called pears in wine and water. To make pears in wine, you must cover the pears with wine, which takes a lot of wine, which costs a lot of money. So lots of restaurants cover the pears with wine and water. Too bad.

The place can be a mad scene at lunchtime, but in the evening it is neither packed nor deserted, which makes it a pleasant place for a pleasant dinner.

• BRUSSELS

115 East 54th Street
LUNCH, MONDAY TO FRIDAY; DINNER, MONDAY TO SATURDAY.
Closed Sunday.
Reservations, PL 8–0457.
Credit cards: AE, BA, CB, DC, MC.
Very expensive.

New management. Victor is in ever-courtly attendance, offering sound wine advice to whoever asks for it, with the courtliest manner on Manhattan Island. Behind the bar in the cozy cocktail lounge, the statue of the young boy continues to perpetually relieve itself into a champagne cooler. The large dining room, with its delicately patterned maroon-and-gold wallpaper, walnut beams, heavy chandeliers and soft light, is as muted and old-world as ever. And, as ever, reading the elaborate menu is more rewarding than eating the foods it lists. What arrives on your plate is clean, studiously prepared, but it is not only utterly without inspiration but actually devoid of the quality of French food. It has no character. An occasional dish is good, nothing is ever actually bad, but if you come here five times you will invariably find yourself searching the menu for something you have not had before, in the hope of finding a dish you would gladly order twice.

In the old days, for a first course you would order the Anguilles au Vert à la Flamande—cold eel in a jellied green sauce, with a bit of garlic. It is sturdy stuff with a texture that appealed to few. Nowadays it is rarely available—perhaps because the desirable small eels are not to be had, as you are told, but more likely because the dish is rarely ordered. You can have Pâté de Fois Gras de Strasbourg en Gelée; it comes from there and it is *en gelée,* and that's about all you can say for it. You can have Jambon de Parme; it is that kind of ham, and there are better kinds of that kind. You can have Toast à la Moelle aux Champignons; the dish is toast with marrow *and* mushrooms, and this mushroom is very nicely sautéed but that one was soaking wet when they sautéed it, so it is stewed instead. The lobster bisque is nice and spicy, and your waiter will pour either brandy or sherry into it, but neither liquor nor wine can rescue this soup from its inferior lobster.

You order Pompano Grenobloise, and the fish seems fresh enough, but at this restaurant, as in most places in New York, Grenobloise means Grenobloise minus mushrooms. Even so made, the dish can be good if the floured fish is rapidly sautéed in very hot butter, but here the process is carried out much too slowly, and instead of a crisp crust you get a soft, breaded exterior. The roasted pigeon is OK, with its canned peas; Tournedos Niçoise turns out to be a filet mignon of unexceptional and unexceptionable quality, with a delicious sauce Béarnaise, and a garnish of one stewed tomato to justify the regional name, and another wet mushroom, this one as a cap, to make the dish look like something special. One of the best dishes in the house is the Noisette de Chevreuil Grand Veneur. This restaurant imports some excellent venison—it is well aged, tender and sweet, and served with a good dark sauce that is sweetened and thickened with cream. The à la carte vegetables are not much, but as you might hope in a restaurant of Belgian pretensions, the braised endives (called chicorées) are very good—the vegetable is cooked in consommé and lemon until it is limp, dark and strong.

The Crêpe Soufflé (vanilla flavor) with crème Anglaise (vanilla flavor) is better than ice cream. The thick strawberry mousse lacks the flavor of fresh strawberries.

There is a captain here (just one), who frowns at every order, looks at you as if you were crazy, snatches the menu out of your hand to read it, to prove that what you want does not exist. He studies it carefully, and sure enough, fails to find the item you request, and you must (gently, now) show him the entry, by pointed finger. He takes your victory as a sign of the declining times, writes, waits for further instructions, frowns again and starts the process all over.

If only Victor could cook! He *does* know how to sell, and if you don't watch out, he'll let you try his 1860 Madeira at $4 a drink.

★★ LE CIRQUE

58 East 65th Street
LUNCH AND DINNER.
Closed Sunday.
Reservations, 794–9292.
Credit cards: AE, DC.
Very expensive.

There are flashes of such talent in the kitchen that one must recognize the possibility that, with time, this may become one of the couple of dozen or so best French restaurants in New York. And there is a sign other than the occasional excellence of the food. It is an almost unfailing rule that any restaurant that serves both French and Italian food is no good at either—the breadth of the menu is a search for a broader clientele, and a signal that someone in charge cares not what he serves, as long as it sells. This place serves several Italian dishes in addition to its preponderance of French food, and you can tell that this is not an economically motivated pandering to the supposed tastes of the wished-for customers. The handful of Italian dishes are not the standard New York items, they are on the menu because someone who decides what is being served here likes to serve them, which is a heartening sign that the place is governed by an ego, not a calculator.

This establishment is built into the Mayfair Hotel, where no restaurant was before, and they have chosen to go the route of Champs-Elysées posh, which is, in this version, harmless enough—but it has dragged in the most uniformly stuffy crowd outside Quo Vadis. The softly lit room is papered in an ivory-and-tan trellis pattern, with pastel murals, in a certain low order of French humor, of monkeys doing human things—Le Cirque is The Circus; in one mural we have monkeys chatting, in another dining, then dancing, then flirting . . . they stop short. The furniture is Louis the Something (with oval-backed chairs in pink upholstery); there are mirrored columns, flowers on the tables, candlelight; and a gentle murmur from the well-breds that besport themselves along the taupe banquette of glistening suede that meanders through the room. It is all very other-worldly, with nary a black or a beard or a denimed derrière in the place —they could have called it Le Musée—but perfectly comfortable in its anachronistic way.

To begin with one of the Italian items, you may drop $5 for a delicacy which is styled Carpaccio Toscane—three small thin slices of superb raw beef, served with a cold green sauce. The meat is freshly sliced from the filet, and the sauce is a thick composite of minced capers, parsley, a bit of garlic, a touch of anchovy, and oil—a good idea is to wrap one third of your sauce in each slice of meat and eat with your fingers. To begin with one of the French items, you may sacrifice $3.75 for Crêpes Le Cirque—these are a usual thing, two pancakes rolled up and stuffed with curried seafood, mostly crabmeat, served with a mustard sauce (a pool of it on one side of your dish) and a spicy tomato sauce (another pool, at the other side)—nice, but nothing special.

When the soup of the day is hot leek-and-potato, do not pass it up. It is simply a buttery broth (chicken-stock base), infused with the flavor of leeks, with a layer of crunchy bits of potato at the bottom of the bowl—elemental and very satisfying.

An ambitious duck, and, by and large, a successful one. Called, without commas, Le Canard Rôti au Citron Pommes et Raisins, it is a very good rich bird, against which the sharp flavors of citrus rind, the sweet and spicy taste of cinnamoned apples, and the plump ripeness of dark little raisins are all perfect complements. La Selle de Pré Salé Desossée Grillée is your lamb as beef, a thick steak of it, served with a mustard-and-tomato sauce (like an excellent barbecue sauce). The sauce is not needed—the lamb steak is good just the way it is. Pretty good vegetables, including zucchini that is sugared and browned until leathery.

A limited number of desserts of interest—an unlisted Tarte à la Tatin is just a humdrum apple tart covered with a whipped cream that is all air; the chocolate cake is rich, moist, solid without being heavy.

★★ CLOS NORMAND

42 East 52nd Street
LUNCH AND DINNER.
Closed Sunday.
Reservations, PL 3–3348.
Credit cards: AE, BA, CB, DC, MC.
Medium-priced.

This is a lovely restaurant; the food is usually good, often excellent; the service, once you get past the officious host, is intelligent and industrious; and the prices, though moderately expensive at lunch (à la carte), are very reasonable at dinner (prix fixe), as a result of which the place does almost as much business in the evening as it does at noon, which is rare for all but the most *haute cuisine* of New York's midtown restaurants.

There are dozens of French restaurants in New York in the East and West Forties and Fifties, and the daytime office population in these neighborhoods is so dense that it's almost impossible for a restaurant to fail unless it is shut down by the health department. So it's admirable when any of them goes to the trouble, first, of preparing the conventional dishes with care and originality, and second, of augmenting the standard French menu with unusual dishes.

There is pâté all over town, but the terrine served at lunch here is of game, and it is pink, moist, rich, and accented with crisp nuts and firm black truffles. In the evening you may wish to pass up the terrine, however, because a crock of fluffy liver mousse, strong and perfectly salted, is placed on the table to divert you while you read the menu, and perhaps decide to start with Moules Normande, one of the best mussel appetizers in New York. This is a giant pot of at least two dozen fresh mussels that have been steamed in their own juice, milk, wine, herbs and shallots; the tangy white soup that remains when you have eaten the mussels is worth the $1.75 premium alone. Even jellied consommé is good here—cool cubes of strong beef broth. And the pink Bayonne ham, served with ripe melon, is tender, just a little smoky, and sliced elegantly thin.

This restaurant makes some of the better quenelles in New York, and though they are served with what the menu calls lobster sauce, it's not the usual sauce Nantua. On the other hand, the word "lobster" doesn't seem quite right either. The white dumplings come in assorted shapes, which gives them a pleasant homemade look. They are tender, not rubbery, intensely flavored without being fishy, and they are covered with a strong brown sauce containing mussels, fresh mushrooms and breath of lobster. Well, lobsters are sky-high. At lunch there is a seafood quiche which is loaded with huge chunks of pink-skinned crabmeat.

Clos Normand is one of the few places that consents to prepare a rack of lamb for one person. It is served in the juice of the lamb, not converted into a sauce, and the meat is smeared with a potent amalgam of garlic, shallots and herbs. The duck with figs is a juicy bird, but the figs are only a garnish and do not enter into the preparation, and are canned, anyway, so you are disappointed if you expect something that lives up to Le Caneton aux Figues.

Most fixed-price dinner houses do not include a salad in the price of your dinner.

Here you not only get a salad, but a great one—tender Boston lettuce, crisp watercress and loads of thinly sliced raw mushrooms in a truly French dressing of mostly oil and mustard, with just a little vinegar.

The Mont Blanc here is disappointing—a commercial meringue, an excessively sweet canned chestnut purée and whipped cream. It's just too much. In its original form this dish is made with *crème fraîche,* not whipped cream, and *crème fraîche* has an edge to it that can relieve the overwhelming sweetness of the purée. Better are Les Délices du Chef, which are little babas covered with a runny custard and toasted almonds, all in a puddle of powerfully sweet caramel sauce. The Crêpe Surprise is a browned crêpe around a ball of pecan ice cream, all in the same honeylike caramel sauce—sort of a French sundae. There is a sensible policy here of stocking only one or two cheeses, but of keeping them at room temperature, and available in good condition. You get a large pot of very good coffee.

Tan plaster walls, beams, rough-hewn wooden pillars, rustic-looking wall sconces, banquettes of coarse red wool, and large, delicately shaded murals of foggy Normandy—cities, towns and a beautiful long beach in hazy sunlight. This is one of the prettiest restaurants in town, though it is rather crowded and noisy, which tends to offset the effect.

The proprietor here is a stiff type who peers at you dubiously over his steel-rimmed glasses. He considers it a sin to seat anyone at once, empty tables or no, reservation or no. His stiff frame collapses and is reassembled into a limp posture of abject respect when big spenders show up. But he is a minor obstacle, and he wilts under a firm complaint.

★★ LA COCOTTE

147 East 60th Street
LUNCH AND DINNER.
Closed Sunday.
Reservations, 832–8972.
Credit cards: AE, BA, DC, MC.
Expensive.

La Cocotte is now a large restaurant—a small front room, a somewhat larger back room, and a spacious room downstairs built into what was once the garden. It still has some of the feeling of a garden because two of the walls are almost entirely of glass, through which a little foliage can be seen, and at lunch, a little daylight. The other walls are papered—huge green ferns. But as the room was added on the strength of the profits and success of the two rooms above, it is deplorable to have it filled so densely with such tiny tables—sixty-or-so eaters, in a glass-walled room, create a deafening ambience, and tables thirty inches square are an affront to the food turned out by the very professional kitchen.

La Cocotte is a very classy restaurant—everything is clean, neat and relaxed. And nothing can be more comfortable than the East Siders who take it over for dinner. The people who come here for lunch are comfortable too; they have found a restaurant where the daytime prices are competitive with some of the most mediocre French restaurants in New York, but where the food is far better—on occasion, superb.

At dinnertime you are served a little something to hold you while you look at the menu—on occasion a mélange of green peppers, radishes, cucumbers, celery, salmon, and mackerel, in a good vinaigrette; another time a dish of celery root rémoulade; and so on.

"Coquille" is a word that is so familiar on New York appetizer listings that one almost automatically reads right by it in the search for something more interesting. But *coquille* means "shell," the contents can be anything, and here the dish is called Coquille Thermidor, not St. Jacques. The contents are sautéed mushrooms, tender little shrimp and red-skinned lobster meat, as well as scallops, all in a sweet, thick Thermidor sauce, the whole sprinkled with cheese and lightly browned just before serving. The search for a mussel variant has led to Moules Mignonette, which is soft, well-cleaned, steamed mussels, out of their shells, marinated in vinegar and pepper, and served with lemon, which gives the dish even more sparkle. The plate of Hors d'Oeuvres Variées is indeed *variées,* but you will have to hunt through it to find something worth a tumble. The oysters here are good, though the management operates under the delusion that tiny ones are better than big ones. And there are the usual smoked salmon, shrimp cocktail and a good pâté de campagne, with the pistachio nuts without which the East Side would not put up.

The steak tartare is very good. The meat is ground just before the preparation, and it is moist and red, which is the basic requirement of a dish made with raw meat. However, if the captain spends too long making it, the Tournedos Périgourdine, destined for the same table, may get overcooked while the tartare's middle-of-the-dining-room preparation is interrupted by the demands of diners who should but can't be assisted by any of the numerous waiters who are standing about in clusters discussing politics. Aside from the timing problem, the preparation of these tournedos is quite expert—the sautéed truffles and sautéed filet mignon are covered with a superb madeira-flavored brown sauce. But the addition of a cap of pâté de foie gras is ridiculous—it's wrong for the dish (the flavor of the pâté is overwhelmed by the beef, sauce and truffles), and it's clearly aimed at the kinds of customers who are the more delighted the greater the number of fancy ingredients they find on their plates.

One of the best dishes here is the rack of lamb (served for two). The delicate, very young baby lamb is studded with garlic, roasted and carved across the ribs, to produce eight long slices of pink meat. These are moistened with a light sauce made in the roasting pan, sprinkled with parsley, surrounded with the now denuded ribs and served with watercress and some very good Pommes Anna (a cake of sliced, seasoned potatoes baked in clarified butter to the point of brown crust, and soft, white interior).

There is a delicate dish of sautéed veal scallops moistened in a cider-based sauce; and a good grilled bass covered with sauce Choron (tomato-flavored Béarnaise). The salads are of excellent crisp greens in a very tart and mustardy vinaigrette.

La Cocotte serves cheese at room temperature. A good Brie is usually available, although, to avoid horrifying customers who point and sniff at a slightly white, hard center, it is often overripe, too runny and past its best flavor.

There are nice fruit tarts, a good coffee mousse, flaky and creamy Napoleons, perfectly decent Cherries Jubilee, and a light and refreshing crème caramel, etc. The wine list is rather brief for a restaurant of this caliber.

★★ LE FONTAINEBLEAU

998 Second Avenue (near 53rd Street)
LUNCH, MONDAY TO FRIDAY; DINNER, MONDAY TO SATURDAY.
Closed Sunday.
Reservations, 752–8088.
Credit cards: AE.
Medium-priced.

Jarring wallpaper, wood paneling craftily contrived to look like plastic, banquettes and booths upholstered in orange icing, paintings that would be rejected by the Washington Square Art Show—all under a crimson acoustical ceiling. The only solution is to dim the lights. The food is good or better, the service knowledgeable and polite.

The snails are plump, tender, flavored by the herby stock they were cooked in, moistened by a buttery sauce that strikes a heady balance between garlic, shallots and fresh parsley. The rabbit pâté, of which you receive a substantial slab, is somehow soft and moist even though it is made up of good-size chunks of firm meat—lots of salt, plenty of fat, a garnish of clear minced jelly that has a potent beef-bouillon flavor, and little pickles, crisp and sour. The Jambon de Bayonne, several thin slices of ham neatly covering a good-size plate, is dark mahogany, slightly fibrous but tender, and smoky. And the Artichoke Vinaigrette is obviously poached in more than salted water—the flavor of the vegetable is somehow emphasized without being distorted, and the vinaigrette is a conventional but excellent mustard-flavored dressing.

Le Fontainebleau is one of a dozen or so restaurants in town where you can get sweetbreads that are, despite the natural richness and oiliness of this meat, light and delicate. They are floured, gently browned and served with chanterelles that retain a woodsy taste despite being canned, and with a purée of broccoli made by chopping the vegetable rather than mashing it, so that the purée has a soft pebbly texture. The same talent for sautéeing is applied to the calf's liver with raisins—the meat is crisped to a deep blackish brown, but it is done so quickly that the interior remains bright pink and moist—the accent of plump, sweet raisins is startling but right. You get a good tournedos here, though the serving is small by local steak standards—good meat, accurately prepared, in a mushroom sauce that is smooth and polished.

One is attracted to the title "Poulet de Grain au Whisky." Well, there is little hint of liquor in the buttery white sauce, but the bird has a browned skin and tender meat, and the unalcoholic sauce is buttery and rich—you eat most of the sauce with the meat, the rest of it with the excellent rice (cooked in broth) that comes with it. Not much fish on the menu, but the striped bass with hollandaise is flawless, if uninspired.

Skip the soufflés—they are $5 extra for two people, available in any flavor you want, very prettily risen over their baking dish, but simply too heavy. You are much better off with the good versions of standard stuff—pastries, a nice rich chocolate mousse. A few good cheeses, at room temperature and in good condition, are also available.

• KATJA

225 East 58th Street
LUNCH, MONDAY TO FRIDAY; DINNER, MONDAY TO SATURDAY.
Closed Sunday.
Reservations, PL 1–5488.
Credit cards: AE, DC, MC.
Very expensive.

Regard the pretty restaurant. Consider how elegant to enter on the gleaming black-and-white checkerboard marble floor, to walk it past a shimmering crystalline bar to the velvety, lawnlike green carpeting on which spacious tables are spaciously placed at the back of this grand and airy room. Note the glassy sconces on mirrored walls, the twinkling chandeliers, the casual greenery hanging and standing here and there. See that at your place is a handsome gold-rimmed plate, monogrammed; that on your table stands a slender silver vase, fresh flowers within; that your drink is prettily served in a plump wineglass. And what do you note of the more fundamental aspects of the place? The splendid display of cold foods: a lengthy bass on a lengthy platter; a side of cold smoked salmon with a sharp carving knife beside it; tiers of fruit, bowls of berries. There are even a couple of reassuring rough-and-ready notes: the kitchen, with whitewashed brick walls and hanging copper pots, is exposed, and it looks honest; and wandering here and there are the waiters, who, despite the posh of the place, show white aprons beneath their black jackets; both of which suggest (though not prove) that the business of the place was not forgotten when all this attention was given to the appearances.

So, at first blush, the place is assuring. You have a sense of rightness, style, even panache. You may even comfort yourself with the thought that whatever may eventually be served you, a place so carefully rendered to attract a certain New York crowd deserves high marks for that effort if no other.

But at second blush a few flat notes craze the fragile harmony. What the devil are these ghastly, murky, five-and-dime oils doing on the walls? And what of this spotlighting, designed, for one thing, to call attention to the huge samovar behind the display table, but somehow contrived to shine directly onto your retina? And in such posh surroundings, and at such (read on) Olympian prices, must one wrinkle one's garments on banquettes of slick vinyl? At $14 the steak, $7 the plate of noodles, $1 the cup of Café Américain (the official title), give us please velvet, to preserve the press on the well-tailored bottoms of this spendthrift clientele.

At Katja there *is* a Katja. She is depicted on the matchbooks, but she is better in person—a charming, pretty, smiling, tasteful greeter, all poise and confidence and just the right amount of unnecessary chitchat as you enter. One wishes that her apparent sense of proportion were reflected more fully in the appointments, and at all in the preparation and pricing of the food. As it is, the net effect of this place is of a hype, and hypes are OK if they are perfect, if we are so thoroughly charmed that we do not mind being fooled. Oh, those oil paintings, they gave it all away.

Scrape up $4.25 for a slab of Terrine of Wild Duck with Truffles. It's a fair choice —there are substantial chunks of duck and slivers of truffle in the moist ground meat and fat, and the surrounding jelly is well-intentioned and harmless. Or you can put together a Selection from the Cold Table—at a piddling $3, it does not include the aforementioned terrine, but only such equally forgettable numbers as fresh mussels and a couple of halves of hard-cooked egg, both under green mayonnaise, slices of undistinguished cold meat, some of that cold bass (overcooked and a bit mushy) with the same green mayo, and a chunk of ripe melon, all with garnishes of cucumber salad, sliced tomato, grated carrots.

A certain familiar red soup is referred to on the menu as Ukrainian Borschtsch. The transliteration from the Cyrillic to the English alphabet is no worse than the interpretation of the native dish in this local kitchen. This is the version of beet soup made with meat, a rendition that is usually served hot. Here it comes cold, with a dollop of sour cream in the center of the broad deep plate. It is perfectly refreshing, complete with crunchy beets and carrots and slivers of firm and fibrous meat, but it lacks the character that a substantial dose of sour salts imparts, and because it is cold, it has been largely de-fatted (otherwise it would be cloying), and this deprives it of a certain richness. Another innocuous dish.

Oblivious to blunt self-contradiction, Katja lists Homard Parisienne ($12) under Le Buffet Froid Moscovite. This is one-half (½) a cold chicken lobster, one-half a lemon and one-half a tomato, with herbed mayonnaise. It amounts to slightly less than one-fourth (¼) a child's repast. Only slightly more substantial is the Schaschlik Flambé, a skewer of morsels that arrives aflame. The bits of lamb are apparently pre-cooked and flamed to be reheated along with mushrooms and onions that have suffered from the same treatment. The scalloped potatoes that accompany are inappropriate in a couple of ways. As the schaschlik is served on rice, do we also want potatoes? And if we do want potatoes, tender and nicely buttered as they may be, should they be flavored with, apparently, garlic powder? The steam-table broccoli is limp.

The dessert cart arrives with a small selection of the small selection listed on the menu. The pretty berries turn out to be dejected and soft, and the sauce zabaglione they are served in is a soft, tasteless custard. You try the Sarnowskaya, which is explained to you as "mousse cake," and you undergo a heavy, brown experience, a bit wet, with here and there the maraschino cherry.

• LAURENT

111 East 56th Street
LUNCH, MONDAY TO SATURDAY; DINNER, DAILY.
Reservations, PL 3–2729.
Credit cards: AE, DC.
Very expensive.

The restaurant is grand, but the food and service are sometimes barely upright. Laurent is a splendidly spacious, gracious, comfortable spot. You enter from the street into a high-ceilinged, dimly lighted lounge, with a handsome bar and well-spaced tables. The room has a feeling of blue velvet, of a twilit night under a clear sky. It is cushy, unhurried, almost timeless (until closing time). Farther in, there is a large dining room —a typical hotel dining room (this is the Lombardy Hotel)—lofty, brightly lit, with carved columns, illuminated paintings on the paneled walls, draperies, red velvet banquettes, green hedges over the partitions that divide the places along the walls, fresh flowers on every table, and an air about the place of old gaiety, wealth, leisure, civilization. Ah, if only they could cook.

"A nice appetizer for the little lady?" and you look around to make certain you are where you are. Yes, it's Laurent all right, and that was your captain speaking. The lady, and everyone else, would very much like a nice appetizer, but she is a little disappointed to find that at one of the more expensive French restaurants on this planet, there is not a first course on the menu that could not be found in a West Side bistro, with the possible exception of the caviar. You may expect that the pâté, styled "Terrine de Faison et Mallard aux Pistaches," may be a little special, but the ground meat has lost the flavor of the original game, and though the spicy loaf is perfectly good with its sweet sauce, there are more honest ones around town at half the price. Smoked trout is smoked trout, it's true, but Laurent does make a little effort to dress it up. It is served surrounded by a delicate minced jelly that is made from a clarified *court-bouillon,* with a respectable sauce of sour cream, a bit of horseradish, and lemon, which is very nice on the processed trout.

The menu lists Red Snapper au Fenouil, and you inquire of the waiter if the flavor of fennel is achieved with a liquor, fennel seeds or real fennel, and you're assured that the fish is made with *branches of fennel.* Sure enough, when the fish arrives, what can only be described as a stick is conspicuously removed from atop the fish before it is served. If you can taste the fennel, you have a powerful imagination. The fish is breaded, grilled and served with lime, and it is not worth bothering about. You're impressed with the sound of Tournedos of Venaison Lorenzo, and get perfectly nice venison, in a sauce that has been populated by an irrelevant, unrelated collection of such things as *stuffed* green olives, almost exactly as they came from the jar, rubbery mushrooms, capers, pine nuts. When sautéed meat is to be served in sauce with vegetables this way, the ingredients have to be warmed together for a while just before serving, or else you end up with something that looks impressive but tastes like a warm salad. And when the ingredients are no good to begin with, it tastes like a *bad* warm salad. Some of the vegetables are good, including Zucchini Niçoise—the vegetable only slightly cooked, in a garlic-flavored sauce of tomato and oil. The salads are good, if not meticulously picked clean of browned leaves.

There is a very dull listing of desserts, but—now for the good news—they make terrific soufflés here. Order your soufflé, and the captain informs you that it must be for at least two people and should be ordered at the start of your meal. You point out that the menu makes no mention of either restriction and that according to the restaurant's stated schedule, there is time left to make two soufflés, maybe three, before the place closes. You must insist. They come in all flavors, are light, and are the only way to redeem some of the dinners you get here.

The wine is served by a perfectly nice but silly-looking fellow in striped clothes with a chain around his neck, a key, a metal dish, and all that. The list is fairly extensive, but there are no bargains available.

★★★ LE LAVANDOU

134 East 61st Street
LUNCH AND DINNER.
Closed Sunday.
Reservations, TE 8–7987.
Credit cards: AE.
Very expensive.

You enter to a vestibule heavily hung with citations, diplomata, certificates of achievement, ratifications of victory, confirmations of award. You are duly impressed, you proceed to the dining room, and you decide that the chef's honors are not for originality if his restaurant's appearance is clue to his creativity. This is Paris posh, as middle as class can be, with a crimson velvet banquette circling the room under ivory walls, dark mirrors, scenic and sunny oils, bronzed sconces. There is potted greenery in each corner, flowers on every neatly-set table. Down to the red carpeting, you have seen it all before. The French restaurant in New York is such a successful institution, that newcomers are happy to get lost in the crowd.

Your *déjà vu,* however, will wane when you eat, for Le Lavandou, particularly when you select from its list of specialties, produces some very classy fare. Accordingly, you opt for La Cassolette d'Escargots des Pinèdes, and receive, blessedly, a small baking dish with six snail-size declevities, in each of which, besides a plump and tender snail, you will find a few crunchy pine nuts and a clear and buttery sauce, mildly herbed, and amply flavored with Pernod. You are happy with one specialty, so next time you try another, specifically La Quenelle de Brochet au Pernod (did the man get his recipes from the back of a Pernod bottle?). The little dumplings of pike are firm, tender, and peppery, with a bright and clear flavor of fresh fish—that is to say, what any good quenelle de brochet would be; but the house ennobles the already aristocratic dish by serving with it a smooth white sauce that is heady with Pernod and populated by half a dozen fresh mussels—lovely.

Veering from the red-letter items, you encounter Asperges de France Hollandaise, and the way they got those French asparagus spears to the USA is by can. Well, withal, they speak only faintly of the tin, and as white asparagus are so rare here that few have a notion of how they taste when fresh, they seem quite delicious in their preserved form, cool and sharp; but this establishment's Hollandaise lacks sufficient lemon to undo its exceptional richness. Once more eschewing the featured dishes, you ask for the Terrine de Canard Truffée, and you are brought a wheeled serving stand, from which you are served any number of things in addition to the listed terrine, which is spicy and rich: a head cheese that is an array of textures, from nodules of white fat, to a cool jelly, to chunks of fibrous tongue; take it or leave it, but a "pâté en croûte" that is not in a crust, one that is predominantly ham and pork, accented with whole filberts; and a mousse of chicken liver that is light, loud, and rich.

Returning to the list of specialties of the house, you find the least likely kind of thing you will want after four pâtés and terrines—Le Cassoulet du Chef Toulousain. Well, have it anyway. This is a heady and heavy composition of meats, birds, and sausages in a thickness of beans. The pork and pigeon are moist, the sausage is fragrant of fennel, and the final heating of the dish with a sprinkling of bread crumbs provides a crusty contrast to the moist ingredients.

To something more refined, Les Délices de Veau aux Chanterelles. It arrives prettily enough, the glistening meat and mushrooms colorfully surrounded by crisp string beans, grilled tomatoes, and browned zucchini. The excellent veal pale—almost creamy —and the chanterelles moistened by a polished dark sauce. But in a dish like this, the sauce is all, and this one is low on character—perfectly good food and all that, but unexciting.

Le Tournedos aux Cêpes Sauce Truffe, however, is something else. The perfectly grilled beef is dressed with a sauce that is creamy, sweet and mingled with the extremely delicate mushrooms—the cêpes are best eaten alone, for their fugitive flavor is masked by strong meat. The sauced tournedos is garnished with a disc of goose liver pâté which is sprinkled with bits of truffle, and this, in its way, adds fat to the dish, the filet mignon being the leanest of beef.

Birds, too, as in La Dodine Pintadotte Périgourdine, in which goose liver and truffles play parts again. A breast of chicken has been removed from its bone, wrapped around the delicate mousse of liver, browned until the pale meat is thoroughly cooked and the liver warmed, and served in a beefy, truffle-studded sauce. It is garnished with fluted mushroom caps, zucchini in a thick tomato sauce, crisp carrots, and green beans.

There is a white cake with pink sherbet, flavored with anisette; good tarts served with dollops of whipped cream; a chocolate mousse wrapped in plain cake and whipped cream, sprinkled with shavings of chocolate for identification. Buttery petits fours arrive with your coffee.

If you wonder about the name "Lavandou," your waiter explains that it is a town in Provence where the chef took his holidays when he was a "leetle keed." You may be certain that in Lavandou they do not serve up your bottle of ordinary wine in one of those silly wine baskets.

★★ LE MARMITON

216 East 49th Street
LUNCH, MONDAY TO FRIDAY; DINNER, MONDAY TO SATURDAY.
Closed Sunday.
Reservations, 688–1232.
Credit cards: AE, BA, CB, DC, MC.
Expensive.

Le Marmiton has been around for a long time, but a few years back it moved into these new and well laid out quarters, a commodious dining area that is French Provincial in intent, but Grand Rapids in the rendering: there are beams on the ceiling, but they are smooth and polished; the copper pans on the walls are lacquered, shiny and undented, and have never been near a stove. But Provincial France, after all, can only be found in the French provinces, and the place is comfortable, with plenty of room in the aisles for the serving carts, and with tables for two along the banquette which are large enough for dinner dishes, for the little red pots that hold more of your stew or whatever, and for wine, glasses, sauces, and so on. This is a sedate place with, by and large, sedate customers, which is to the good, because the room's principal shortcoming is its superb acoustics, and a noisy party anywhere in the room undoes the whole tone.

As in most French restaurants of this caliber in the East Forties and Fifties, the menu is standard French New York, but a few of these familiar dishes are particularly well made, and there are a couple of other items that are actually minor breaches of custom.

Some of the first courses are on display (along with cheeses and desserts) on a table near the front of the restaurant. Among them is a pâté, in its jelly, in the pot in which it was baked, so you know from looking, as you will later from tasting, that it is made on the premises. It is also stored for a few days before it is served, so that the flavors blend, but not too long, which would be ruinous. And because it is out of the refrigerator hours before you eat it, its meatiness and mild flavor of spices are at their peak. This is not a great pâté de campagne, but it is perfect in its way, and sometimes the pot is left on your table for a second slice, if you want it; and if it is not, you can send for it.

Coquille de Fruits de Mer, usually called St. Jacques, is also a local commonplace, but here it is made of good fresh scallops, shrimps and fresh mushrooms, in a tender sauce that is perfectly browned just before it is served. There is often a quiche du jour —asparagus one day, mushrooms another, and so on. They are not made to your order, so of course they have fallen, but they are tasty, and of good ingredients. The Moules Ravigote are of perfectly fresh, tender mussels, and when mussels are so carefully made they retain a strong, sparkling flavor of the sea, but unfortunately, what Le Marmiton calls "ravigote," the rest of us call Russian dressing, and these mussels deserve better treatment. Decent snails and clams, and oysters in good condition.

Boeuf Bourguignon is such a regular around town that one almost invariably reads right by it, but this is one of the places where it is quite expertly rendered. The cooking is long and slow, so that what started out as tasty but tough stew meat has finally become positively soft, but with no loss of flavor; and the same process—long, slow cooking—provides a sauce, here made with plenty of wine and a strong stock, that is thick without the benefit of a thickener. The dish is best when the sautéed mushrooms are added a few minutes before it is served. That detail is not faithfully carried out here —the mushrooms have been waiting for you since the dish was made, and they have lost their texture. This does not ruin the dish, but it deprives it of a very nice touch.

Another main course that is good but could be better is the Grenadin of Veal Normande. This is browned veal in a creamed sauce of Calvados, white wine and sautéed mushrooms. It is a crime to start out with wonderful ingredients like those, and then, apparently, not taste the sauce for seasoning. That final salt and pepper you cook in just before the sauce is creamed is what makes the difference between a nice sauce (what you get here) and an excellent one, in which all the flavors are brought to life.

The Lobster Marmiton is a perfectly broiled lobster, stuffed with very decent crabmeat and mushrooms, served with butter that is better than butter. It is flavored with shallots and fresh parsley—splendid stuff to dip lobster meat in. Probably the most unusual dish among the main courses is *cold* Duckling à l'Orange, en Gelée. The dish is made with canned mandarin oranges, but it is excellent nevertheless. The duck is moist, covered with sections of mandarin orange, and embedded in an opaque aspic that is heavily flavored with the liquid from the can. Good in winter, splendid in summer.

The menu lists some very ordinary-sounding desserts, but better, unlisted items are usually available: sometimes fresh strawberries in a crème Anglaise that has been liberally flavored with Grand Marnier. This dish is served only when the house has managed to obtain perfect strawberries, and it is the best dessert in the place. If it is not available, there is usually a special mousse in addition to the chocolate—the latter is more heavily flavored with coffee than what you find in most places. But the other mousses are more interesting. They are actually flavored whipped creams, and the almond mousse (which is really an orange mousse topped with burnt almonds) is superb, feathery and very sweet.

Le Marmiton insists on jackets and ties, and in other ways encourages a "respectable" clientele. The shorter your skirt, the longer your parade through the restaurant; you may even be led to the remote little room to the rear. Those privileged to sit in the main room won't even notice your knees as they go by, for they are discussing higher things: "After your divorce, can you get your name back, and get back into the social register?"

"I think I'd have to behave for a few years, and I'm not sure I can do that."

The service is professional, available and intelligent, whatever you are wearing.

★★ LE PÉRIGORD

405 East 52nd Street
LUNCH, MONDAY TO FRIDAY; DINNER, MONDAY TO SATURDAY.
Closed Sunday.
Reservations, PL 5–6244.
Credit cards: AE.
Very expensive.

Like father like son like father. At least that is the intention. Le Périgord sired Le Périgord Park, beheld its work and decided to emulate it. Le Périgord gets an E for emulate, which, the *Random House College Dictionary* tells us, means "to *try* [italics added] to equal or excel." The word also connotes some degree of success, and, it must be credited, Le Périgord is a better restaurant today then it was before it was attracted to its offspring's ways. The *cuisine* is a bit more *haute,* the captains a bit hautier (nothing serious—you just have to bellyache a little bit about the first table you are led to if your face is unfamiliar to his tuxedoed majesty, said table being perhaps a pitiful little island that stands in the center of the flow of traffic between the front and back rooms), and the prices up more than 20 percent in the last couple of years.

To make all this appropriate, there has been a bit of sprucing up. The intentionally-comic-but-not-in-the-way-intended murals in the back room have been replaced by sylvan scenes, though the marbelized mirrors have been retained. You are better off in the front room, which is larger, where there is a bar, where the action is—it has a festive ambience, it is where the regulars are seated.

But assuming you do not mind throwing your displeasure around or, alternatively, suffering your own disposal into the back room, you can eat well at Le Périgord. At lunchtime there is a saucisson chaud that is commendable more for what accompanies it than for itself. The sausage is properly spicy and oily, really a rather substantial item for an afternoon appetizer (and one wonders why it is offered only then and not in the evening), but it comes with impeccably poached little new potatoes, abundantly buttered and sprinkled with parsley—gloriously elemental potato. What price an appetizer of potatoes, please? You can also get a pretty terrific Terrine de Canard—a coarse pâté rimmed with white fat, moist, spicy and rich; shrimps that actually taste fresh, which is unlikely, but one is willing to be fooled by artful freezing; an excellent cold poached bass, flaky and sweet, garnished with crisp little marinated mushrooms; a firm artichoke, served with a thick tart dressing. This restaurant still pushes its Mousse de Brochet Tout Paris as a *Spécialité,* and these quenelles are very good, with a clear bright flavor of fish, albeit the dumplings are a little bready. The sauce, however, is outstanding, thick and honeylike, the whole dish fortunately served with a little mound of white rice, the perfect vehicle for the extra sauce.

If you eat around, and you do so for variety of food rather than for changes of scenery, the thing to do is to try the rarities wherever you are. Here one of the rarities is Poulard Poelée Demi-Deuil, which, as anyone who reads French knows, is a semi-despondent chicken, its ambiguous mood honored by swatches of black truffle worn under its translucent skin. The poached bird is very good, very moist, and it is served in a doubly thickened, very buttery sauce made on a base of chicken stock. The bird and its sauce are accompanied by rice that has been pepped up with bits of yet more truffle, and by celery that has been poached with garlic.

You can save a $3 upcharge by not bothering with the bouillabaisse. The assorted seafood comes in a quite delicious, heavily garlicked and saffroned broth, and the chunks of hard, garlicked toast that are served on the side are great when soaked in the liquid, but the main features have not been treated so well. The bass fares best—fresh and flaky—but the clams are toughened in their overlong cooking, and the lobster tail (not lobster, lobster tail), frozen, of course, is simply bad.

A veal roast of the day is rather coarse, a sole in mustard sauce rather rubbery, though the sauce itself is rare for a mustard sauce in that it has the clear tangy flavor of the spice without being overpowered by it.

This is a busy restaurant, apparently busy enough to turn over enough cheese so that what you get is new and newly brought to room temperature—thoroughly ripened Brie, earthy and sexy between chalk-white skins; Roquefort that is at once buttery and sharp.

Poaching fruit in wine is a simple thing rarely done well—the wine must not be watered, and the fruit must be firm to begin with, and still firm when the process is stopped. They do it well here, sometimes peaches, sometimes pears, and the fruit, in its sugary and syrupy wine, is positively springlike. An excellent blueberry tart—plump berries, untouched by sugar, their sweetness natural, sprinkled with bits of pistachio nut, on a dark and flaky pastry.

★★ LA PETITE MARMITE

5 Mitchell Place (near First Avenue and East 49th Street)
LUNCH, MONDAY TO FRIDAY; DINNER, MONDAY TO SATURDAY.
Closed Sunday.
Reservations, 826–1084.
Credit cards: AE, CB, DC, MC.
Expensive.

Even among the best French restaurants in New York you will not find the consistency and reliability of La Petite Marmite. The menu is conventional (almost boring in the appetizers, your eyes may glaze over as you read the listing of desserts), with a few flashes of originality among the main courses, but it is virtually impossible to obtain a plate of food here that can be called "off." In addition, the service in this comfortable place is available, attentive, intelligent, unobtrusive. To come here is to take no chances. But it is more than that—the food is not only right, but good, sometimes better than good.

La Petite Marmite has enjoyed success since it moved into these quarters under new management a few years back, and what was once a makeshift-looking place had its skin smoothed with an overdue refurbishing. The uninspired appointments—dim floral wallpaper, wood paneling, idiotic little oil paintings, red velvet banquettes—have nothing to recommend them individually, but their sum effect is greatly more pleasant than the parts, particularly if you remove your glasses.

Those familiar appetizers are commonplace only as to the available assortment—the items themselves are of superior quality. There is, for example, the smoked trout available in many French restaurants around town, and from the admittedly excellent flavor of the product, it can be judged that it all comes from one smokery. But the trout you get here has not been waiting for you and drying out in the process—you get three shafts of the oily meat (three fourths of a trout, that is), and it is flaky and moist, utterly freed of bones, and served with a sauce that is a perfect balance of horseradish and cream, though some versions, in which the cream is whipped stiff before it is combined with the horseradish, have an airier texture. The Maquereau au Vin Blanc, an equally familiar item, is equally good, in the coarse way of this dish—the marinated fish is pungently sour, oddly flavored with *cloves,* garnished with the limp, sweetened onions of the marinade and decorated with slivers of fresh tomato. Order ham and melon, and you get thinly sliced huge sheets of dark, marbled, smoky meat over juicy, sugary melon; order saucisson sec and you get a platter of three-inch discs of a salami that is at once succulent and spicy.

Of course La Petite Marmite serves a petite marmite—a powerful broth with chunks of meat and crisp vegetable reposing at the bottom of the little crockery pot.

A nice little big deal is made of showing you the main courses in the pans before the food is served onto plates. Here comes your duck, for example, nestled into an oval pan, the skin dark-brown, as you can see, and the meat moist and slightly fatty, as you will soon discover. You will also discover that the orange sauce is not orange at all, but a deep mahogany, and that its meaty flavor, with vague overtones of herbs and liquor, is only subtly touched with fruit. Le Tournedos au Poivre Vert is a very substantial slice of filet mignon, aged and tender and tasty, grilled accurately, and served coated with a polished dark-pink sauce flavored with uncured pepper. At lunchtime you can get a simple roasted chicken here, browned and buttery, and served, as are most of the main courses, with little balls of roasted potatoes that have had thin brown skins formed as they cooked in drippings—lightly salted, crisp and quite delicious. Also at lunchtime, during the warm weather, there is on occasion a special of cold roast sirloin—rare, tender, served with superb hot mustard and with cold string beans that are crisp, barely poached, lightly tossed in a mustard dressing—excellent summer food. This establishment seems to know what it does especially well, and, happily, the Bass Amandine and the calf's liver with raisins are still on the menu.

The waiter confides that the cheese is in and out of the icebox from one meal and from one day to the next. You are grateful for the information, particularly as it deflects you toward the chocolate mousse—thick, yet airy, sweet, with a dense flavor of dark chocolate. On lucky days there is a roulade, a dark moist cake rolled around crushed raspberries and a lemon-flavored cream; and on most days there are tarts—lightly browned fruit on good pastry. For purists there is purity—huge ripe strawberries, solid and sweet, or a little mound of raspberries, juicy and fragrant of their own perfume, both with good unsweetened whipped cream.

A relaxed place with a starchy clientele. The management, however, does not favor the stiff collar and silk tie over shapeless denim. Contrary to the rule in many restaurants, unknowns are led to the best tables in the house if they are available—bad corners are given to the last customers rather than to the least-known.

★★★ LE PONT NEUF

212 East 53rd Street
LUNCH, MONDAY TO FRIDAY; DINNER, MONDAY TO SATURDAY.
Closed Sunday.
Reservations, PL 1–0373.
Credit cards: AE, CB, DC, MC.
Expensive.

There is no explanation for this restaurant's continued lack of exalted reputation, except that the place does not look like what it is—one of the half dozen or so best French restaurants in New York. Where is the grandeur, the spaciousness, the golden light illuminating muraled expanses? Where are the captains, and where are the impeccably tonsured magnates and their chic companions? Where, for that matter, is there anything visible to set the place apart from dozens of West Side bistros and East Side rendezvous? Only on the menu and on the plates. The listing is diverse, unusual and ambitious; and the dishes are, almost without exception, of character, distinctive and, moreover, good to eat. Picking out Le Pont Neuf from among the crowd of its competitors requires that ability to spot the star in the chorus line or, lacking that, a moderately discriminating palate. This is a professional establishment, as it has always been. Over the years the quality of the food has remained high, and the service, which was never bad, has improved—you can expect alertness and thoughtfulness from the waiters, intelligence and a thorough knowledge of the menu from the host. All this in a restaurant which is comfortable, a little informal and, it must be admitted, rather commonplace in appearance. You will find the plaques and folksy murals, and so on, dreadfully familiar—almost everything else, therefore, surprising.

There is a little blackboard mounted just outside the front door, whereon, in admirable tradition, are listed special dishes of the day, usually of seasonally available foods. Among these, often, are the crab "fingers" for which the restaurant has something of a reputation (that is, among those to whom the place *has* a reputation). The crab claws are battered and deep-fried until they are crusted to a dark golden brown, and they are served with a sauce of mild mustard and heavily herbed stock. Sometimes Moules Vinaigrettes are chalked on the board, and these are recommended too—the mussels are the tiny sweet ones, perfectly fresh, and served cool in a tart vinaigrette laced with minced Bermuda onions and lots of fresh parsley. The restaurant still makes some of the best quenelles around—tender dumplings of fish served with a smooth sauce flavored with crayfish. What distinguishes these quenelles from the run of the mill is their lightness and the vivid, sweet flavor of fresh fish.

When good venison is available, the blackboard sometimes lists venison stew. You have to be insane to pass it up. If this is not the best venison dish in New York, there is a miracle worker somewhere. The meat is marinated twice—in oil and vegetables, and then in wine. After it is stewed, the thick winy sauce is smoothed with currant jelly. The meat is almost unbelievably tender, still pink, vaguely sour in a way that contrasts perfectly with the gravy; and the stew is served to you surrounded by a great wall of chestnut purée, happily not sweetened to a candy, but prepared for what it is—a delicate vegetable with a nutlike flavor.

Bouillabaisse, we all know, is not *really* bouillabaisse once you get very far from the Mediterranean. But we do not sit around moping about it, right? We are mature, right? We do the best we can with what we have, right? Well, the best that Le Pont Neuf can is very good—a giant pot of *strong* briny broth, with clams, shrimps, chunks of lobster in the shell, and slabs of local fish. The thing is made right—rapidly—so that no ingredient has been toughened and no flavor has been lost. What with all the dipping of bread deep into the broth, holding the lobster with the fingers to suck out the meat, and generally abandoning all politesse, one slumps back in one's chair and gives oneself over to dreams of a warm wet napkin. No sooner dreamt than had. Your hot napkin replaces your bouillabaisse pot as naturally as your salad follows that. Good salad, too. Firm endives and crisp watercress in a creamy mustard dressing.

If there is one discomfort in this restaurant, it comes of the difficulty you will encounter concentrating on your own food when such delights as the superb rack of lamb is being carved for the people a table or two away—this is still one of the best racks of lamb in town, served for two, with little roasted potatoes, artichoke bottoms, and mushrooms in an herby lamb gravy.

At $7 the Soufflé au Grand Marnier should be better. It *tastes* delicious, sweet and liquored, with a perfectly browned dry crust, sprinkled with sugar. And it is served with a flawless crème Anglaise flavored with additional Grand Marnier. But the interior of the soufflé itself is a bit heavy and pudding-like. If you want to spring for a fancy dessert in this place, you are better off with the Crêpes Normande—next to which Crêpes Suzette taste like lollipops. The dessert is composed of thin pancakes and a thick sauce of orange rind, whipped cream, honey, Cointreau and Calvados, and it is superb.

• QUO VADIS

26 East 63rd Street
LUNCH AND DINNER.
Closed Sunday.
Reservations, TE 8–0590.
Credit cards: AE, CB, DC, MC.
Very expensive.

Quo Vadis is a high-priced, overstuffed hype. Once in a while you hit a really terrific dish here, but most of the food is simply passable. The dining rooms are decorated to the eyeballs, but the taste that inspired them is so banal, pompous and eclectic that the tastes that emanate from the kitchen are immediately suspect, and an experienced diner without professional obligation could take one look and leave.

The crimson carpeting is as velvety as the matching banquettes. The walls are silken. Crystal droplets depend from the wall sconces. There are somber paintings, of which one can say that they are genuine paintings. Nude statuary.

The dish of raw vegetables contains dirty radishes and canned olives. You may doctor the cocktail sauce that accompanies your crabmeat, shrimp, clams or oysters with the Tabasco that is presented alongside the Oysterettes. But of course this is a fancy restaurant, and you wouldn't order those anyway. You would order, if you're on your toes, Champignons Forestière au Gratin, and you would get one of the best dishes in the house—mushroom caps stuffed with minced stems and baked in a buttery cheese sauce that is lightly browned. The process brings out an overwhelmingly strong mushroom flavor. But if you're less fortunate you'll select the Pâté du Chef—a perfectly decent pâté, no worse than you can get in many West Side bistros, but at $3.50 it's a laugh, if you can laugh. Crêpes Quo Vadis are curried scallops in a pancake. At one time this dish was made with shrimp, lobster and crabmeat, in hollandaise. They haven't changed the name, and the item is still listed under *"Nos Spécialités."* They have simply reduced the cost, raised the price and insulted the public.

The listing of *Spécialités* is pretty amusing—it includes such masterpieces of the chef's talent as Beluga Caviar, Foie Gras de Strasbourg and Nova Scotia Salmon. By coincidence these are also the most expensive appetizers on the menu.

Perhaps you would like Le Caneton Rôti Normande. Sounds like something special, no? No. Roast duck, not crisp, some stewed fruit on the side. If they sold you the fruit by the pound in a jar, you could make the dish yourself at home! The Suprême de Volaille Gismonda is breaded chicken strewn with mushrooms; and the roast lamb is roast lamb.

Off in a corner of the kitchen somewhere, while the rest of the fellows are laughing it up, there is a vegetable cook who takes his job seriously. Among the à la carte vegetables, the delicious Aubergine Provençale is sautéed to the brink of being burned, and sharply flavored with garlic. The celery is braised in a rich brown gravy, and the asparagus, carefully scraped down to the soft white core, is served with a thick hollandaise into which no more butter could conceivably be incorporated, though it lacks lemon. The vegetables that accompany the main courses are very good too—including fresh, crisp, sweet string beans and very heavily buttered and spiced spinach.

They wheel over the dessert cart. You ask for the menu. They point out the delicious items on the cart. You insist on the menu. They inform you that the best things in the house are before your eyes, on the cart, but they promise to bring the menu as a reward after you have ordered. You point out your preference for having the menu before your eyes at once. It's an hour before closing. Soufflés? The waiter falls all over himself at the hysterical impossibility. Crêpes Suzette? His partner must also be carried off. The second team comes on. Cerises Jubilée? They embrace to hold each other up. You can have strawberries, oranges in liqueur, cake, ice cream.

There is a cover charge, surreptitiously listed as one of the hors d'oeuvres. It has a bitter taste.

• LE STEAK

1089 Second Avenue (near 58th Street)
DINNER.
Reservations, 421–9072.
Credit cards: AE, DC.
Medium-priced.

You've heard of a tourist trap? This restaurant is a New Yorker trap. Same thing, but the deception is more carefully contrived, and the place is packed with New York businessmen, their customers, comrades and companions du jour, enjoying their special knowledge of this special out-of-the-way place, which serves a single, not so special, prix-fixe steak dinner. This dinner is hardly a dinner at all—the salad converted into the first course, French fries with the steak but no other vegetable, dessert and coffee. There are enormous economies in so limited a selection, which can be reflected in (1) perfectly prepared food, or (2) low prices, or (3) increased profits. Here the economies are channeled mainly into (3), and the food is only moderately good, the price no bargain.

One's (everyone's) dinner begins with a large salad of romaine lettuce and chicory, dressed with a good vinaigrette, and continues with what the menu refers to as "Le Steak Maison—steak served with unique herb sauce from Provence & thin French-fried potatoes." One area in which American cooking outshines the French is in the preparation of steak. The American method leaves a band of scored fat on the steak, which adds to the flavor and prevents overcooking at the edges. At Le Steak the steak is trimmed before grilling, and as the meat is not well marbled to begin with, the steaks are mediocre (though cooked as ordered). The mysterious sauce from Provence is a Beurre Maître d'Hôtel (parsley butter, with lemon, salt and pepper, here augmented with basil) in which the steak is basted. Before serving, the waitress goes through gestures of finishing the preparation over an alcohol burner on a serving stand. Actually, there is nothing for her to do but remove the food from the platter, put it on the plate and serve it, as the preparation is complete when the steak leaves the kitchen. Then the accompanying French fries are given the same magical toss over the fire on the steak platter, hocus pocus, abracadabra, and *voilà!*, steak and potatoes.

The French fries are good, but as the kitchen staff has little else to conquer (or to offer), an effort should be made to do them as well as they are done in any second-rate establishment in France. The reputation Le Steak has for its *pommes frites* must be attributed to the abysmal quality of most New York French fries rather than to any particular excellence here.

One may have either cheese or dessert. The cheeses are Brie and Camembert, from those four-inch export circles found in supermarkets. But they are served at room temperature, and can be acceptable. The Gâteau Maison is a chocolate excess. La Surprise de Monique, described as "parfait with chestnuts, whipped cream & grilled walnuts," is made of canned, candied chestnuts, good ice cream and whipped cream, and walnuts that have never seen a grill. The balance of the inspired selection: Peach Melba, chocolate mousse, crème caramel, fresh fruit. Wines are overpriced from a very limited selection.

With all its faults, the restaurant somehow adds up. The food is fairly good, the service, though bored, is efficient, and the room is cozy. The regulars who pack the place are, of course, never disappointed, so one is surrounded by happy people. And though the value is illusory, one is not being beaten out of very much.

The barmaid has eyelashes two centimeters long, a death mask of make-up, and an expression of such cosmic urban ennui that to have her got up in the puffed-sleeve peasant blouse of a French milkmaid is the moral equivalent of serving goat cheese on Melba toast.

Le Steak has an emblem, a girl and a bull, with the former running from the latter, which has a certain validity.

★ LA TOQUE BLANCHE

359 East 50th Street
LUNCH, MONDAY TO SATURDAY; DINNER, DAILY.
Reservations, PL 5–3552.
Credit cards: AE, DC, MC.
Medium-priced.

La Toque Blanche is more interesting for its reputation than for itself. It has been unduly admired for years, though it is surely not without its merits; its regular customers mistake their comfort in its familiarity for excellence, and they prolong its good standing with obsessive patronage. Part of this loyalty results from the fact that La Toque Blanche has kept its prices within reason—with only a handful of exceptions, your slightly superior dinner elsewhere in this part of town will cost you substantially more money (as may your slightly inferior ones). We are dealing here with self-delusion in the service of liquidity.

None of its devotees claim that La Toque Blanche is one of the most sublime, or even one of the best, eating places in New York. They speak of it, rather, as one of those you-can-count-on-it, solid, dependable French Gibraltars of the New York restaurant scene, like Mon Paris or Le Veau d'Or or René Pujol or a handful of others, which is precisely what it is not. In a reliable restaurant you get at least acceptable food, no matter what you order, almost all of the time. But at La Toque Blanche it is possible to begin your meal with an undercooked artichoke that is so cold it seems to have come from the freezer, when even refrigerator temperature is too low; to proceed to a cold poached salmon that was prepared on the day the fish should have been discarded (the bad taste of slightly over-the-hill fish cannot be hidden by the excellent green mayonnaise it is served with); dawdle bitterly over a green salad that is almost all chicory; and conclude with a pear in wine that is suitably purple, but tastes as if the poaching liquid were ink.

Now the defenders speak up. Fool, they say, you ordered the wrong things. Which suggests that La Toque Blanche, in the way that some restaurants indicate that certain dishes are Specialties of the House, should identify some of the items on its menu as The Wrong Things.

Let us assume, however, that you ordered The Right Things, or at least The Acceptable Things. In that case you may begin with the really terrific quiche Lorraine—it is light, as smooth as soft butter, eggy, and studded with substantial chunks of good ham, all on a well-baked, browned, crunchy pastry. Or perhaps the Maquereaux au Vin Blanc —hefty lengths of firm fish in the jellied marinade, with lots of onions, crisp discs of carrot, and an abundance of fresh parsley strewn about. The dish is coarse, but it is so well-balanced, at once so sweet, tart and winy that it is also artful. The Quenelle de Brochet is something less—the little dumpling is more like a fish cake than an intense forcemeat of fish, but the sauce Nantua is rich and smooth, with a strong crayfish flavor. The soups are pretty good, including a Potage Cressonnière that is more notable for its foundations (lots of butter, a good chicken stock and a vivid potato flavor) than for any particularly clear watercress flavor.

In season, much respect is shown here to the Soft-Shelled Crab. They are sautéed rapidly, in butter; they are tender and sweet, and they are well selected, so the shell is crinkly and eminently digestible. Then, for something considerably more substantial, there is a Cassoulet Toulousain—it is good and gamy, the sauce thin and a bit sweet for some tastes; the chunks of lamb are tender and agreeably muttony, one of the sausages is heavily smoked, the other spicy and moist, the bacon slightly crisped, all embedded in white beans that are firm yet tender. This particular dish is served with a warm and juicy grilled tomato, but some of the main courses are accompanied by quite undistinguished peas that are conveniently served in their own little dish, so that they can be moved to the far side of the table.

This place used to serve a spectacular chocolate crêpe soufflée. You never could be sure it would be available, and a couple of recent requests for it have been met with the information that the temperamental gent who prepared it is no longer in the house employ. Perhaps, and there is evidence to support the thought that the desserts are now in new hands. The St. Honoré, the potentially spectacular pastry filled with a lightened custard, is still good, but not the sumptuously rich creation it once was; and the fruit tarts are only a cut above average. Sometimes there is an almond cake, and it is up to the old standard—the eggy custard is sweetened with almond-flavored sugar between its layers of dark and flaky pastry.

La Toque Blanche is a traditional and comfortable New York French restaurant—provincial murals, lots of contented customers, Americanized French waiters (one of them hums the "Star-Spangled Banner" as he works—none of them regard the murals nostalgically), a grumpy bartender who becomes extra-special grumpy when he has to prepare a Grand Marnier-and-tonic.

★★★ LE VEAU D'OR

129 East 60th Street
LUNCH AND DINNER.
Closed Sunday.
Reservations, TE 8–8133.
No credit cards.
Medium-priced.

At night, on this quiet street, the small, brightly illuminated red canopy is an inviting radiance to the loyal and multitudinous following that makes this one of the busiest restaurants in New York. Le Veau d'Or is a few steps down, and the best view of the cozy place is through the street window, where you can look over the whole bustling scene: about thirty tables, rather closely packed, and (from seven-thirty on) enough people for these and a dozen more; the overflow is concentrated at the small bar near the front. (The tables in the front, therefore, are served by waiters who must be at the bottom of the seniority scale, and they mutter *pardon, pardon, pardon* almost continuously as they squeeze past the crowded bar carrying food from the kitchen, and used dishes back.)

Le Veau d'Or is like a club that has survived from the twenties. The room has the ambience of a solid, well-worn casino (there must be a roulette wheel in the back), with its wood-veneer walls; casually placed photos (Paris at work and play); the golden calf (in oils) framed and asleep between the sheets, his head on a plump pillow; and at the front, leaning out over the counter of her little room, contentedly smiling, the coat checker, like a benign concierge. She knows lots of the customers by name, as does the host, but this is a businesslike establishment and customers are seated in order of arrival, habitué or stranger—a practice only slightly compromised by reservations.

Assuredly, the waiter is upon you promptly, but you're not rushed. If you send him away to return later, while you drink your drink or your wine or read the menu, he will return sooner than you intended, but only to provide a few tablespoons of rata-touille, or terrine of chicken, or Moules Rémoulade (the first two are better) to tinker with while you sip and/or read the listings. Here you get some of the best French country cooking in New York, including a saucisson chaud—a thick slice of a red sausage (hung by an expert maker, until strong but still juicy) that has been wrapped in dough and baked until the surrounding glazed pastry is brown, shiny and flaky outside, and slightly greasy where it touches the hot, well-larded meat. If—by some miracle—that doesn't appeal to you, perhaps what you want is the Saucisson d'Arles —a salami-like indelicacy which arrives as a dozen thin, shiny, purplish discs, heavily peppered, and with a hint of sweet spices, like nutmeg and cinnamon. The pâté is mostly liver, but elevated by a surprising bounty of truffles throughout. Of course for those who fear the hidden ingredient, there is Parma ham and melon—the species of melon varies with the season, but it is almost invariably ripe and juicy, and the limp, pink slices of smoky ham are tender, briny and slightly high.

There is strong onion soup—you are offered good grated cheese, and after you accept, you discover that the soup was already loaded with it; the watercress soup is thick and has a vivid flavor of fresh green watercress combined with an herby chicken stock and potatoes.

On occasion there is rabbit on the menu (Civet de Lapin); this is a fricassee of marinated meat cooked in red wine, with the sauce thickened (it must be told) with the blood of the rabbit, to all of which mushrooms are added at the end. This dish of tender, fibrous slices of strong meat in the thick, dark sauce is tremendously hearty, the kind of thing to which the mind turns when the stomach is emptiest. The Poussin Rôti en Cocotte is, as the title states, a very young chicken. It is roasted until browned, and served with mushrooms and onions that have been cooked in the butter and drippings that the bird was cooked in.

Tripes à la mode de Caen is offered on almost every French menu in New York, but this version is one of the few that seems to have benefited from the long cooking that yields a thick, almost glutinous sauce, and tender, only slightly chewy tripe. The sautéed chicken livers are browned and tender, and the sautéed onions they are mixed with have been cooked until they are thin, almost black strands, powerfully flavored, and perfectly offset by the cake of scalloped potatoes that accompanies many of the main dishes here—such as the very rare, tender roast lamb, served in its juice.

You may have noticed that not much is made of fish here—the herring, smoked salmon and mackerel in white wine are offered as appetizers, and Sole Amandine as a main course, but the restaurant is best at the kind of hearty food that is based on meat or fowl, and that is what you should make your meals of.

Among the desserts you will find nothing unusual—the Parfait au Rhum is notable for the strength and abundance of the rum, and the cheese for its generally good condition.

The popularity of Le Veau d'Or is the result of its strict consistency and its generally high standards. The place could have moved to larger quarters a long time ago and been reasonably certain of filling the additional tables; the prices could be raised substantially and still be below those of many lesser competitors; and newer customers could be treated with the contempt that many fashionable restaurants seem to enjoy dispensing. But Le Veau d'Or seems to be better than that. It has its shortcomings, but they are mostly not of the management's making—if people pour in through the front door, no one can be blamed. If you arrive at nine-thirty of a Saturday night, you may be guided to the bar with the advice that you have a little drink while you decide on a nice place to have dinner.

Wine from $7.50 is the only overcharging Le Veau d'Or is guilty of. The management seems to have a very simple attitude toward choosing wine—they offer mostly wines shipped by Prosper Maufoux, and this pretty much assures that you will get a good bottle.

The regulars who eat here seem attuned to the place, and they mostly eat with dispatch and get up to leave, which means the wait at the bar is often not as long as the size of the crowd suggests. If you wish to linger a bit, there is a good *marc* available, and no one will rush you if you order more coffee.

Haute Cuisine

These are the restaurants that attempt to duplicate the best food of France. Sometimes they come close.

Of the best in France the *Guide Michelin* says: "In these restaurants, price has no meaning." In these New York aspirers, it has a definite one: the prices don't vary with the quality, which goes up and down, but apparently with the square of the cost of living—or at least the cost of living well, which only goes up. You won't mind the bill when you hit one of these places on a good day.

Most of these restaurants list a few dishes as specialties of the house. Take their word for it, they know whereof they specialize. If you are not, as a matter of habit, going to drop $30 to $50 per person for dinner in these restaurants, then don't order by habit either. Even in the least of these restaurants there is a chance you'll get a spectacular meal if you spend the few extra dollars for the red-letter items.

Gentlemen (and other males) may be required to wear neckties, females may be forbidden pants. Phone ahead. Within the rules, the best clothing procedure is an arrogant display of your most casual duds. You'll be taken for a millionaire who doesn't have to prove it.

★★★★ LA CARAVELLE

33 West 55th Street
LUNCH AND DINNER.
Closed Sunday.
Reservations, JU 6–4252.
No credit cards.
Very expensive.

La Caravelle is a simply decorated, not very large restaurant, with murals of sunlit Paris parks. The room is lighted by sconces here and there on the rosy-pink walls. Certain things immediately suggest excellence. On the tables the crystal, flatware and linen are sparkling and clean. And within ten feet of any table, at almost any time, there is someone ready to hear a request and take care of it promptly; and the demeanor of these people, though it is always proper, is never stiff.

And then, of course, there is the food: Oysters Bercy, in which the oysters are first poached in their own liquor, and then returned to their shell halves to be quickly glazed and browned in sauce Bercy—a white sauce with a fish base, to which sautéed shallots, white wine and parsley have been added. When made perfectly, the oysters remain as tender and juicy as when they were raw, which is how they are done here—a fabulous first course. Of all the dishes on the menu, only one is called a specialty. This first course —La Mousse de Brochet Havraise—is pike prepared as if for quenelles, but cooked as a large loaf. Over a slice of this loaf is poured a cream-enriched white sauce to which mushrooms and tiny shrimp have been added in abundance. There are also some lovely Mussels à la Moutarde—tender, utterly free of grit, served in a sparkling mustard sauce.

Of La Caravelle's main courses, there is a rather famous duck. Duckling Bigarade is available, and it is very good, but the Duckling au Poivre is something else. The bird is rubbed thoroughly with pepper and then roasted—not in itself a startling thing, but when it arrives, a sauce smitane, not mentioned on the menu, arrives too. This sauce —sour cream, white wine and stock—is an inspired contrast to the crisp-skinned, highly seasoned bird.

Among the fish, there is a wonderful Bass Grenobloise. The fish is floured lightly before it is sautéed, to form a crisp, brown exterior; the inside is flaky, and the whole is brilliant and tart in its dressing of capers and lemon; and, still in the fish family, there is a Sole Murat—browned potatoes, artichoke bottoms and sautéed tomatoes over a perfectly breaded and browned fileted sole.

La Caravelle also serves excellent steaks, including tournedos of beef on artichoke bottoms, with bone marrow and bone-marrow sauce—called Tournedos Masséna.

What we call arugula, or rocket, the French call *mâche,* and someone from this restaurant gets to the market each morning before anyone else and buys all the small tender leaves, leaving the larger and tougher ones for the grocer on your corner. This green is usually just one ingredient in a salad, but when the leaves are small it makes a very refreshing dish by itself—just right before some of La Caravelle's excellent desserts, which include Crêpes "Ma Pommes," a variant of Crêpes Normande, in which slices of apple sautéed in butter are added to the sauce of cream, butter and apple brandy. There is a good selection of cheeses, which is a good idea, because sweets are served with your coffee—cat's tongues, puffs of pâte à chou filled with custard, delicate chocolate sticks, and whatever else the baker, in his fantasy, thinks would be a pleasant little remembrance to diners near the end of their meal.

It has always been said that people not known to the management are relegated to the back of the room, and this place does have a remote corner in which even the only mildly paranoid might feel ostracized. Well, there is *some* truth in it. Actually, it would be more accurate to say that people well known to the maître are seated at the front. The back is not set aside for strangers, but for people who, the management feels, do not become the place. On one evening a gentleman who had apparently just emerged from a poodle barber was escorting a young lady who had neglected to put on some of her clothes. They were seated in Siberia, but they enjoyed some very good food back there. No matter where you are placed, you are treated courteously.

★★ LE CHÂTEAU RICHELIEU

48 East 52nd Street
LUNCH, MONDAY TO FRIDAY; DINNER, MONDAY TO SATURDAY.
Closed Sunday.
Reservations, PL 1–6565.
Credit cards: AE, BA, CB, DC, MC.
Very expensive.

There has been a Château Richelieu in New York for many, many years, and one at this spot for more than fifteen. The ownership has not changed. Mr. Robotti was always the proprietor, but he made his big money in other enterprises. When he amassed enough, he took a good piece of it and created the restaurant of his fantasies. Those who enter here are thereby privy to Mr. Robotti's private visions. What he visioned was a distinctly posh place, with mirrored walls and crimson walls of silken damask reaching to a lofty ceiling, deep banquettes of glistening French blue and plush red carpeting. The walls of the grandiose room are adorned with gilt sculptures (back-lighted), grand displays of cut flowers stand here and there. The restaurant is in Technicolor.

The customers are in gray: substantial, corporate types in gray suits, their spouses in gray hair. If they consort with other than their spouses, they are not here. Here is for grim marking of birthdays, ritual pretheater dinners. They are called "Mr. This" or "Mr. That" or "sir" by the fawning captains. If you look like you "don't belong" in the place—that is, if you seem to be stretching your budget for a special night out —the captains turn on the boredom and the short answers. Like most such types, however, they readily revert to servility if they are merely looked at with a bit of contempt. A glance of amused scorn is *very* effective. It is not necessary actually to *say* anything.

Journalists want to dislike this restaurant. Its trappings are too obvious, the food too pretentiously *haute cuisine* in such a worn-out way, with an almost endless list of incomprehensible modifiers scattered over the menu: this is à la Parisienne, that Royale, something else Diplomate, Maréchale, Jurassienne, Grand Veneur, Marguery, Henry IV, Lucullus, Rothschild. If you know someone who doesn't like all those fancy sauces, this is what he doesn't like and probably doesn't understand. But for what it is—fancy food—it is pretty good. And you can get good versions of dishes that are so familiar that almost everyone has forgotten what they can and should taste like.

For example, Oysters Rockefeller about as well made as you can find them in New York. The oysters are filled with a spinach stuffing that has been seasoned and flavored with Pernod, and they are baked until the buttery filling is bubbling and browned, but not too long, so the oysters themselves are juicy and tender. The whole thing is permeated with the licorice fragrance of Pernod. This is a very substantial appetizer, and there is no rule against having two orders (one dozen) as a main course. Smoked trout is on many menus, and it is almost always the commercially available stuff—good as long as it kept refrigerated and moist. The sauce, however, is the restaurant's contribution, and in this place it is fabulous—sharp horseradish and airy whipped cream. One wishes the fish itself were not a bit dry, and that the lemon, artfully serrated, did not look as if the artist came in only once a week. There are snails, plump and tender, in a sauce that is deep-green with parsley and more heavily flavored with shallots than with garlic.

Among the fancy main dishes is one styled Ris de Veau Braises Financière, which is to say sweetbreads braised in stock and served in a wine sauce to which the braising liquid has been added. One looks in vain for the truffles the dish is ideally made with, but the sweetbreads themselves are so hearty and rich, the sauce so sharp and deep—the perfect contrast to the sensuous meat—that it's hard to quarrel with it. Les Médaillons de Veau Vallée d'Auge is a typical Normandy preparation of veal. Thin slices of the pale and tender meat are browned, as are some fresh mushrooms, and the two are served in a sauce that is mostly Calvados and cream. This is a simple dish, made with good ingredients. The Noisettes d'Agneau Mascotte consists of slices of roast lamb (very rare) in a sauce made of the roasting-pan juices, to which browned artichoke hearts and delicious little roasted potatoes have been added. The à la carte vegetables are very expensive, but they are carefully prepared. The grilled mushrooms, for example, are fresh, well-browned, crunchy and fragrant.

There is an unspoken agreement among the more thrifty (to put it nicely) New York restaurant customers and the more entrepreneurial (to put it bluntly) New York restaurant captains and waiters. When salad time comes, toward the end of dinner (not long before tipping time), the parsimonious diner considers his finances and orders something like one salad for two, or three salads for five, or whatever. The functionary considers *his* finances and portions out plates of salad that are more copious than anyone wants, charging according to the number of salads ordered. He is, as you see, in the salad business, but with no costs. The watercress and endives are fresh and crisp, and the oily dressing, with freshly ground pepper and just a little mustard, is first-rate.

A good dessert cart, including, at times, a hot Christmas pudding—a dark, spicy and sweet amalgam of nuts, fruits, rinds and brandy, served with a heavily liquored and rather liquid hard sauce. The chocolate mousse is rich and thick, and is served in a cakelike crust, with excellent whipped cream. The tarts are something rare—the usual fruit and pastry, but with a layer of marzipan. Now, marzipan is out of the world of pastry into the world of candy, and unless you have a special liking for the stuff, you may find these tarts a bit much.

This place is known for its lengthy wine list. The prices at the low end are insane: $12 for a bottle of ordinary Beaujolais. But the prices are not proportionately higher for wines that are many times better. To save a few dollars you may drink what the wine list refers to as "Native wines." There is a cover, but those entrepreneurs sometimes forget to include it in the final calculation. Business is business.

★★LA CÔTE BASQUE

5 East 55th Street
LUNCH AND DINNER.
Closed Sunday.
Reservations, MU 8–6525.
No credit cards.
Very expensive.

This is one of the prettiest restaurants in New York. The murals set in the ivory walls are not the bland background illustrations that panel many of New York's midtown French restaurants—their colors are brilliant, painterly; and their presence is assertive and actually delightful. (It's as if you entered a restaurant where you have learned to suffer the Muzak to savor the mousse, and found the Muzak replaced by Mozart, and the speakers by Stern, Rose and Istomin, in the flesh). The curved back wall is a gorgeous, panoramic view of a Mediterranean harbor vibrating in subtropical light, dotted with hundreds of little boats and surrounded by a density of tile-roofed houses. There is a sense of casual, elegant gaiety about La Côte Basque. The table linen is of soft red-and-green striped cotton, there are flowers on all the tables, and if you're not swooning just to be here, the side chairs may help—they sway to the tune of about five degrees from the perpendicular. It's true, this grand relic is opening up at the seams. La Côte Basque, Henri Soulé's fun house, built to look like the transformation of a manor house into a party retreat, is stiffening and cracking. It's not only the chairs, of course. Everything about it is less. The food is less. The utter relaxation of its former self is now rendered in dismal imitation, by captains who exchange a few casual remarks about this and that as the menu is explained, add a few more as the food is served and—disaster!—keep talking as that moment arrives when you're ready to convert food, wine and conversation into dinner, the moment when a professional captain would instinctively absent himself. La Côte Basque is now a museum. Perhaps the thing to do is drop in, look at the pictures and leave. Not that you can't get a good meal here, but you may get the wrong idea; this is not the Côte Basque. The place is legally entitled to the name, and its lineage is impeccable, but the restaurant is trying to survive by perpetual imitation of itself. The real thing has to be re-created, every day, by the creator, and Soulé is dead.

Some restaurants in New York are known as places where married men take women to whom they are not married. To La Côte Basque they take their wives. The close-tonsured, iron-gray heads barely turn to the stone faces on their left or right. At the little place around the corner from the office, these guys would be leaning, squirming and patting with every virile anecdote. There the food doesn't matter. Here, where it *is* the thing, it will not invariably offset the company, though when it is at its best it equals the food of the old Côte Basque.

Among the dishes which are of that quality, you may number an unlisted item that is occasionally available—a mousse of sole, served with two sauces. The mousse itself is fluffy and firm, yet it has a deep, clear flavor of fresh fish. It is served with an herby white sauce, made with a well-flavored *court-bouillon,* and a delicate brown sauce in which there is a distinct flavor of wine. If you begin your dinner with smoked salmon, you'll find that La Côte Basque obtains the best (you couldn't beat it at Zabar's), and on occasion forgets to serve oil with it. You want the Terrine Maison? Good idea. It is made with chunks of ham and tongue in among the pork, and it is fragrant with garlic. The plate of hors d'oeuvres includes some excellent crisp shrimp in, it must be admitted, very good Russian dressing; crunchy mushrooms that have been marinated to a turn in oil and herbs; a refreshing salad of tuna and celery, amalgamated in a clear-tasting vinaigrette; dressed tomatoes; and hard-cooked eggs in thick house-made mayonnaise, which raises the pedestrian to a position of semi-nobility. The billi-bi is odd—this cold soup in the version served here lacks the al-most overwhelming concentration of mussel flavor that characterizes most good ren-ditions of it. This one is spicy and briny, with the mussels detectable as an aftertaste, but it is delicious nevertheless.

If you're going to spend what it takes to have dinner at La Côte Basque, spend a lot more and have the best. The Noisettes d'Agneau Edouard VII are offered at a large premium above the regular fixed dinner price. It's not that the lamb is so splendid— it is good, but of the American kind, which means mild and not gamy; and it's not that the accompanying vegetables are short of disgraceful, because the little balls of roasted potato seem re-roasted and the artichoke heart is overcooked—it's that the sauce is thick without seeming thickened, it is meaty and buttery without being cloying and it is utterly infused with the nutlike flavor of truffles—the sauce is dense with little black chunks of the stuff.

Fine. But what does one make of this Côte de Veau aux Cèpes? The mushrooms are nice, but the sauce is raw—raw wine and raw stock, hardly melded, and insufficiently enriched, so that it seems like a kitchen cocktail, and the veal chop itself is coarse. The Caneton aux Pêches is not bad, but in a restaurant of this caliber, the sauce and the fruit should be a creation, not a combination—not peaches in sauce of duck.

A group of early diners inquires about the cheese at seven-thirty, and they are told that it is still "very cold." This is La Côte Basque! The cheese should have been removed from the refrigerator at three or four in the afternoon. The customers do not order much cheese? At these prices, if one in twenty wants cheese there should be a substan-tial selection at room temperature. If that is impossible, it should not be listed on the menu. At ten o'clock the cheese is still pretty cold. Good cheese, but cold—strong, gamy goat cheese, with that lovely, vaguely chalky texture; creamy, biting Roquefort. But cold.

Perfectly rendered soufflés; a mille-feuille of thin, crinkly layers of pastry and a filling of thick cream; fruit tarts that are of good fresh fruit.

★★★★ LE CYGNE

53 East 54th Street
LUNCH, MONDAY TO FRIDAY; DINNER, MONDAY TO SATURDAY.
Closed Sunday.
Reservations, PL 9-5941.
Credit cards: AE, DC.
Very expensive.

When Le Cygne was young, aspiring and not quite succeeding, it offset its short-comings (1) by underselling its *haute cuisine* competitors and (2) by making much of its elaborate service and suave *politesse.* There are now clear signs not only that Le Cygne has arrived but that Le Cygne knows it and is relaxed in the knowledge. The lid has been taken off the prices, and they have been permitted to reach their unnatural level; and the mindless reverence that once infused the demeanor of the host, captains and waiters has been replaced by a bemused savoir-faire that bespeaks a cool confidence not only in themselves but in what they are selling. The captain smiles lightly as he listens to and answers your questions about this dish or that—"Why do you ask all these questions," he seems to be saying, "when whatever you order will be superb?" Not only superb (by and large), but virtuosic—the kitchen, apparently bored by merely turning out, six days a week, terrific versions of the dishes listed on a fairly elaborate menu, keeps itself in shape with fanciful, ever-changing augments thereof. This is one of those restaurants where one may eschew the menu and just ask for the day's specials (to avoid eating the same old thing, day after day)—the main courses tend to be roasts (excellent, but not fascinating), but the appetizers are complex, often startling surprises, and you should not pass them up lightly.

Among these miracles, on occasion, is a quiche in which you will discern minced sweetbreads and strong green olives, and the singular effect of this particular combination of ingredients is to render the spicy quiche at once stronger and richer—the custard is light, firm and perfectly browned, and the crust is dark and crunchy. This is to run-of-restaurants quiche what love is to larceny. Another off-the-menu, elegant variant on a mundane theme is the saucisson chaud—an amalgam of well-spiced coarse meat, with plenty of fat left in, wrapped in a flaky pastry that is warm and moist with grease. It is served here with a deep sauce instead of the usual jar of mustard on the side, and that little touch lifts the dish well above the level of ordinary charcuterie. It is to run-of-restaurants saucisson chaud what Watergate is to larceny. Yet a third unlisted appetizer, sometimes available, is an almost unspeakably delicate feuilletée filled with striped bass and herbs (a feuilletée is a stuffed puff pastry, and the pastry here is almost fugitive in its lightness—just as you have begun to experience its flavor, it is gone). The fish and herbs, however, are clear and vivid, and the white sauce (made with a fish stock) that is poured over the tender dish is like liquid marble—weighty, polished.

Of course, there are first courses that *are* listed on the menu, and available whenever the place is open. The greatest of these are not the Moules à la Moutarde. Understand, they are flawless, and if you love mussels you will love this dish because the mussels have a clear fresh taste, and the sauce is vibrant with the flavor of good strong mustard, but the dish will bring to mind other good food you have had before, it will not astonish you—can't have that! Not to say that the listed items never make it—the Little Necks des Gourmets (ghastly name), for example, are perfectly tender and sweet, which means that their baking, under a topping of mushroom purée and a little bit of garlic, is very carefully controlled. The six mollusks arrive in a pool of buttery clam broth with parsley—you spoon the briny liquid over the browned mushroom topping before swallowing the freshly moistened morsels. There will be a good bit of the broth left over when you have finished your clams—if you are concerned about your girth, you drink it from a spoon, otherwise you eat it soaked into chunks of the excellent bread.

L'Emincé de Filet de Boeuf Bercy (a lunchtime dish) should not be read as minced beef. The slices of beef are small, but their sautéeing is so carefully attended to that each slice is like a perfect miniature steak, pink within, browned outside. The meat itself is extremely tender but with no loss of texture, and the sauce it is served in is made with an exceptionally sturdy beef stock and red wine that would be quite good enough to drink even with this exceptional dish. If there is a dish in this restaurant that is quintessentially French, it is L'Escalopine de Veau au Champagne—three slices of delicate white veal, sautéed in butter until a few points and edges of the meat are chocolate-brown, most of the surface just sprinkled with flecks of brown, the meat taking on the nutlike flavor of heated butter; the meat is served with a delicate white sauce, the abundance of which is more than enough for the little cutlets, a circumstance that is provided for by a mound of superb rice—huge firm kernels (apparently cooked in stock, so they are very tasty) which you slide through the sauce before consuming it. Butter, perfect meat, a simple sauce and a simple starch—perfect French food.

Le Caneton Smitane is still on the menu, and though it is still not up to the version served at La Caravelle, it is much improved from what it was a couple of years back. The bird itself is at once sharp and rich, with a perfectly browned skin and ample moisture in the meat, but the sour-cream sauce, though much better than the old version (which tasted far too strongly of raw sour cream), is now obscured by the excellent bird instead of providing a contrast to it. The dish is merely delicious.

The Quenelles de Brochet which are served at lunchtime are very refined pike dumplings in a crayfish sauce that is at once oceanic and honeylike. One of the three dumplings is surmounted by a sautéed mushroom, a sort of lark. The mingling of sweetness and of the two distinct seafood flavors is an amazing harmony, the mushroom a grace note.

Wonderful mocha mousse, made with excellent chocolate and what tastes like a fresh brew of strong coffee. A pear tart in which the fruit is in an eggy custard, on a breadlike pastry—delicious, but not sweet, it takes a position toward the end of a meal that is more like cheese.

But, of course, almost everyone skips that kind of stuff and orders soufflés. It is something to observe them emerging from the kitchen—they are browned, but not deeply, which will lead you to expect that they are a bit unfinished and will promptly collapse. They do not. They are simply made with such exquisite care that they are moist but not wet, firm but not breadlike, light but substantial. Try the one that is served with a sauce of Calvados and minced apples—the vibrant liquid and crunchy apples are a perfect sauce to the tender and sweet soufflé.

The service that was once hovering is now attentive, but there are still a few idiocies. At the busy lunchtime there is a sheet of paper in a glass on every table which is designed to give you the impression that each table has been assigned to a specific reservation, in case you want to refuse the first table you are led to. Of course, if you look at the sheets of paper, you will note that they are blank—you are led to a table selected by Mr. Whim. But in the slower evenings the whole business of seating is handled with much grace, and couples are offered side-by-side tables for two if neither member wants to face the wall. Best of all, the clientele is not what the steep prices would lead you to expect. During the day there are, of course, midtown executives reinforcing their own sense of importance. But much of the crowd, at lunchtime as well as in the evening, are relaxed pleasure lovers rather than big spenders (though of necessity in this place they must be the latter as well); it is not all sharkskin suits and sculptured hair—this is a classless restaurant in every sense except the economic.

★★★★ LA GRENOUILLE

3 East 52nd Street
LUNCH AND DINNER.
Closed Sunday.
Reservations, PL 2–1495.
Credit cards: AE.
Very expensive.

If the customers at La Caravelle seem to consist, in large measure, of corporate board chairmen, the customers at La Grenouille include a great many company presidents. Not only are the presidents about a decade younger, but their corporations are about a century newer. However, there's no point in holding on to your riches and waiting for them to become old when La Grenouille is serving lunch and dinner six days a week right now; and if you have good reason to believe that La Caravelle will seat you beyond the Arctic Circle, eat at La Grenouille, where there is a front and rear, certainly, but no remote corner, and even unknowns are sometimes seated in the tropics.

The dining room is unprepossessing—apple-green walls and crimson velvet banquettes. Someone came up with the idea of gracing the place with flowers—they are in every corner and on every table—and this touch of Mother Nature creates a feeling not of all outdoors, but of a little more space than there actually is.

The food at La Grenouille is slightly erratic, but occasionally achieves heights that can cause a diner to drop his fork at first bite. (In this rather noisy establishment the event goes unnoticed.)

If you haven't been to Europe in a number of years, have the terrine de campagne at La Grenouille. There are few dishes served anywhere in this country that are so evocative of France. Or you might choose some of the excellent, paper-thin Bayonne ham, served with ripe melon. Bayonne ham is the best ham on earth, and this is some of the best Bayonne. La Grenouille serves a justly famous plate of Hors d'Oeuvres Variées. It includes crisp celery root in a very surprisingly lemony rémoulade, cucumber salad with a touch of mustard in the dressing, as well as a superbly poached artichoke heart vinaigrette, and the aforementioned terrine. The Clams Corsini are a superb specialty—the littlest of littlenecks cooked in white wine, butter and garlic, and sprinkled with fresh parsley. They are tender, delicate, almost soothing, and they are at once sweet, tart and aromatic. And though celery broth may not sound very exciting, this broth—apparently the essence of the Creator's original notion of celery—is a sublime elevation of beef broth, which makes every petite marmite in town seem like a bowl of bouillon made from a cube.

The main courses do not invariably measure up to the openers, but they often reach heights of such balanced perfection, delicate or strong, that the occasional lapse is easily overlooked. The *grenouilles,* as you might expect, are excellent. Legs from only the littlest frogs are used; they seem fresh rather than frozen (a great rarity in New York), and they are so elegantly and delicately breaded, so superbly crisped by the light sautéeing in garlic, oil and butter that one could easily consume about three hundred of them, with a bottle of wine, in an hour's time. They are served with a strongly concentrated reduction of sautéed tomatoes and a perfectly boiled potato. However, the Quenelles de Brochet, with Pernod and tarragon, sound more interesting than they are. The quenelles themselves are a bit too delicate (they seem to have forgotten they were once fish), and the sauce (only slightly flavored with Pernod) is imaginative, even singular, but it somehow doesn't add up.

Kidneys are a humble food, but here they are raised, if not to an aristocratic level, at least to a comfortable middle-class status, with a sauce of mustard and port wine that brings the flavor around to where it is encountered as if for the first time—not as the acidic and aggressive taste that most people above the level of poverty simply avoid, but as a strong, gamy meat that requires a powerful sauce to tame it. The roast chicken is perfectly browned and delicious; it arrives at a point of such moistness and crispness that one imagines a gentleman in the kitchen paying attention to nothing but this one bird, waiting for the exact moment when it must be snatched from the oven.

Everyone in this place seems to have soufflés for dessert—toward the end of a mealtime they can be seen streaming out of the kitchen by twos and threes. And they are good—especially the delicate raspberry one available in summer; the strawberry, moistened with a strawberry sauce to which tiny seeded and skinned lemon sections have been added; and the chocolate, which is served with whipped cream or with a crème Anglaise flavored with Grand Marnier, or both.

The service here is excellent, but not invariably available; on occasion a bit of arm waving is necessary to get a waiter's or captain's attention. The tables are close together by the standards of any restaurant—some are actually inaccessible to serving carts— and by this time the management ought to have found larger quarters or sacrificed a couple of tables for the comfort of customers who must shell out the proverbial arm and leg to obtain what is, admittedly, some of the best food available in this country.

★★★★ LUTÈCE

249 East 50th Street
LUNCH, MONDAY TO FRIDAY; DINNER, MONDAY TO SATURDAY.
Closed Sunday.
Reservations essential, PL 2–2225.
Credit cards: AE.
Very expensive.

What sets Lutèce aside, most noticeably, from its *haute cuisine* competition in New York, is the idiosyncratic domesticity of its rooms. You expect to find coats and mufflers hung on the coat hooks just inside the front door. The little upstairs bedrooms, which seem only temporarily converted to dining rooms for some extraordinary party, may well have pairs of slippers in the corners—certainly there are suits and dresses behind these closet doors. The downstairs garden room, despite the formal rows of tables, has the quality of a small plot of urban backyard upgraded by a devoted fanatic who is bound and determined to incorporate a bit of country into his town house; the wicker chairs, trellises and colorful linens create a picnic atmosphere that is not undone by the refined food. Lutèce is housed in a narrow brownstone, and the traffic areas are constricted. If you arrive just behind a few other diners, there is barely a place to stand while they identify themselves, hand over their coats, and get started toward their table. The tiny bar, with its plain marble tables, is dominated by a Parisian street scene—you sit in a wicker chair to sip your apéritif. The stairway and the upstairs hallway are one-fat-man wide. The crystal chandelier, sconces with their little lampshades, flower paintings, tapestry, misty wallpaper and mirrors seem like the unplanned accumulation of several generations.

The à la carte dinner menu lists soups and broths as the first course, which is one way of going, but if you're planning to sample the hot hors d'oeuvres before your main course and to conclude with one of this restaurant's sublime desserts, make your soup a thin one, which means Consommé Tortue, your turtle soup. This is a really stiff, profoundly flavored broth, the color of mahogany, with bits of turtle at the bottom of the cup, their delicate, pliant texture a perfect contrast to the able-bodied stock. The waiter adds a good bit of sherry when the stuff is served. Turtle soup is probably the only dish of purely English origin that the French have enthusiastically embraced, and the version served here is so satisfying that it really seems to possess the health-giving tonic quality often attributed to it. Maybe it's the sherry. There is also an excellent Crème Saint Germain (your pea soup, without frankfurters), and a Consommé de Volaille (your chicken soup, without noodles). They are very good, but if you are positively famished, have both a cold and a hot hors d'oeuvre, because these are really singular for New York.

Lutèce offers a plate of Pâtés Assortis, consisting of four pâtés, any one of which is superior to ninety-nine of a hundred others. There is a pâté de fois gras that successfully carries out the pâté-de-foie-gras miracle—the gamy flavor of pork forcemeat, side by side with the perfume of goose liver. The others are coarser: a pâté of game flavored with herbs and truffles; a pâté de campagne with a crunchy surprise of hazelnuts, maybe every third bite; and a pâté en croûte, the least of the lot—fatty, bland, a difficult thing to appreciate in this flavorful company.

Among the hot hors d'oeuvres there is one that is served only at night, and only for four. If you're not interested in tasting several dishes, or if you can see your way clear to coming here several times, or if you simply insist on having one spectacular dish before another, *and* if you have three companions, order the Saumon Farci en Croûte. This masterpiece is presented as a large, raised crust that has been permitted to char at the extremities, so that it is perfectly browned over most of its surface. It is cut into four substantial slices and served. The crust itself is flaky and delicate. It is filled not only with a layer of salmon, but with one of pike, and the two kinds of fish retain their distinct characters, and the whole thing is surrounded with a velvety white sauce which is made slightly tart with sorrel.

The snails at this restaurant may be the best in New York. They are plump, tender and well flavored of the wine and stock they were cooked in, and baked briefly, in little individual pots, with a fragrant, herbed butter.

Many of the dishes here read like those concoctions of multiple items, which, usually, are sure signs of second-rate food. But here there is no hokum. The Quenelles de Brochet avec Cuisses de Grenouilles (pike dumplings with frog's legs) are made up of light, firm, moist ground pike, with fresh-tasting frog's legs inside, served under a syrupy, dark-pink sauce Nantua which has a strong flavor of crayfish. This dish is all you need to justify a bottle of cool white wine.

The Poulet en Croûte Lutèce is a little chicken filled with a mushroom stuffing, baked in a crust—a moist young bird, deliciously prepared. There is also duck, made here with peaches; the duck is almost unbelievably juicy for one that is quite obviously thoroughly cooked, and the sauce is equally unbelievably sweet for one that is not the least bit candied or cloying, but rather, bright and stout.

The most noticeable characteristic of the food at this restaurant, the care of its preparation notwithstanding, is the excellence of the basic ingredients. This is particularly obvious among the meats. If you order the Médaillon de Veau aux Morilles, for example, you'll notice that the meat is blanketed with sweet wild mushrooms, that it is browned to a crackling crust, and that the sauce is creamy and rich, which, of course, is all very nice. But the dish would be only a fraction of what it is if the veal were not the best obtainable—white as milk, tender, almost buttery, and fresh as a new bloom. The Mignon de Boeuf en Croûte Lutèce is beef of equal quality, in a brioche—Beef Wellington improved a hundredfold by simplification.

As to the lamb, it's almost horrifying to see the Carré de Pauillac Persillé (rack of lamb) carved into chops. This is the youngest lamb you ever get, with a clear, clean flavor, cooked exactly the way you order it. At Lutèce you expect the eye of the meat to be carved in long strips and served garnished with the ribs. There is no law about it, but good rack of lamb somehow tastes 5 percent better when it is carved that way.

The salads here are merely of good greens (watercress, endive, tender lettuce) in perfect vinaigrette. As Mother said, you can get the same thing at home, but you probably don't. And the cheeses are sometimes a bit old, as if they were re-refrigerated when not sold at one meal, and brought back to room temperature for the next.

The desserts are not as flamboyant as in some of the restaurants around town. There are no crêpes prepared at your table, no soufflés to be ordered in advance. But what they serve will serve. The Tarte à la Tatin is a simple apple tart, made in the usual way, with raisins, and flavored with cinnamon, but it is somehow cooked until the apples are deep, deep brown (but still firm), and the pastry is dark and crinkly. There is a good chocolate mousse, flavored with Grand Marnier; a bombe of thick mocha and hazelnut ice creams and airy whipped cream; and a frozen raspberry soufflé on a thin layer of dry cake, with a clear, sweet sauce.

But a restaurant is not all food, nor is wine the balance. You look at the wine list, you summon the captain, and order. Now, the captains here have a reputation for being unruffled, a reputation they deserve. But poise is not the primary qualification for being a captain. This suave aplomb, which so impresses (they have been called "attentive," "smooth as silk," "seductive"), conceals the fact that they are often less than straight with customers who have not attempted to seduce *them*. Their ready answers are not invariably honest answers. You are told that the wine you ordered is all gone. You point out that a number of wines on the list are obviously gone, since they have been crossed off, but that your selection is *not* deleted. Your captain does not address himself to this piece of logic, but repeats that the wine you ordered is gone. You select another wine. It, too, is not available. Now you are just playing. You ask for this one, that one, another one. All are listed. None is available. Does Lutèce not wish to sell wine? Of course Lutèce wishes to sell wine. But it wishes to sell wine of *its* choice to customers it does not know, while preserving the limited stocks of rarer wine for its friends. They seem very gracious in the act. They do not push high-priced wines. But the wine they sell to you for, say, $12 is just as profitable to them as the $20 bottle they save for regulars. It's true that it's almost impossible to get a bad bottle of wine in this restaurant, but if you have been saving your pennies for a year or if you can afford to eat here six times a week, you are proffering the same brand of money and you are entitled to the same treatment. There are only two ways to deal with this situation. You can order your food and wine, and if the wine is refused, you can explain that you don't want the pants without the jacket, and to help the captain save face, suggest that perhaps he can "find" one or two stray bottles. The other way is simply to give up, and let the captain select a good, inexpensive wine.

The attitude of the captains here is that anyone who is not known does not deserve to be, and that their own perfection is unblemished. On one occasion a captain here recommends the cheese, and it is merely tolerable. On another he forgets about cheese and sells half a dozen desserts. When you remember cheese and point out his omission, he lies. The cheese, he says, is not in good condition this night. You insist. The cheese is brought, and sure enough, the Pont-l'Evêque, Brie and Boursault are perfect, as you would expect on a Saturday night. He prefers to put them back in the icebox for Monday rather than admit he looked your table over and figured you didn't know from cheese.

Lovely crystal, good china, fresh flowers. Here and there bottles of wine breathing for customers who ordered them in advance. You want a Campari and soda? Your soda is a split of Perrier. You want a Calvados? You get a spectacular *grande fine.* You wish to hang around for a bit? You have already been served some decent petits fours with your dessert, and soon you are brought a tray of good candies, including glazed orange sections that squirt fresh juice when you bite into them.

But wouldn't it be nice if the menu provided straightforward English-language translations of the French dishes? This would eliminate the need for most of one's truck with your unctuous captain. "Good selection," he says when you have chosen your dinner, and you are expected to expire with relief. Who asked you? is the only rational reply.

Other idiocies. If the establishment wishes to set house rules about what you should wear, the least it can do is to announce them when it accepts reservations. At dinner, only one menu per table lists prices, the captain makes a stab at who is the host and he hands it to him. People of low economic position who share (how crass!) the cost of their dinner deserve to be inconvenienced. Ask for additional menus with prices.

This is now the best kitchen in New York, but it is not the best restaurant.

★★★ LE MADRIGAL

216 East 53rd Street
LUNCH, MONDAY TO FRIDAY; DINNER, MONDAY TO SATURDAY.
Closed Sunday.
Reservations, 355–0322.
Credit cards: AE.
Very expensive.

The difference between the new Madrigal of a few years back and the older Madrigal of today is little more than time and its ripening and mellowing effects. Take, for example, your host, the diminutive gray-haired chap with the smile. That thin arching of the lips once scarcely concealed his distaste for some of the sources of his livelihood. Little as he liked it, and from the first, for every bearer of old money that walked in his front door, two with new came to see. On the theory that the old has been multiplying for generations (and apparently unaware that fecundity is a property of youth), Le Madrigal raised its already exorbitant prices in search of a level at which mere high-earners would wince, while coupon-clippers would go on never even reading the right-hand columns of their menus. The fixed-price dinner has been replaced by an à la carte listing in which the lowest-price main course is $9.25, which means that if you consume nothing else, your food bill will be $10.75 because there is a leetle item in leetle print at the top of the page—Cover Charge $1.50. And if a couple of people eat and drink in this place with regard only to what they want, not to its cost, they will part with $65 or more before they leave. So what do you think happened? Right. Today, for every bearer of old money that walks in the front door, two with new come to see.

So, saith the wise man, if you can't divorce 'em, love 'em, and your host, along in years and loath to enter senescence without wisdom, has taken the advice. He now smiles with equal warmth on bankers and loan sharks, ambassadors and middlemen. His staff follows his cues; this has become one of the city's most cordially run dining rooms, and in the waiters' and captains' pockets and in the house bank account, all kinds of money happily comingle.

Always one of the prettiest restaurants in town, and one of the most comfortable if you avoid the cramped little "garden" room appended to the rear, you must now enjoy it without the pleasure of stiffing the captain. The place is all sunny golden light, and nowadays the men in uniform seem to give off some of it. If your party includes fetching young things, you may get an extra dose.

On your left as you enter is a pretty array of platters, the makings of a refreshing plate of Hors d'Oeuvres Variés, including slices of perfectly ripe but not the least bit soft avocado; tomatoes of rare redness and flavor for these days, and (touch of old elegance), the tomatoes are skinned; mushrooms, the stems trimmed down to a stump, so that they are crunchy little nuggets—they have been marinated in oil, vinegar and herbs; two kinds of saucisson sec—one peppery, the other smoky, both sausages firm, dark-red and abundantly fatted; chickpeas that are crisp—there is someone in the kitchen here who does not let a thing cook too long—and dressed with an oil that is fragrantly flavored with bay. You can have excellent ham, tender and smoky. The fresh clams and oysters are served on deep plates that have been filled with crushed ice—the littlenecks are *tiny*. The smoked trout is the usual thing, firm and flaky, and what differentiates one place from another as far as this dish goes is the horseradish sauce —this one is thick and heavy, made with cream that has been whipped until very stiff, and strong fresh horseradish.

If two of you want fish, you qualify for "Striped Bass Flambée Madrigal (For Two) $21.00 (45 Minutes Waiting Time)." This is a variant of the famous dish of Provence in which *loup* (a fish of the Mediterranean) is cooked over burning fennel branches. The real thing cannot be made in New York because *loups* do not frequent the Atlantic, but this will do. The fish is poached with the fennel branches, delivered to within viewing distance of your table, the twigs of fennel still protruding from the core of the fish, and flamed in Pernod, yielding, at the bottom of the pan, a buttery broth with a fennel flavor. Your captain separates the meat of the huge fish from the sticks and bones, piles it onto a couple of plates and spoons the sauce over it. The sauce is rather obvious, but it is good anyway, and the fish used here is impeccably fresh and thoroughly cooked without being in the least softened—a gay dish.

More in the tradition is the Caneton à l'Orange, and the one you get here is the honest article, not candied duck—the sauce is deep, slightly acidic, polished, velvety; the bird is moist and oily, without a trace of excess fat, wrapped in skin that has been browned to a glistening reddish umber.

If the two who had fish want to go all the way together, there are well-made soufflés, their tops like huge golden mushroom caps above the white porcelain soufflé dishes, available in all the standard sweet flavors, at a not falsely modest $7.50. The dessert cart carries an unabashedly sweet, thick, almost sticky chocolate mousse; a bowl of whipped cream that can be spooned on the mousse or on the strawberries (a couple of unripe ones here and there) in kirsch; a rich bread-and-butter pudding; crisp pears cooked in white wine and sugar. The platter of petits fours is no longer served only to the captains' favorites—everyone gets his freebies.

Vestiges of the days when they were trying so hard to keep the riffraff out—at the bottom of the menu: "Appetisers [*sic*] Served and Not Followed by a Main Course will be charged as a Main Course"; and "One Portion Served for One Person Only." Nothing worked. The rowdies are still here, guffawing and giggling as they stumble out.

★★★ LE MISTRAL

14 East 52nd Street
LUNCH AND DINNER.
Closed Sunday.
Reservations, 421–7588.
Credit cards: AE, DC.
Very expensive.

There is a certain sadistic pleasure in finding formerly hard-to-get-into French restaurants half empty at dinner hour. These places now grant telephone reservations before hearing the caller's name, they politely seat walk-ins off the street at five minutes *after* official closing time, and they treat tourists in Sears, Roebuck clothing like visiting royalty. Of course it took a recession, the crackdown on expense accounts, and an accelerated migration of the middle class to the suburbs to achieve this state. Certainly, when business picks up, if it does, restaurateurs will forget their lessons, prosperity will seem to stretch endlessly into the future, and the shrewd but unknown New York restaurant goer will resort again to certain well-tested tricks: "This is Dr. Smith's office. The doctor wishes a table for four at seven-forty-five." (MD's get terrific treatment.) "This is the Canadian consulate. The cultural attaché requires a table for two at eight-fifteen." And so on.

Le Mistral was never the worst offender in this regard, since it was never the most popular of the "fancy" French restaurants. Because of its location it is and always has been packed at lunch hour, but these days it is one of the best restaurants in New York for a leisurely midweek, *haute cuisine* dinner. The customers are few, but not so few that the place feels deserted; the lovely room—murals of sunlit southern France, fresh flowers, rough plaster walls, dark-stained beams and comfortable red velvet banquettes —is most pleasant when not crowded; and the staff has the time to give customers the attention they need.

In addition to its listed first courses, Le Mistral usually has available a cold poached fish with a cold sauce. The perfectly cooked bass is served with a rémoulade that is more than the usual seasoned mayonnaise—it takes onions, capers, herbs and anchovy paste to really make this sauce, and that is how it is put together at Le Mistral. Among the appetizers, there is a very good terrine with nuts and truffles, and a nice selection for a plate of Hors d'Oeuvres Variées, including beautifully marinated fresh mushrooms, hearts of palm, mackerel, and the usual vegetables—celery root, cucumbers, and so on.

Technically the table d'hôte dinner at Le Mistral includes an appetizer *or* soup, but the captain will sometimes overlook your mistake in ordering both. The best reason for making the error is billi-bi. At Le Mistral it is served hot or cold, and it's a good idea to try both at the same dinner. In the cold soup the flavor of mussels predominates, but when the soup is heated, the strong taste of cooked cream emerges and blends with the ocean taste of the broth. The same soup, but completely transformed.

There is a wonderful trout dish prepared according to one of Madame Prunier's famous fish recipes. Trout Grenobloise is prepared by sautéeing trout filets in butter, sautéeing a few mushrooms in the same butter, and then pouring them over the trout, with a few capers and some lemon juice. A simple and splendid dish.

There is also a Chicken Alexandra—sautéed chicken in a rich white sauce (here made pink with a touch of tomato). And for more lusty appetites, a Sauté de Boeuf Châteauneuf-du-Pape—chunks of filet mignon over which is poured a sauce of pan juices and wine, thickened to the appearance and consistency of warm chocolate—powerful stuff.

Le Mistral's salad dressing is very strong—with that much mustard, do we need that much vinegar? It's a good idea to describe the kind of dressing you want when you order your salad.

The desserts include a chocolate mousse the house pushes as a specialty, but there is nothing special about it except for the lumps of pure chocolate throughout the rather pasty mixture. There is an excellent Crêpe Soufflée of Grand Marnier, and good strawberries, even out of season.

The purchase of a bottle of wine in this restaurant is really a big deal. The captain brings the bottle you ordered, carrying it like a nurse showing a newborn baby—the left hand under the cork, as if the neck will not support it, the right hand under the torso at the bottom. He slowly slides a well-manicured right thumb under a few salient words on the label, and simultaneously the words are intoned, as if the customer were being taught to read. "From the House of Joseph Drouhin," he declaims (all kneel), and the customer bows his head in assent.

★★★ LE PÉRIGORD PARK

575 Park Avenue (at 63rd Street)
LUNCH, MONDAY TO FRIDAY; DINNER, DAILY.
Reservations, 752-0050.
Credit cards: AE.
Very expensive.

This restaurant, the aristocratic offspring of the plebeian Le Périgord, is one of the most elegantly designed eating places in New York. The large main dining room is brightly lighted with an ivory glow that is at once so soft and intense that it seems like gentle sunlight. There are crystal chandeliers and gold-colored banquettes, and apparently to ensure that the classical surroundings not create an atmosphere of overbred restraint, there are irreverent wall paintings of strolling characters in puckish garments who regard (or disregard) the proceedings with a jester's humor and superiority.

A few steps up is the second dining room—vaulted tan stucco ceilings, booths of dark wood and leather, and dim light; and a few steps farther up, the same furnishings in an intimate, low-ceilinged third room.

Le Périgord Park has one of the most reliable kitchens of the French restaurants in New York, the service is competent and professional without being stiff, and the regular clientele, many from the surrounding neighborhood, seems comfortable and keeps the rooms busy.

The food is not invariably to one's taste, but it's a matter of disagreement, not failure—the results are the intended ones, if not accepted ones. Terrine de Canard Truffée et Pistachée is a case in point. This is a powerful, livery terrine, at once refined and strong, but somehow the pistachio nuts seem out of place, too discordant; however, the garnish of celery root, in a very mustardy rémoulade, is a lovely touch. This terrine, on the good bread served here, with cold white wine, is a pleasant way to pass the time while waiting for main courses, as are the Clams aux Fines Herbes et Vin Blanc. These sweet clams are carefully baked with parsley, white wine, and most important, the juice of the clams; one wishes that only the tiniest clams were used because the larger ones overpower the delicate broth, both with their strong flavor and heavy texture. The appetizer of cold striped bass, with cucumbers and sauce rémoulade, is superb—a rich fish in a rich sauce, with crisp, dressed cucumbers as the very refreshing, tart relief.

Business is good at Sunday dinner. This is partly because most of New York's other fancy French restaurants are closed on Sunday, and partly because the splendid special main course every Sunday is the roast lamb "comme en Provence." The meat is excellently roasted—crisp outside, pink within—lightly flavored with garlic, and moistened with a glaze of good stock and the strong pan juices that lamb provides. There is a very good roast pigeon every day, but it is uninspired—called Le Pigeon dans Son Jus, it could use a little of someone else's *jus*. An unadorned roasted bird can be a masterpiece, but it requires a perfect bird and a perfect hand—someone like the chap who sees to the roasting of birds at La Grenouille.

Something on the menu is called Truite Inspiration du Chef. This, to begin with, seems to be sea trout, or else not a live fresh-water trout, which is not a misrepresentation, simply a disappointment. The chef's inspiration is a chocolate-brown sauce with mushrooms; it is very good, but he does a little better when he goes by the book. Good salad—lettuce and endive in perfect condition, the dressing made with excellent mustard.

There is a lot of flaming of desserts here. Mousse à l'Armagnac is a fire for $2 (over the prix fixe); and soufflés of any flavor, at an extra $2.75. But the cart of pastries and other sweets is more interesting: very light Floating Island; fluffy chocolate mousse; beautifully bronzed apricot tarts. After a large meal the bright pink raspberry mousse is a perfect sweet conclusion without too much weight.

Unusual Cuisines

These are restaurants that specialize in national styles of cooking that can be found in only a few or, at most, a few dozen restaurants in New York.

It's inexplicable, but by and large, the rarer the cuisine the more reliable its exponents. There are only a couple of Danish restaurants in New York, only a few Czech or Swiss restaurants, merely a handful of Armenian ones, but almost every one of these places serves decent food. You won't find a Japanese, Indian or Greek restaurant on every other block, but these places are beginning to proliferate, and sure enough, if you try several of them, you'll get the bad with the good.

You may find a few French or Italian dishes on the Middle European menus; Chinese dishes at the Indian restaurants; Greek dishes in the Armenian places. And almost everywhere there will be steaks or chicken sandwiches or omelettes or some such. These deviations from authenticity are designed for those odd members in dining parties who don't wish to try foods that are strange to them. It's a good rule to stay away from this stuff and instead do as the Romans do.

★ ARARAT

4 East 36th Street
LUNCH, MONDAY TO SATURDAY; DINNER, DAILY.
Reservations, 686–4622.
Credit cards: AE, DC.
Medium-priced.

Does it mean anything to say that this is a typical Armenian restaurant? With the demise of Sayat Nova, the Armenian restaurants in New York are so alike (in appearance) that one is tempted toward the dubious syntax of "This is an *identical* Armenian restaurant." Much red upholstery, golden draperies, carved wooden partitions, crystal chandeliers, all very Eastern-posh and Hollywood-harem. There is a back room in blue and ivory—probably left over from another restaurant.

Armenian dried beef is very much an indelicate Armenian delicacy, but New York's Armenian restaurants rarely list it because its flavor, to the uninitiated palate, may seem rank. It is surely strong, tastes aged rather than cured, gamy rather than smoky. But it is good meat, cool, dark, fibrous and loud. A few slices and you will be a convert.

This is an inconsistent restaurant, and though you can get as good a dinner here as at The Dardanelles or The Balkan Armenian if you order the right items, the menu offers more opportunities for ordering the wrong ones. Two appetizers to avoid here are the midia dolma (baked stuffed mussels, served cold) and the enguinar (artichokes cooked in oil and lemon, with carrots and onions, also served cold). The trouble with the mussels is that they are greasy, the sweetness of the sweet spices excessive, the texture of the pine nuts lost. And the trouble with the artichoke is that the heart and stem have not been perfectly separated from the leaves, which seems to prevent the flavor of the other vegetables from permeating the artichoke. But Ararat seems to do best what its competitors will not do at all: chi kufta, superfluously described on the menu as "Armenian tartar steak," is then further described as "lean ground raw lamb and seasoned cracked wheat garnished with chopped fresh onion and parsley . . ." This is extremely rich stuff, the sharpness of the raw onion almost essential if you are going to finish the substantial serving. There are also good versions of cheese boreg (cheese, wrapped in pastry and served warm), and imam bayeldi (eggplant, baked in oil, with tomatoes and onions, served cold), and tarama (the paste of red fish roe, bread, garlic and lemon), but if you go out of your way to come to this out-of-the-way place, the things to start your dinner with are the dried beef and the raw lamb.

Of course there is moussaka, composed of a layer of eggplant, another of ground lamb, a top one of heavily cheesed white sauce, the whole thing oozing spicy red oil. And, equally of-course, there is shish kebab—tender blackened chunks of good lamb, skewered with slices of tomato and onion. But the real winner is boud skara, a marinated lamb steak, the meat lightly seasoned, seared and rare—this is a strong dish, partly because the lamb here is a little gamy, and partly because it has been made even louder by its marinade. That weird dish called harpoot kufta is also served here. This is the elaborate construction of hollow balls of cracked wheat, stuffed with seasoned ground lamb, and served in broth. At its best, each of the three elements of the dish is distinctive—the cracked wheat crusty, the lamb oily, spicy and succulent, the broth hot and clear. The version served here is perfectly good to eat, but the elements are somehow all blended together. Too bad.

To an Armenian, fruit compote is not something you put on menus for sick people. Armenians take fruit compote seriously. The one served here is made with prunes, dried apricots, apples and pears. The four fruits are cooked with lots of clove, and the final dish is strong, sweet, winy. Good nut pastries and puddings and bread cooked in syrup, all of them available with kaimak, the exceptional Armenian cream that is as sweet as ice cream and as rich and thick as butter, with which you will need a cup of the potent coffee served here—half coffee, half sediment.

★ THE BALKAN ARMENIAN

129 East 27th Street
LUNCH, MONDAY TO FRIDAY; DINNER, MONDAY TO SATURDAY.
Closed Sunday.
Reservations, MU 9–7925.
Credit cards: AE, DC, MC.
Inexpensive.

This is a very satisfying little Armenian restaurant. The tables may be small, the service plodding, and the decorations a bit silly, what with Oriental rugs, and paintings that are not merely primitive but atavistic, on the dark walls. But it is a relaxed neighborhood restaurant, set in its ways, not trying to make a buck any faster than it made one in the past, and accordingly, one is treated simply as a hungry human rather than as an element in a financial program.

Watch out for the generalizations, but Armenians are generally very proud of their background. The intensity of this pride varies from, at one extreme, the belief that Armenians are the greatest race on earth to, at the other extreme, the conviction that Armenians are the greatest race on earth and that Armenia is the fount of all that is worth preserving in civilization. The menu here makes a modest contribution toward the defense of these propositions, itemizing, at no charge, "The Birth of a People," "A Few Famous Armenians," a short history of The Balkan Armenian restaurant itself (during Prohibition, shish kebab was 50 cents, and arrack was sold in demitasses), and a tabulation of the world distribution of Armenians, the upshot of which is that most Armenians live in Armenia.

The list of dishes does not hew slavishly to the Armenian line, making it possible to have tarama as a first course—the famous paste of roe and moistened bread, flavored with lemon. It is served here in a wonderfully well-balanced version, thick, but moist enough to spread, and heavily flavored of roe. The cold stuffed grape leaves, however, are overly oiled and dilled, which gives them a slightly sour taste, and the cold yogurt soup, with barley, is garnished with a level teaspoon of dried mint, like a spoonful of dust. The stuffed mussels (with rice, pine nuts and currants) are good, but rather heavily oiled and light on the allspice, the seasoning that can make this dish surprising and stimulating.

The main course of hot grape leaves (with meat in the stuffing, and quite another dish from the cold appetizer) is really delicious. The leaves have not been rendered limp and retain their slightly papery texture; and the filling, of rice and gamy ground lamb, is accented perfectly by the strong, tart, homemade yogurt served with them.

The shish kebab is of good meat, perfectly broiled; and the patlijan silkme—a heavy and extremely satisfying amalgam of sautéed eggplant and pot-roasted lamb—is powerfully flavored and rich. As in all Armenian restaurants, most of the main courses are based on lamb, and since the meat used here is tender and highly flavored, the main dishes are invariably satisfying, if never elegant. (The mushroom kebab is a standout exception—allegedly of fresh mushrooms, the dish is made with the canned variety, and it is a bore.)

The usual desserts of thin-layered pastry, walnuts and honey are available here in all the usual shapes—flat baklava, rolled checkme, etc. The pastry is crisp, the nuts crunchy, the honey thick and sweet, and what more can you ask? Avoid toulumba, which, the menu frankly admits, is a cruller, though it fails to point out that it tastes like the drugstore version.

There is a famous story of a lady seated on a park bench, babe in arms. "What a lovely child," remarks a passer-by. "You should see his pictures," says the lady.

"Ask to see our Kodachrome pictures of Armenian dishes," says the menu.

★★ CEDARS OF LEBANON

39 East 30th Street
LUNCH AND DINNER.
Reservations, MU 6–9634.
Credit cards: AE, BA, CB, DC, MC.
Medium-priced.

Good and cheap, even by pre-inflation criteria. Once a seedy place with plastic tablecloths and splintery walls, Cedars of Lebanon has been COMPLETELY REDECORATED and now looks like all the successful Armenian restaurants in New York, even though it is Lebanese. But, miraculously, the shift to posh has not been attended by a parallel movement to steep. Here—amid the pictorial velvet rugs hanging on rosewood walls, ornate chandeliers, sculptured red napkins standing on white linen, and swarthy waiters in red jackets and bow ties—you can still get a complete dinner for $4 if you select from the lower-priced main courses and restrict yourself to the on-the-dinner appetizers. Employers seeking to attract staff to this unfashionable neighborhood can point out the fringe benefits of working far from the temptations of Saks and Bloomie's and near the $3 lunches at Cedars of Lebanon.

Precisely what distinguishes the dishes of Lebanon from those of Syria, Egypt, Turkey, etc., is, one feels certain, well-known to the Lebanese, Syrians, Egyptians, Turks and etceterese. But in New York the restaurants of these countries offer menus that are indistinguishable from one another. No matter, we do not come to study, but to eat, and one begins here with a little plate of oily hot peppers (pale gold) and a basket (plastic gold) of triangles of flat bread, cut from the circle. The moist heat of the peppers is alleviated by the dense, bland bread. The bread is double-layered, like an envelope, and after you have dispensed with the peppers, studied the menu and ordered the first courses, you may fill a few of the envelopes with homus, the Middle Eastern paste of chickpeas and sesame oil. The version served here is among the best in town—freshly made each day, thick yet moist, so redolent of the flavor of sesame that the stuff tastes almost like halvah, soft, slightly grainy, rich and heavy. The mashed eggplant with sesame oil (which all the world knows as "ba ba ghannouj") is not particularly notable for the vividness of its eggplant flavor, but the baked vegetable is freshly mixed with an abundance of oil, spices and garlic, making it nice and gooey, a hint of texture lent by the eggplant seeds. Here are not New York's best stuffed grape leaves, though it is not easy to put your little finger on the problem—they are a bit too loglike, rather overly sour, the leaves somewhat tough; none of these grossly offensive, but the total off the mark in several directions at once. Listed under the salads, but served as an appetizer, is a sparkling item called tabboule, which consists of very coarsely chopped parsley, minced scallion greens and little chunks of tomato, all dressed in oil and lots of lemon juice. Mint leaves belong but are not in evidence; the scallion greens are visible but rare; and in the company of the fragrant parsley, the bits of tomato are a textural note rather than a flavor; but the resilient parsley, fragrant and slightly chewy, is especially stimulating when stirred up by the tart lemon and the other, more fugitive ingredients. This is a good place to come to with a few people—an assortment of these appetizers, each on its own little plate, arranged in the center of a table, is a lovely and tempting sight.

Kibbee is many things, in its most primitive form raw ground lamb and cracked wheat. When it is taken beyond that stage, it is called Kibbee This or Kibbee That. Among the Cedars' kibbees is one called Kibbee Shish Barak, in which the kibbee is stuffed into sausage-shaped patties of yet another lamb mixture—lamb and pine nuts —sautéed, and served in a lemony broth that has been enriched with yogurt. The meat is spiced, the grainy outer layer hardened to a crunchy crust, the inner filling soft and moist—you alternate bites of the little dumplings with spoons of the sour and creamy broth. Then there is couscous (Class, what is the distance between Lebanon and North Africa?). Couscous is also many things, ranging from a fiery vegetable, pasta and semolina stew augmented by several meats, to sweetened steamed grain, eaten as a dessert. The Cedars' couscous is approximately what most people think of when they hear the term—a broth containing grain and vegetables (here the grain is fine and slightly nubbly, the chickpeas crunchy, the onions tender and sweet), surmounted by browned chicken that is thoroughly cooked but still tender and moist. The thing comes off as an Eastern competitor in the chicken-in-the-pot stakes and wins handily. Naturally there is shish kebab, but this one is not made of great lamb, which is a matter of immateriality when the lamb is (a) only one step below the best and (b) either stewed or ground. But in shish kebab you are eating chunks of lamb that have been marinated and broiled, which is a revealing preparation. It is on the menu because the public expects it to be on the menu in Eastern restaurants, but at Cedars of Lebanon you are better off with the more complicated and more highly flavored lamb dishes.

Your waiter escorts you to the display of desserts at the front of the restaurant and explains the desserts to you. Then the proprietor rises from his table near the display of desserts and explains the waiter's English to you. The best thing in the place is something they have decided to call Ladyfingers—a log of sweetened ground walnuts that is baked in a wrapping of buttered onion-skin-thin filo pastry, cooled, and moistened with honey just before it is served. The worst is something called Bird Nest, which is apparently made of pistachio nuts and mothballs. In between are good versions of two varieties of baklava—the standard thing and a variant in which cheese is substituted for the walnuts. The Lebanese coffee is thick, strong and delicious.

★★★ CHALET SUISSE

6 East 48th Street
LUNCH AND DINNER.
Closed Saturday and Sunday.
Reservations, 355–0855.
Credit cards: AE, CB, DC, MC.
Expensive.

If you believe what you see, and if, therefore, you are frequently disappointed, you must come to the Chalet Suisse, if only to reinforce your confidence in first impressions. The place is immediately prepossessing: comfortable, elegant rusticity—rough plaster ivory walls, dark beams on the ceiling, soft lighting; the large tables are surrounded by wooden slat-backed chairs with cushions on the seats. They are occupied by comfort-loving regulars, who look like they have been coming here for many years without losing any of their taste for the place—at lunchtime they fill the restaurant, at dinner the place is quieter but far from dead. Whenever you come, if you linger, even to the point where you are the last customer, dawdling over a superfluous brandy and a second cigar, you are attended to as if time had no end.

The owners, man and woman, are ever-present, unobtrusively overseeing, not above filling your wineglass or coffee cup if your waitress is engaged elsewhere. And the waitresses, these incredible waitresses in their nifty, crisp, pretty Swiss costumes—they know the menu utterly, and they explain it thoroughly, concisely; they are watchful and available. And thoughtful. "Is it all right with you if I take some of this veal back to the kitchen to keep it warm until you are ready for more?" "Yes, of course. Very good idea. And by the way, while you're at it, if you don't mind, will you marry me?"

If you flinch at the idea of eating brains, how do you feel about *cold* brains? Just as ivory-white and slippery as the hot kind, but also kind of clammy—they are marinated in a lovely dressing, with minced, pickled vegetables (crisp), parsley (fresh) and capers (sour); you get a lot, and it is delicious. Pretty much the same color and texture, but hot—actually steamy—is the Onion and Cheese Pie, a kind of quiche actually, but predominantly cheese and very pully. The cheese, of course, is from Switzerland, and it has a strong, nutlike flavor that is quite powerful when it is hot and browned. Even stronger-tasting is the Bundnerfleisch—a smoked beef, served in thin slices, fibrous and peppery.

Nine times out of ten, when you read a menu introduction like "SPECIALTIES of our Executive Chef Mr. Erwin Herger," you know you're being sold what you don't want to buy. That kind of pronunciamento almost never precedes a dish of the quality of Médaillons de Veau aux Morilles, and when you're told, additionally, that these are "The finest Veal Steaks in a rich Cream Sauce with imported Mushrooms," you have every right to expect that you are in a boob trap. Unfortunately for rules of thumb, but happily otherwise, the dish is as good as its description. The veal is very pale, and lightly sautéed, so that it is moist and rosy, and the sauce is thick, buttery, well herbed and strongly seasoned; the morels, of course, are sweet and crinkly, and you are served a quite astonishing abundance of the expensive little things—as well you might be, for the dish is $12, à la carte.

There are humbler items on the menu, like Liver and Kidney à la Suisse, a fricassee of browned slices of liver and kidney made in a strong stock; you soak up the thick brown sauce with hunks of the good bread you get here. Naturally, there are fondues. And if you don't mind working for as well as paying for your sustenance, the cheese fondue is worth struggling with, particularly if you let it bubble for a while over its flame —it improves with extra cooking. The dish is made with good cheese, a little kirsch and a touch of garlic, and the knowing drink the vaguely sparkling white wine called Fendant with this dish—a good one is available here.

Excellent vegetables: the spinach is strong, lightly seasoned with nutmeg; the string beans are fresh and moist, and they are served in a little bundle, wrapped in a strip of bacon; the rösti potatoes are moist and salty under their perfectly browned crust.

The desserts are as successful as the dishes on the rest of the menu, but the listing is not especially interesting. The chocolate fondue, of course, is made with superb chocolate as well as hazelnuts—you dip the almost black stuff out of its pot with bits of pastry or pineapple or sections of mandarin orange. The Aargauer Rueblitorte is a sweet, crunchy cake of carrots and almonds topped with a dollop of whipped cream that is so startlingly light, so happily unsweetened, so elemental, that it is like a sniff of country air to a lifelong city dweller.

Chalet Suisse has been around for decades, and it has never been better. The dining room has always been well managed, but the food was not always this consistently good.

Plenty of good Swiss wine on the list.

★★ COPENHAGEN

68 West 58th Street
LUNCH AND DINNER.
Closed Sunday.
Reservations, MU 8-3690.
Credit cards: AE, CB, DC, MC.
Medium-priced.

This is a wonderful restaurant in many ways, but one wishes that the host and hostess would turn it over to managers who are not enslaved by the petty pecking order of an established restaurant with an established clientele.

An apparently unrecognized couple arrive for dinner, and though the room is only half filled, they are seated at a small table behind a post, while a larger table beside it (as well as many others elsewhere in the room) is unused for the balance of the evening. When two beautiful young ladies arrive for lunch in casual dress, the plump, dimpled, blond boss lady sizes them up as in over their heads (and anyway, we all know that women alone don't spend) and leads them to a rarely used table in a remote corner; eventually she has it set up for eating, while better-situated tables, all ready with their rolled napkins, flowers and crystal, wait for customers who never come. But the host and hostess are minor obstacles; the waiters one deals with after they are out of the way are far more courteous, and the food makes it easy to overlook the deficient hospitality.

Danish food is famous for "det kolde bord" (a more or less elaborate buffet), and smørrebrød (open-faced sandwiches, available, in good restaurants in Denmark, in imponderable variety). At this restaurant the buffet is served at lunch and dinner, the sandwiches only at lunch.

The buffet table at Copenhagen is circular, so one can begin at any point, but the standard place to start is at the herrings and other cured fish. One marches from his table to the buffet, takes a plate from the stack and begins. There is sweet herring in a tart curry sauce, and a pickled herring with dill and cucumber, both of which are stimulating; a very strong smoked herring which is positively invigorating; and a mustard herring, with dill, which, by comparison, is merely refreshing. These, with a few slices of smoked salmon and a helping of cold beet salad are a good selection for the first trip. When all is consumed, with, it is suggested, beer and Akvavit (the Danish caraway-flavored stimulant, which is brought to the table in a bottle sheathed in a sleeve of ice), one waits a moment for the plate to be removed and repairs to the buffet for a fresh plate and some milder seafood. There is a whole cold salmon under a blanket of mayonnaise, sprinkled with little shrimp. Take some of that. Then there are some very nice halves of cold boiled lobster. Take one or two of those. Enough for this trip, except perhaps for a little potato salad. Return to your table, arrange for some more beer, and perhaps a second Akvavit. By this time the waiter will recognize you as the salt of the earth, and he may suggest a double Akvavit, for efficiency and economy. Not a bad idea.

Mousse of liver, cold roast beef, cold roast duck and chicken, melon (it could be riper) and an excellent smoked ham are good reasons for a third trip (very good with beer and Akvavit). Avoid the half-dozen hot foods, because they range from bad to worse. At this point one may decide to repeat one or two previously eaten items, or ease into dessert with some strawberry preserve and cottage cheese on plate number four. Desserts proper are served at your table, and they include a delectable apple concoction with whipped cream and sweetened pastry crumbs, a light lemon chiffon and a chocolate mousse, all served by the waiters in gigantic platefuls.

At lunchtime the menu that one is handed does not mention the availability of smørrebrød, but many of the customers are seen eating open-faced sandwiches. The waiter must be asked for the smørrebrød list—a slip of paper on which you check off your selections. The selection is meager, by Danish standards, and outrageously expensive by any standards, but the sandwiches are excellent. They are decoratively composed by the artist in the kitchen, who always begins by covering the bread with a half-inch layer of butter.

Many of the sandwiches are of items available at the buffet, but there are several additional interesting possibilities: the good smoked salmon with scrambled egg; a little tartar steak with egg yolk, capers, horseradish, onions and beets, which is sensational; seasoned roast veal, reclining under aspic and onion rings; and cold roast duck with beets, prunes, orange, apple and red cabbage. It's quite amazing to see how successfully so many items are combined on a normal-sized slice of bread. Simpler sandwiches of Blue cheese, egg-and-tomato, and so on, are also available.

Copenhagen has an extensive list of hot foods on its menu, but they are generally of less interest than the cold buffet and smørrebrød. There is a boiled codfish, with mustard sauce and horseradish, which is apparently heaven to a Dane but slightly stupefying to anyone else; and Danish fricadeller, the national dish of Denmark— meatballs served with red cabbage and potatoes—which is also mainly for the homesick.

Three kinds of Carlsberg beer available: light, dark and elephant. Décor is *nouveau* Danish Bronx, with gold banquettes. No pipe smoking.

★ CZECHOSLOVAK PRAHA

1358 First Avenue (at 73rd Street)
LUNCH AND DINNER.
Reservations, YU 8–3505.
Credit cards: AE.
Medium-priced.

There are three well-known Czechoslovakian restaurants in the Seventies near First and Second avenues. Ruc is rustic; Vašata is like a comfortable European upper-middle-class café; Czechoslovak Praha is the most Americanized of the three—soft lights, carpeting, golden draperies, a separate barroom with (color) TV, plastic flowers (tulips and daisies). The main dining room is dominated by a huge black-and-white engraving of the city of Prague. If you don't want to look at that, there are two tables at the front windows, and you can look at First Avenue. Sometimes there is music, and if you make arrangements you can have "Happy Birthday" played (not sung) by a duet of one stout man on accordion and one thin one who plays a huge metal clarinet that sounds like a tenor saxophone. Notwithstanding the slightly vulgar touches, this is a comfortable and well-run place. The bad taste is the kind of bad taste that is in good taste, the kitchen turns out food in the kind of good taste that tastes good, and the service is winning. The customers, as in all the Middle European restaurants in this neighborhood, relax into the ways of the old country—the talk is polite, and when the food comes, there is much less of the talk.

The delicious headcheese, mostly tongue, in a firm and cool jelly that is heavily peppered and herbed, is served with minced onions and garnishes of olives, small tomatoes and radishes. It's unthinkable (well, a mistake) not to accompany this stuff with the superb beer from Czechoslovakia (Pilsner Urquell) which is on tap out by the TV. The beer is just as good with what is called Prague ham, but the ham, though it may be from Prague, is not the smoky, fat-rimmed thing you get at Vašata—it is just OK. An experienced restaurant goer will read Eggs à la Praha and smugly say to himself, "A lot of fuss about a couple of hard-cooked eggs." Wrong. It's true about the eggs, but the salad of chopped ham and pickles in mayonnaise, with a couple of slices of lemon squeezed over it, is sparkling and appetizing; there is no question but that it is made daily because there isn't a trace of that held-in-the-fridge flavor which ruins many mayonnaise salads. There is a similar salad, called Gypsy Salad, which is just as good—coarsely chopped beef, chicken, green peppers and onions in mayonnaise.

At the coarsest, but by no means lowest, level of main courses, there is a suggestive Czechoslovak Sausage Platter. You are served up three firm cylinders: number one is Jirtnice—pale, hot, moist and vibrant; then comes Klobasa—red and very potent; the third is Debrecinka—spicy, fatty and explosive. Of course you'll want beer. For something more relaxing there is Boiled Beef with Dill Sauce, one of the best boiled beef dishes around, in that the meat is not poached to extinction—it is served, oddly, off the bone, in thin slices. It is tender, but still textured and tasty, and it comes with a creamy sauce that is infused with a powerful flavor of fresh dill and parsley. Up the scale of culinary refinement by a degree, to what the menu calls Rabbits in Cream Sauce —peppered joints of rabbit in a slightly tart sauerbraten-type sauce, with caraway. You eat the extra sauce on slabs of bread dumpling. And finally, to the pinnacle—roast goose, with a crinkly skin, firm dark meat and a pitcher of strong consommé to liven it up as you slowly work your way through the huge portion.

The vaunted fruit dumpling dessert is a comedown—a canned peach in a dumpling under a mixture of sugar and cottage cheese or sugar and poppy seeds. It is heavy stuff, but it would be good anyway if the fruit inside had any character; the menu reads Fruit Dumpling *in Season*—we learn from this that canned peaches have a season. The strudels are pretty good—poppy-seed strudel, or nut strudel, or apple strudel; the pastry is flaky, the fillings are moist and fresh, and they are sprinkled with powdered sugar.

★★ THE DARDANELLES

86 University Place (near 12th Street)
LUNCH, MONDAY TO SATURDAY; DINNER, DAILY.
Reservations, CH 2–8990.
Credit cards: AE, CB, DC, MC.
Inexpensive.

There are only a handful of Armenian restaurants in New York, and they are all pretty good. They look very much the same—like a Hollywood notion of a middle-class Arabian living room. Serious art (framed prints of mosques), red broadloom, wood paneling, brass sconces with dim amber lights and textured wallpaper are typical. The Dardanelles goes all the way. The restaurant is just as conventional in its menu—authentic Armenian food, all right, and mostly well prepared, but selected, and in some instances modified, for the local palate.

The best of the familiar appetizers here are the fassoulia poulaki (crunchy white beans, lots of dill, stewed carrots and celery, all in plenty of thin oil), cheese boerek (a warm appetizer of a strong egg-and-cheese mixture, with parsley, in a flaky pastry) and enguinar (the heart and core of artichokes, in the shape of large mushrooms, cooked in oil with onions and carrots; the artichokes are firm and soft, and they take on the flavors of the vegetables they were cooked with). But the chickpea spread (homus) is terribly bland, the stuffed mussels are greasy and absurdly overflavored with cinnamon, and the cold stuffed grape leaves are wilted, with a mushy and sugary filling of rice and pine nuts. The hot yogurt soup is good, but no mint at all would be better than the dried mint used here (and everywhere else).

There is at least one outstanding dish which you will not find in many other Armenian restaurants. It is called harpout keufta, and is a mixture of spicy ground lamb and pine nuts shaped into balls and rolled in cracked wheat before cooking, and served in a thick and strong meat broth. There is an excellent baked lamb shank, tender and not stringy, and a very good chopped-lamb dish called Scarra Keufta—two broiled banana-sized patties served with cracked wheat and rice. If you ask for Lulé Kebab, you get the same dish, but powerfully and deliciously flavored with red pepper. Of course there is shish kebab, made with tomatoes, onions and green peppers; better lamb is served elsewhere, but this is good.

The usual desserts are above average here. The baklava is served slightly warm—the walnuts and almonds are crunchy, the pastry crisp, and the honey clear and pure.

There is a very rich ekmek kadayiff, an overwhelmingly sweet pastry made by baking toasted bread in honey; it is served with kaymak, the concentrated cream of the Middle East. This cream has no sugar in it, and is composed of butterfat and milk solids—its dry flavor and texture are the perfect complement to honeyed desserts. The Armenian coffee is one delicious gulp from a tiny cup.

The waiters here, at first impression, look like TV Arabs—smooth and sinister. They are, in fact, mostly young students, eager, polite, helpful. On Friday and Saturday evenings there is an oud player or two. They also wail softly. Very nice.

When busy, this is a festive restaurant, and it gets its share of the Village's diverse populace (impoverished poets explaining economics to their middle-class girl friends, who are paying; members of the N.Y.U. faculty debating the meaning of tenure in a discontinued department).

★★ GAYLORD

50 East 58th Street
LUNCH, MONDAY TO FRIDAY; DINNER, DAILY.
Reservations, PL 9–1710.
Credit cards: AE, BA, CB, DC, MC.
Medium-priced.

New York seems to expect a kind of economic authenticity in its restaurants of foreign cuisine. If a country is not among the so-called advanced nations, its New York restaurants must be cheap and seedy. Consider, for example, the Spanish Pavilion and Toledo, posh Spanish restaurants, now both defunct, while a couple of dozen comparatively grubby Spanish restaurants have survived, in some instances thrived, for years. Notice that grandeur in Chinese restaurants was accepted only when it became generally recognized that China was not a nation of starving peasants and scrawny coolies.

Oblivious to this law, an international chain of high-class Indian restaurants has taken on the New York market. They have made it in Bombay, Delhi, Hong Kong, Kobe, London and Chicago, which is enough to give anyone confidence. But will New Yorkers support an Indian restaurant while the sub-continent is economically substandard? Sub-likely.

Gaylord is a luxuriously and colorfully appointed place. The main dining room is rimmed with plump comfortable sofas; the chairs that face them from the other side of the ample tables are high-backed and covered with pale-blue, soft wool. At your place there is a giant plate of gleaming brass. There are chandeliers of the same polished metal. Hanging along the cloth-covered walls are tall macramé lamps of pale string interwoven with patterns of brilliant color. In between there are panels of hanging beads with, behind them, back-lighted, translucent pictures of Indians doing Indian things.

The place is frequented by moneyed Indians, and if there are enough of those in New York, they may be able to carry the restaurant. Moneyed Indians, apparently, are accustomed to extremely polite but very leisurely service, which is the only kind anyone gets here. You will be treated very well, but not necessarily right away. When he comes, however, the captain (or whatever his Indian title is) will explain the menu to you patiently and informatively, and if you have already made your selections and he considers them badly matched, he will tell you so, and why. Then he goes away, and you nurse your wine, and you nurse it and nurse it. The quality of the food you finally get indicates that it is made to your order, which explains the delay; and if you are sitting near the front of the dining room, you can watch it being made—there is a windowed wall, behind which a couple of men in white kitchen linen, their skins gleaming, their performances enveloped in clouds of steam and smoke, prepare some of your dinner. The glass is soundproof, and their labors are like mime.

If you are a sampler, you may begin here with the Special Indian Hors d'Oeuvres, which will provide you with a taste of samosa—a deep-fried pastry filled with fresh peas and potatoes; of pakora (which is a generic term for vegetables that are coated with a paste of chickpeas, and deep-fried) made with ripe plantains (big bananas to you), very sweet and moist; of shami kebab, spicy patties of ground lamb; and of papadum, a crisp, spiced wafer of fried unrisen bread. None of the food here is particularly spicy, but it has an unmistakable quality of authenticity—it has character, singularity. These first courses, though you may find them in more potent versions in other Indian restaurants, do not seem to be compromised for the American palate. They seem, rather, to be refined urban versions of strong Indian food.

There is an extensive assortment of main courses at Gaylord, including very good versions of some of the most familiar Indian dishes. The Tandoori Chicken is bright red, moist, firm, with the nice flavor of the edges being slightly burnt. The Boti Kebab (skewered lamb) is of cubes of meat that have been marinated in curd, onions and spices, and broiled with raw onions—very good. A quite different lamb dish is the one called Lamb Pasanda—the meat is marinated in yogurt and stewed in cream with sweet spices, mainly cinnamon—very, but not excessively, rich.

There is an item on the menu called Tandoori Prawns. This is a bastardized dish, because seafood is not part of the original tandoori cooking, but that should not bother you, particularly as this illegitimacy seems to have been the result of love. The prawns have been marinated in herbs, they are oily and slightly spicy, though their brilliant redness makes you expect something hotter than what you get, and they are coolly garnished with minced onions, cucumbers and tomatoes.

The dish called Chicken Bhuna Masala seems Western, which should not prevent you from trying it. The chicken is stewed in an herbed sauce of vegetables, dominated by tomato—the flavors are strong without being spicy, as of fresh vegetables and herbs highly concentrated.

With all of these things, one may choose from an assortment of side dishes: Special Indian Pickles are inflamed zucchini—it is not necessary to actually eat them, just wave them around to clear the air. The paratha here is not the rich deep-fried bread you get in most of New York's Indian restaurants—this version is comparatively dry and may seem tasteless if you have come to like the oilier kind. The nan, which is the closest Indian bread to Western bread, in that it is baked (and then lightly browned), looks nice, long and puffed, but is rather bland.

The desserts are like candies. For $1.50, the menu informs you, you make "Selection from Trolly (Any two pieces)." The man wheels over the trolly and you point to Rasgalla and promptly regret having been seduced by the pretty little balls that taste precisely like chalk in rose water, which is close to what they are. You try the pistachio candy, an excellent heavy pistachio-dominated nut cake—much better.

If you have eaten highly flavored food, a thoughtful man may come around and offer you dried anise and cardamom seeds. Hold out your hand, and he will spoon some into the palm. You place them on the impeccable cloth before you and meditatively chew them as you talk, fancying yourself all the while a philosophical Indian with all the time in the world. The seeds *are* refreshing.

★ INAGIKU

111 East 49th Street (Waldorf Astoria Hotel)
LUNCH, MONDAY TO FRIDAY; DINNER, DAILY.
Reservations, 355–0440.
Credit cards: AE, BA, CB, DC, MC.
Expensive.

Marriott Japan, with rice paper and red carpeting. Instead of the Grille Room or the Pub Club, we have the Kinkaku Room, Hida Room, Hakone Room, Kamakura Room, Imperial Room and Nikko Room. However, you wait for your table in the Cocktail Lounge, where, just as in the old country, the bar is lined with swivel stools, and the little cocktail tables are surrounded by deep armchairs. And just as in the good old USA, when the waiters and waitresses crowd around the service bar, waiting to pick up drinks, there is a bit of covert grabbing and overt giggling to while away the moments. The dim referents of the various rooms are a shrine, a farmhouse, a Japanese inn, a forest resort, but from the gilded beams and walls to the tables with trap doors in the center (which, when removed, reveal apparatuses for at-table cooking) to the jewel-like odds and ends on the tables, to the kimonos on the waitresses, the whole thing is Hollywood. If you don't believe it, get a load, if you are of the correct gender, of the holy urns that are set aside for your precious bodily fluids in the men's room.

To which, of course, are drawn our city's visitors, commuters by day, conventioneers by night. Inagiku is a pocket of un–New York in the heart of the city, a refuge for those who come here but whose hearts are in the sticks. Male diners must wear jackets and ties—one wonders what treatment a kimonoed male would receive.

There is some confusion about where you eat what. The Kinkaku Room ("The artistic centerpiece of the new Inagiku, this golden-canopied room evokes the splendor of the famed Golden Pavilion Shrine (Kinkakuji) that was constructed in 1424 . . .") is where you eat tempura, at a large, circular tempura bar; the Hida Room (". . . recalls the traditional Japanese farmhouse of a thousand years ago"), which is popularly referred to as the Steak Room, is where you eat, you guessed it, steak, as well as broiled chicken and fish, served on wooden paddles at a little bar. In the rest of the place you can order anything at all, and, idiocies aside, the food is good, sometimes very good.

Of the lighter foods that are pushed at lunchtime, there are excellent sashimi, impeccably fresh raw fish with the usual seasonings, and a singular delicacy of fish roe on seaweed which is moist, cool, salty and grainy. Suonomo is a light and appetizing little dish of vinegared cucumbers and crabmeat, with lemon—sparkling. The tempura (deep-fried shellfish and vegetables) is prepared of fresh shrimp or lobster, crisp zucchini and other veggies. The lobster is sweet meat, but this shellfish does not lend itself as well as shrimp to the tempura treatment, particularly at Inagiku, where the frying medium is weighted heavily to peanut oil, the nutlike flavor of which is good with shrimp but obscures the lobster. At noontime you can give yourself a good introduction to this restaurant by ordering Shokazen, an assortment of meats and seafood served in a compartmented tray. It includes very good chicken teriyaki, charcoaled and oily; cool chunks of moist duck; slices of powerfully salted fish, moistened with soy sauce and garnished with bright orange strands of fresh ginger; sausages of gummy, spiced rice, to be dipped in either the spicy soy sauce or the sweet one; garnishes of intensely flavored pickles.

At night the menu is dotted with items the authenticity of which is dubious. You can usually determine whether a dish is local or imported by whether the name of it is given in English or in transliterated Japanese. Steamed Clams, for example, though steamed in sake and scallions, and fairly tasty, is an invention for native tastes, and the clams are rather large and tough. There is even a Japanese Surf & Turf, styled Inagiku Special, and described as "The finest cut of aged sirloin in strips, with tender selections of lobster broiled as only Inagiku does it . . ." Whatever you order, you get a bowl of salad—iceberg and red cabbage. The broiled beef dishes are of excellent meat, the sukiyaki of the same meat and good vegetables, artfully prepared at your table—the latter may be the thing to have, because delivered platters of food at dinnertime are often cold in this very busy place.

Naturally, you will wish to conclude your dinner with Green Tea Ice Cream.

★★ JACQUES' TIK TAK

210 East 58th Street
LUNCH AND DINNER.
Reservations, 753–5513.
Credit cards: AE, DC.
Medium-priced.

Several decades ago the city was favored to have dozens of restaurants that were open several hours past midnight. Usually there was music, and often the kitchen would take orders right up to closing hours. These were cafélike places, noisy and gay. Often there was dancing, and often the clientele was predominantly of one European national extraction, and most customers were well-known to most of the other customers— every night was reunion night. The new Tik Tak is attempting a revival of that tradition, complete with late hours and live music. But in an effort to appeal to more of the city's population than just its Hungarians, the management has sacrificed the very thing that gave those old places character—a consistent national flavor, from the appointments to the music to the food to the waiters. The new Tik Tak serves Hungarian food, but that is as far as it goes. The place looks like the dining room of a Colonial motel; the waiters, often as not, have little understanding of the menu; and the music is cocktail-lounge piano, belted out by a dark-skinned lady who probably doesn't know a gypsy air from a balalaika.

If you frequented the old Tik Tak, you will recognize your host, Jacques. He will assure you that his mother, who, he says, ran the kitchen in the old place, is still with him and is still in charge of the cooking. He gets around to saying this so often in the course of a brief conversation that you soon suspect a fabrication.

You suspect it again when you are served the little dishes of vinagered cucumbers that arrive with the bread and butter in almost all of New York's Hungarian restaurants. This version is excessively sweet and watery, when it should be sour. But you may request the alternative coleslaw, and you get a dish of superbly crisp shredded cabbage accented with bits of red and green peppers.

Then there is the food you pay for, from a menu that is almost an exact replica of the old one, including the fabulous first course of brains and eggs, and it is the unmistakable moist amalgam of chopped brains and very lightly scrambled eggs, made slightly hot with a healthy dose of strong paprika—exceptional food. The stuffed green peppers are filled with spicy meat and rice, and they are served in a thick red tomato sauce that is sweet-and-sour of lemon and sugar—a meaty dish. Tik Tak also offers an item entitled Mushroom Fritters, served with something referred to as Sauce Tartar. The dish is not kind to the potential of mushrooms—they are breaded and deep-fried and served with a mayonnaise that has been sweetened and then thinned with lemon. The elements simply do not add up.

Much is made of the Erdelyi Fatanyeros (served for two) at a mere $18.50. The collection of breaded-and-fried meats and grilled sausages arrives as an edifice on an armature of skewers, the tower of meats on a foundation of fried potatoes, surrounded by that coleslaw, pickles and tomatoes. This food is so heavy, it may well seem more Czechoslovakian than Hungarian. The sausages, slits in their crackling casing, are dark-brown, juicy, spicy and lightly blackened; the veal, originally tender and pale, is overwhelmed by a heavy breading which you may wish to peal away to get at the delicate stuff within; cutlets of chicken, chicken livers and pork chops all get the same leaden treatment. One of the best items on the plate is the potatoes—well-browned, slightly greasy and heavily salted; at a diner they would be called home fries.

The old Tik Tak was noted for its stuffed roasted chicken. This one is pretty good, its cavity filled with a moist stuffing of bread crumbs and chicken livers bound together with egg. But the original was browned to a rather miraculous extreme without drastically overcooking the meat under the skin, and the stuffing was more potently spiced, giving it strong character, if no finesse. This is simply a safe version of the original. The Veal Shank is braised and roasted, to the point where it, too, sports a well-browned crust, but the meat within, like much roasted veal, is virtually tasteless.

If the old place had one specialty more important than another it was the house onions, variously called baked onions or fried onions, and in this dish the new Tik Tak is the equal of the old. They regularly accompany some of the main courses, but you ought to order a big plate of them whether the food you choose comes with onions or not. The onions are served in thin threadlike circlets, lightly battered, and fried to a point of browned, airy sweetness—none is ever left on the plate.

For dessert there are, of course, strudels, including a warm, heavily lemoned cheese strudel in a flaky crust, sprinkled with fine sugar. And, of course, there are palacsintas, the Hungarian crêpes here served with fillings of a warm apricot preserve, or with cheese and raisins; if you wish, you can have one of each in the regular serving of two —they are both elegant sweets.

Wines are something of a problem. The best wines on the list are the French ones, and they are ridiculously overpriced. The best Hungarian table wine is only OK, but reasonably priced. The thing to do is to drink beer or nothing during your dinner, and then drink sweet Hungarian Tokay with dessert. The Tokay is crisp, strong and exhilarating.

When most of the tables are taken and the air is filled with smoke and conversation and the lights have been turned down, the place may remind you of those old Lower East Side cafés. But unfortunately the customers do not know the parts they are playing, and the place empties out at around midnight, just when the gaiety should be starting up.

• MYKONOS

349 West 46th Street
LUNCH, WEDNESDAY AND SATURDAY; DINNER, MONDAY TO SATURDAY.
Closed Sunday.
Reservations, 265–1590.
Credit cards: AE, CB, DC, MC.
Expensive.

It is said that the customers at Mykonos dance in the aisles. Not true. What is observed are the convulsions characteristic of noise shock. (This diagnosis is proven by the fact that when the noise stops, the convulsions stop too.) Said noise is germinated by humans having at a piano, an organ, drums and bouzoukis, magnified by electronic amplification equipment and delivered by *eight* loudspeakers in a room in which an un-plugged-in strolling violinist could be obtrusive.

Though Mykonos is expert in the generation of good noise, it is not so consistently successful in the preparation of food. There are a number of very good Greek first courses: a rather subtle avgolemono, made with well-flavored chicken stock, just a little lemon and—surprise!—finely minced carrots; a very light, yet strongly roe-flavored taramosalata (the pink paste of red roe and moistened bread); and superb hot stuffed vine leaves filled with ground lamb and rice, flavored with mint, and covered with a velvety and thick avgolemono sauce, much more lemony than the soup. The vine leaves themselves are superior to the ones you get in most Greek restaurants in that they have a leafy taste, not unlike spinach.

There are two appetizer assortments. The cold one is called Mykonos Special, and is billed as "a variety of Greek delicacies." Among them is a slice of eel reminiscent of a fish market at closing time, but the rest of the platter—a nickel's worth of feta cheese, a tablespoonful of vegetables in mayonnaise, a couple of inches of octopus, one (1) olive, a smidgin of eggplant spread, and a golf ball of taramosalata—is pretty good. The trouble is that if you find anything you really like, you eliminated it in the finding, and if you don't like any of it, you are stuffed anyway. The hot assortment, called Mykonos Taverna, is a mélange of chicken livers, sausages (cocktail frank), sweetbreads and hard-boiled eggs served in a (salty) gravy. This serves to convert the diverse items into a dish—very hearty, and it makes a very adequate lunch.

Listed under roasts is something called Arnaki Galakto Souvlas, which is described as "roast baby lamb country style." Give us, please, city style, where the lamb is crisp outside with a bit of blood within. Here the lamb seems braised rather than roasted, it is gray and the flavor has been cooked out. It is served with string beans fresh out of the can. There is Kalamarakia, which is deep-fried squid (the little squids arrive in great numbers on your plate, tentacles entwined, all happily crisp). The moussaka here is rather dreadful—overwhelmed by allspice, topped by tasteless custard, filled with greasy ground lamb, and with only the thinnest layers of eggplant. If you hate Greek food but dig sound (have you heard "Granada" sung by a Greek contralto with bouzouki accompaniment?), there are plenty of simple broilings on the menu.

The usual nut and honey desserts are here, augmented by Flogera, a tube of crisp filo pastry filled with what an otherwise brilliant wit described as custard's last stand.

This is a handsome restaurant. The main dining room has a wine-colored ceiling with huge wooden beams, Greek folk murals in the great arches along the walls, and jutting out from one wall and extending over a number of the tables, a life-size buxom lady from a ship's bow. (People keep looking up.)

If you want simply to hear the music, not feel it, there is a small dining room, called the taverna, at the very front of the restaurant and separated from the main dining room by a broad tunnel in which there is a bar on one side, and on the other, a display of the owner's records—she sings. The taverna is dark (the main room is brightly lighted) and paneled in the manner of a hunting lodge; there are candles on the tables and a white stucco mock fireplace adorned with Greek pottery.

The prices in this restaurant are simply crazy—not only after nine o'clock, when the so-called entertainment has begun, but all the time. And the special lower-priced table d'hôte lunches and dinners offer little real selection.

★ NIPPON

145 East 52nd Street
LUNCH, MONDAY TO FRIDAY; DINNER, MONDAY TO SATURDAY.
Closed Sunday.
Reservations, PL 8–0226.
Credit cards: AE, CB, DC, MC.
Expensive.

An order of sashimi, at $4, consists of a small slice of raw squid, one of snapper, and two of striped bass. "This is four dollars?" you ask the waitress. "Yes, because the chef cuts it. You can get it for two dollars at another restaurant, but this is the best *expensive* restaurant." This is uttered with such bright-eyed, innocent enthusiasm that it's several moments before you fully realize that any pursuit of the subtle conundrum germinated by this exchange could lead to more inquiry and explication than you're willing to undertake across a cultural barrier. This may well be the Cadillac of Japanese restaurants in New York—solid and expensive—but it is not the best place for the raw fish dishes. The prices are bizarre, and the fish is not invariably served at that point of sweet freshness past which delicate Occidental olfaction takes offense.

But the cooked food here is so uniformly well made that there are any number of good reasons to visit this popular place. The small order of tempura which the menu suggests you have with your drinks consists of shrimp, fish, green peppers and onions, lightly battered and rapidly fried in hot oil, and each item is in crisp condition. The consommé is available with a selection of added garnitures. The broth itself is hot, clear, faintly flavored, and you can have it with crisp broccoli, firm and slightly rubbery abalone, carrots, and so on.

You may be shocked to see that the Japanese casseroles are cooked right at your table in Corning Ware, on a hot plate, but this does not Westernize the food. One of these dishes, called Hama Nabe, is a stout stew of fresh clams, chunks of bean curd the size of children's blocks, mushrooms, onions and scallions. When you have finished with the solid contents of the pot, you may feel a wee bit unsatisfied, but when you have asked for bowls and drunk the heavy broth, all will be well.

Most of the American customers look at the menu with dismay and end up ordering one of the house dinners, in which the main courses are sukiyaki, teriyaki, yakitori or one of the other Japanese dishes they have eaten before. Turn the page and you will find the à la carte menu, where there are listed such comparative New York rarities as Uni-Yaki (broiled seasoned squid, served with strong pickled ginger), and Shichimi-Yaki (marinated chicken that has been seasoned with red pepper, sprinkled with sesame seeds, and broiled until very crisp and almost black). There are a number of good side dishes too: if you have gotten past the mental block (now, don't deny it) between you and raw fish, perhaps you're ready for raw chicken. Torisashi is just that—the un-cooked, pink chicken meat is sweet and moist, served with cold spinach and shredded roots. If you really are in the mood for culture shock, order a box of Yakinori, which is thin, dried seaweed, several blackish-green sheets of it, each the size of a calling card; its strange, metallic taste is rather marvelous. All this, with the excellent beer from Japan called Kirin, can make a splendid meal.

Nippon is a sprawling restaurant with bare tables close together, rice-paper lamps, a sushi bar, and to your left as you enter, a small bar and lounge, entered over a little bridge, under hanging branches—this was built to the scale of the builders, so keep your head down. At the rear there are tatami rooms where you may eat while sitting on the floor. (Except on weekends, about half the customers here are Japanese, and they, who know a good thing, seem to prefer chairs.) It's more fun than a circus to watch the pink-skinned experimenters on the floor discover that they seem to have an extra thigh.

Parts of the menu are not translated, so naturally, those are the parts you want to know about, but as a blurb at the front of the menu explains, the menu is prepared to emphasize dishes that "are most popular with Americans." How are the other dishes going to become popular if they are kept secret? Most of the waitresses here have difficulty explaining in English the exact nature of the untranslated dishes. They can't all be porgy.

★ PARKWAY

163 Allen Street (near Stanton Street)
DINNER ONLY.
Closed Monday.
Reservations, 575–0612.
No credit cards.
Medium-priced.

The Parkway and its admirers strain for the past, one that is largely unremem-bered, at that. This restaurant is an archeological reconstruction rather than the survi-vor of a tradition, no matter how directly it can trace its provenance to a real Rumanian Jew's real Rumanian-Jewish restaurant on New York's once-mainly-Jewish Lower East Side. The food here is for real, and jollity is jollity, but the culture is moribund, if not dead, its assimilated descendants scattered, and the feasts and celebrations and evenings out are larky, contrived, "something different," not a natural aspect of the lives of the people who come here.

So if you think you can get a glimpse of Moskowitz & Lupowitz or the Café Imperial, where the plump, blue-haired, bejeweled and minked ladies danced with one another while their spouses loosened their collars, lit up huge cigars and regaled themselves with blue stories, forget it. Nor will you be greeted by an eccentric host or served by one of those fabled heartwarmingly brusque, blasé and overbearing Old Country waiters. The Parkway is a museum, so the products may be genuine but the people in charge are merely curators. The proprietor is of such patrician mien and faraway look that he startles you when he doctors your chopped chicken liver with radishes and chicken fat with his own hands; his spouse is cool Viennese elegance, and she will dance with a lady the same day the Pope does; and there is a waiter here whose pug nose, pink hair, erect stance and laborious politesse are to a traditional Jewish waiter what Bushmill's is to cream soda.

But the recipes are in the public domain, the ingredients available; and museums, after all, cannot be faulted for displaying the teepee but not the rain dance.

Many of the best things at the Parkway are free. You are presented with great bowls of pickles: pickled red and green tomatoes, pickled peppers, all exceedingly tart, sweet and garlicked, and all very stimulating. You accompany them with rye bread that is fresh and moist in its crackling crust and with the carbonated water (seltzer) that is served in big pitchers. The bread may be smeared with butter, but the knowing eschew that for the chicken fat (schmaltz) that is served in little pitchers—schmaltz is to butter what a malted milk is to coconut milk.

The stuff you pay for includes, to begin, the famous Chopped Chicken Liver, which is soft, rich, peppery, garlicked, and adequately soaked with chicken fat when you get it. However, the boss may decide he likes you, and he will, right at your place, just the way your mother did when you broke both your hands, add *more* schmaltz, as well as slivered white radishes, and greeven (browned strands of skin that are a pungent by-product of the process of rendering chicken fat), which converts the sturdy food into something that is almost overwhelmingly succulent. Then there is the eggplant, which is simply chopped baked eggplant until you (or the boss) improve it with raw onions, perhaps, or radishes, or the greeven, or lemon, or combinations thereof. For something more elemental but equally rich, there are cold sliced brains—three thick slabs, and you eat them straight. And for something comparatively dietetic, there is pitcha, cold calf's feet in jelly—an acquired taste, but if you have already acquired it (it can be acquired at the Russian Tea Room, where a more refined version is called kholodetz) you will find nothing to fault in these.

The main courses will require a bit of discrimination, for though they are all leaden, some are nothing more. For example, the Broiled Chicken Livers and Unborn Eggs suffers from an overcooking of the livers that is somehow managed without even browning them, and a dozen and a half (count 'em) of the rather tasteless egg yolks that are good as a stray textural surprise in a plate of chicken soup, but as nothing else. The fried onions help. If there are four of you, or if there are fewer of you and you wish to train for a gluttony competition, you may order the Mixed Grill, which includes the aforementioned chicken-liver-and-unborn-egg thing as well as Rumanian steak— a fibrous cut, garlicked and hearty; sweetbreads—heavy and greasy, their delicate flavor lost in the company of . . . ; Karnatzlach—an overwhelmingly garlicked broiled sausage; and duck that is not your usual duck—it is broiled until charred, but with almost no loss of fat, which is quite a combination.

There is boiled beef—a gigantic portion of the wet gray meat served with either red or white horseradish, which are, respectively, hot and very hot. There are side dishes —varnishkes, which are noodles mixed with the buckwheat cereal known as kasha, all heavily buttered; and there are kreplach, bland meat-stuffed noodle pillows. Pass up the potato pancakes (latkes)—they are greasy and almost tasteless.

The desserts vary from not bad to bad—the fruit strudel, with nuts and spicy and hard candied fruit, is probably the best; the apricot Jell-O a curiosity; the mousse an atrocity.

The Parkway is an eclectic place, with marbleized mirrors, plastic walls, Chinese-restaurant chandeliers, draperies, a candelabrum on the piano.

★ RED TULIP

250 East 83rd Street
DINNER.
Closed Monday and Tuesday.
Reservations, 650–0537.
Credit cards: AE, BA.
Beer and wine.
Inexpensive.

There is a sameness about the good Hungarian restaurants in the East Seventies and Eighties. They are invariably the kind of place one would expect to find in Budapest: this one on a fancy boulevard, that one in a workingmen's neighborhood—they are all city restaurants.

A mutation has appeared—a place that is like a peasant's house in the countryside. There are whitewashed walls, a few feet of thatched roof poking into the room from one side of the ceiling, a floor of simulated red tiles, hanging plants, colorful plates and jugs on the walls, bare wooden tables (but for a few that are covered with brilliant-striped cloths under glass tops). The restaurant is neat and clean without being the least bit antiseptic, like an immaculately kept farmhouse. All this is to the good, and some of the food is to the good also, but not all of it, and there is a certain amount of bungling in the management of the dining room that may make you laugh if it fails to make you cry.

As it may be difficult to learn about the menu from the help, here's a guide:

The first courses are the best things in the house, and fortunately, large portions of some of them also serve as main courses, so you may be well advised to order your entire dinner from the upper left-hand corner of the menu, starting, possibly, with what is accurately described as "chilled, creamy, sour cherry soup"—it has a quality, actually, of tenderness, of fruit that is *just* ripe. For something at the other end of the soup continuum there is Gulyas Soup—a strong, beefy broth with chunks of meat in it, flavored with the heavily perfumed paprika used almost nowhere but in these Middle European restaurants. The Hungarian sausage is like an improved model of your kosher frank—made with good meat, plenty of garlic, and tasty fat. It comes in a casing that seems to be crackling from the intensity of flavors within, and it is served with red horseradish, white horseradish, and mustard that is not merely strong but also a little wild. The stuffed pepper is unfortunately served in a tomato sauce that is intolerably sweet, so don't order it. Order instead the inspired Chicken Liver Red Tulip, which consists of chicken livers sautéed with mushrooms, onions and green peppers, in the fragrant fat you get from the chicken itself. (This is also available as a main dish, and fanatics are permitted to have it first and second.)

But we have a problem here with these main courses. The Veal Shank is described as being "crisped in smoked bacon with mushrooms," which it may be, but it has a raw, inappropriately gamy quality, as if it were almost beef. On occasion the delicious pot roast is simply tough. The paprika chicken is good, though undistinguished, and the Lamb Paprikas Cooked in Red Wine is simply a dull stew in which neither the obscure wine nor the abundant red pepper seems to do anything for the meat. But don't fret. Simply order the Stuffed Chicken, filled with its own Liver, Mushrooms and Fresh Herbs, an apt description, and go home happy—the ample bird is crisp, and the stuffing, which utterly fills the half chicken, is moist, spicy and heady.

For dessert, have palacsintas (the famous Hungarian crêpes), which come filled with chopped walnuts (ground fine and mixed with sugar), or with poppy seeds (also mixed with sugar—these are the seeds of singular flavor which taste something like caraway, very slightly like anise, but really like nothing else), or with cheese or apricot jam. The odd Hungarian dessert of sweetened noodles (sweetened with the walnut or poppy-seed mixture, or with the apricot jam) is also very delicious, but for non-Hungarians it's usually simply a bizarre way to conclude dinner. Avoid the palacsintas filled with chocolate and rum and flamed—too much rum, it tastes like a cocktail. And the chestnut purée with whipped cream somehow lacks the outrageous richness that is needed for this dish to work—the flavor is there, but not the assault.

★★ RUC

312 East 72nd Street
LUNCH, SATURDAY AND SUNDAY; DINNER, DAILY.
Reservations, 650–1611.
Credit cards: AE, CB, DC.
Medium-priced.

New York's Middle European restaurants are among the most reliable eating places in town. It's almost impossible to get a bad meal in the Hungarian restaurants that line Second Avenue between 72nd and 86th streets, and the three Czechoslovakian restaurants in the lower Seventies are even better. When you're looking for a change from the familiar round of steakhouses and French and Italian restaurants, think of these places—not only is the food good, and the service positively courtly, but there is a feeling of such contentedness among the well-fed, superbly bourgeois customers that it's easy to forget whatever problems you bring into these adult fairylands.

Ruc seems to be a perfect evocation of home for the members of New York's Czechoslovakian community who regularly eat here. If we can't have Czechoslovakia in Czechoslovakia, they say, well, we'll have Czechoslovakia in New York. And since we are very nice people, we'll even permit these Americans to eat with us.

And lucky you are, because you can have headcheese, for example, a Czechoslovakian specialty—thick, firm slices of chunks of tongue, in jelly, with fresh chopped onions. Or you can have something called Meat Salad Gypsy—a cold mixture of coarsely shredded beef, onions, celery, green peppers and mayonnaise; it's like an excellent chicken salad, but made with red meat. Or you can have ham salad, which is like the Gypsy item, but made with finely minced ham (hold the celery and green peppers), and for an extra 35 cents it comes as Eggs à la Prague; that is, with hard-boiled eggs, a dollop of mayo over the eggs, and a garnish of black caviar.

There are different soups on different days, including an excellent giblet soup, and on other occasions, beef broth with liver dumplings. The dumplings are strong, and just before the hot soup is brought to the table, a large spoonful of chopped parsley is added. When the waiter pours from the silver cup into your large soup dish, you are enveloped by a powerful green aroma.

You won't get goose much better than the goose that Ruc often has on the Sunday menu. The skin is as flaky as a thin pastry, and the juicy and tender meat comes with thick slices of dumpling that you soak in the goose-dripping sauce. On occasion there is Cevabcici—ground veal, pork and beef, with onions and garlic, seasoned, rolled to the shape of sausages, and sautéed until the outside is dark brown and firm. The calf's brains with eggs are a rich, peppery amalgam, obviously done in the marvelous grease you get from ducks and geese. There is a good meat loaf called Prague Roast, and sometimes a roast tenderloin of beef—both are served with an unusual vegetable-based cream sauce that is redolent of celery, carrots and herbs. All the food arrives at your table in good condition; the main courses come with a crisp cucumber salad and either dumplings that are solid and bland, which means they are perfect for soaking up gravy, or else some kind of potatoes. Some of the dishes get this place's amazing sauerkraut; it is apparently cooked for weeks, and is sweet, utterly without acid, at once crisp and tender, and lightly accented with caraway seeds.

Some of the desserts you will not find everywhere. Apricot dumplings, for example, which are apricots, in dumplings, sprinkled with cheese, or with cinnamon, or with bread crumbs, or (best of all) with poppy seeds and sugar. The palacinky here are very good—thin, lightly browned pancakes with apricot preserves. Or if you are really hungry, have an Omelette Confiture—the same preserves in a thin, folded sheet of browned eggs, the whole thing sprinkled heavily with powdered sugar.

The older waiters here are of the European Café School. With napkins over their arms they walk extremely rapidly (they do not run) with their trays from barroom to dining room to kitchen. They make their explanations of the menu breathlessly but patiently. The younger help are blond, pink-cheeked and much admired for their awkward charm.

Ruc is a low-ceilinged place, decorated in plastic Bavarian—suspiciously shiny wood-paneled walls, hanging plates, wagon-wheel chandeliers with lanterns, and so on. The cruder front room holds a bar and three good-sized tables. In the summer this restaurant provides one of the pleasantest places for outdoor dining in New York—a terraced garden under overhanging trees.

Ruc is a good restaurant in which to eat alone, as there is much to see: When was the last time you saw a table of six at which three stout burghers were partnered by three ladies in black velvet hats? Where else are old-fashioned sultry blondes still in fashion, with their cigarette holders and long maroon fingernails? Greta Garbo would be just one of the girls here.

★ SAITO EAST

8 East 49th Street
LUNCH AND DINNER.
Closed Sunday.
Reservations, 758–3114.
Credit cards: AE, BA, CB, DC.
Medium-priced.

For a Japanese restaurant that serves, for the most part, authentic Japanese food, there are some very un-Japanese appearances about this place. What is one to make of the Scandinavian downstairs room, with its wall-to-wall carpeting and armchairs of polished wood and Naugahyde? And what about the upstairs tatami rooms, partitioned off by the kinds of curtains one remembers unhappily from semiprivate hospital rooms? And what of this bartender, he of the unmistakably Japanese features, with his shirt billowing out beneath his dirty vest? And the other bartender—the one behind the sushi bar—who is not very busy at dinner, who occupies himself by crouching in a corner and eating? At least he uses chopsticks.

As in all but the most humble of Japanese restaurants in New York, many of the customers are male Ivy League Japanese middle managers, dressed and tonsured in faithful reproduction of the executive style of fifteen years ago, representing Japanese companies in the United States. Most of these men are in this country without wives, and Japanese restaurants are the social centers of their lives. They come in large groups, in large numbers, as they have been for several years. At Saito the waitresses who serve them have apparently seen them come and go, and have developed an abrupt and slightly contemptuous manner that is in no measure rendered charming by their kimonoed attire; they have adapted the ways of the American hash house to a Japanese restaurant. It's perfectly OK for the Japanese to outperform Americans at everything American, as they seem to be well on their way to doing, but this is ridiculous. Their countrymen pay the waitresses no mind, however, so why should you?—particularly as the food is very good.

Eschew the raw fish—sashimi and sushi—which is good, but it does not have that quality of delicate sweetness you find at some of the places that specialize in those items.

You can order one of the complete dinners, and start with a hot and clear broth. Then, if you proceed to Shabu-Shabu, you may be disappointed to discover that this exotic-sounding and elaborately described dish ("A gourmet's choice," the menu informs you, "a different and delicious," etc.) consists of a platter of sukiyaki ingredients —beef, mushrooms, onions, cabbage, watercress, scallions and bean curd—which you're expected to poach in a pot of boiling broth (water, really, with two slivers of bean curd). Resourceful customers have been known to dismiss the pot, order a pan, and create a perfect sukiyaki on the spot, much to the waitress's annoyance.

You'll probably have better luck if you stick to the à la carte menu. The Oyster Fry, for example, is no bargain at $4 for six oysters, but they are extraordinarily delicate and crisp outside, and sweet and moist within—happily, they use huge oysters. Or you might try the kabayaki—eel, split, broiled until blackened, and served in an enamel box in a shallow pool of soy sauce. This is a strong, almost overpowering dish, and it is likely to heighten your hankering for yet another Kirin beer. You could make a dinner of nothing but the so-called side dishes. There is one called Sakana-No Shiwoyaki which consists of a steak cut of halibut, broiled until crisp with coarse salt, and served with a preserved apricot and tangy, fresh ginger. Another side dish is called Yakinasu—an exceptional order of eggplant (one thick cross section) baked with ginger—powerful flavors. The tempura is splendid—a few shrimp, a bit of fish, and a slice of green pepper, deep-fried in that amazing Japanese way which seems to create a crust out of air.

★★SHALIMAR

39 East 29th Street
LUNCH AND DINNER.
Reservations accepted, 889–1977.
Credit cards: AE, BA, CB, DC, MC.
Inexpensive.

Shalimar is an Indian restaurant situated within an Indian enclave in Manhattan's East Twenties and Thirties. The place is not only a restaurant but something of a community center where Indians congregate, read the pinned-up notices of Indian cultural events, and of course, eat Indian food.

They don't seem to mind the eclecticism of the elements that combine to make up the ambience: the illumination is from those perforated-tin-can lamps that you find in Mexican restaurants; here they hang from a stamped-tin ceiling like the ones you find in old New York saloons; the place is broadloomed; the rough plaster walls are decorated with embedded bits of tile and mirror, in abstract patterns; the background music is sometimes of India and sometimes of other Asian nations. No one cares.

Among the items listed under "Appetizers" are papadums, which are thin deep-fried wafers about the size of dinner plates, with random perforations. The sheets are reddish brown, dry, crisp and salty. They taste like sublime potato chips, though they are made of a bean flour, and they are delicious with the cool relish of spiced raw onions that is brought to every table. Then there is samosa, the triangular pastries that are filled with spiced lamb and deep-fried just before they are served. Despite some strong ingredients, such as garlic, ginger and red pepper, the effect is subtle because the pastry takes the edge off the strong meat filling.

You will want bread, and paratha is a splendid, intensely oily bread of wheat flour fried in clarified butter (ghee). You can have it straight, or you can have a variation called Aloo Paratha which you will probably not like, because you probably will not like a sandwich of oily bread and spicy mashed potatoes. Then again you might. Indians do.

If India has a national dish, it's Chicken Tandoori. This dish is made by marinating whole chickens in saffron, spices (including hot spices) and yogurt, and then roasting them with a coating of clarified butter. This spicy and moist bird is very good with the rather bland purée of lentils called dal that accompanies your dinner in most Indian restaurants.

There is an enormous variety of vegetable cookery in India. Bhindi is a spicy and oily amalgam of onions, tomatoes, okra, salt and spices, fried in ghee. These rich dishes are very good with the cool condiments called raytas. Raytas are combinations of yogurt with one or another fruit or vegetable. The potato rayta is like a very refreshing rather than heavy potato salad; and the cucumber rayta may remind you of cold cucumber soups, except that it has substantial chunks of cucumber in the cool yogurt.

Indian desserts are hard to like, but for the record, something called Rosa Gola is described, in the inflated language of this menu, as "Snow White Succulent Cheese Balls, Rose Water Flavored," which may be translated as chalk balls in rose water. Then there is Gulab Jaman, a pleasant pastry in a thin honey syrup. And there is Firni, a custardlike pudding of rice flour, perfumed with rose water—pretty good.

The waiters are awkward but willing. The menu provides some light reading: "Tipping is usually 15–20% of your bill to cover the services rendered by your waiter. He will appreciate your generosity." "Spices Are Assorted Vegetable Substances with Distinctive Flavors and Aromas Which Give Zest and Piquancy to Food." And more.

★★ SUSHIKO

251 West 55th Street
LUNCH, MONDAY TO FRIDAY; DINNER DAILY.
Reservations, 247–9191.
Credit cards: AE, DC.
Inexpensive.

The neighborhood seems to be picketed, but the pickets are not carrying signs. In this part of town, hard by Eighth Avenue, there is much traipsing, up and down the streets, by bizarrely attired female humanoids whose leisurely gait tells much about their occupation. But assuming that the lure of raw fish is more compelling than their blandishments, or that by reason of gender the latter were not directed your way, you make it to and enter this humble restaurant in the humbler half of the humbler half of Manhattan's midtown. There are gilded paper lanterns hanging in the front window, but there the *luxe* ends. Within, there are splintery bamboo walls, yellow oilcloth on the dozen or so tables, rickety rice-paper lanterns. There are also adornments—a Kirin Beer calendar (scenic), a telephone (pay). Behind it all, the plinking and wailing of recorded Japanese music, and when that lets up, the murmur of the Japanese language. The place has a substantial Japanese clientele, including not just the neat and clean executives that habituate the swanker restaurants on the less humble, East Side half of midtown, but women and children and menials, too, drawn by the low prices and creating, in their aggregate, a more homey ambiance than the aura of officers' mess you experience when surrounded by dozens of close-tonsured black-haired men in impeccable suits.

Long hair is not inherently un-Japanese, and the sushi bar that is the off-to-one-side hub of the dining room is manned by hirsute Japanese youths whose lank hair, casual white garb and offhand manner are no clues to the neat things they do with the vibrantly fresh raw seafoods that are the principal ingredients in the sashimi (seasoned raw fish) and sushi (variously prepared morsels of raw fish and vinegared rice) served here. This is one of the best restaurants for raw fish in New York, and the place to enjoy it is on one of the half dozen stools at the little bar, where you can point at any item on display, ask its identity, struggle with the heavily accented polite answer, try it despite your lack of new information, and have a wonderful time.

You sit down to paper napkins, little chopsticks in a paper sheath; you are brought a warm moist square of terry cloth on a little bamboo canoe, and if you are at a table instead of at the bar or if you want hot food served to you at the sushi bar, a seven-page menu in a hangdog folder, the first page of which is an ardent paean to the pleasures of eating in Sushiko, albeit with some good advice: "Sushi is for the true connoisseur. . . . Eaten with beer, Sake or whiskey, there is no equal in this world." Hyperbole aside, those are the right beverages for this food.

You put yourself in the hands of the youngster behind the bar; he places a clump of moist pink pickled ginger before you, on a little board, the ginger shaped to a pyramid by his nimble fingers. (If you do not enjoy seeing the food you are about to get fingered, eat at a table.) You are started off with slices of dark-red tuna, soft and velvety, around moist rice and a sharp mustard that seems to clear the head. Then some mackerel, distinctly fishy compared to the tuna, also on rice, and sprinkled with sesame seeds on the silvery skin, for a crunchy, grainy accent. Next, though only for willing experimenters, raw abalone, a tough and inky-tasting and cartilaginous meat, with a stormy-oceanic flavor that calls for a calm interlude of raw squid—a very rich, almost buttery raw seafood that is enhanced by a moistening of soy sauce.

The second movement also begins with the tuna theme, but in this variation the fish and rice are formed into cylinders within a wrapping of crinkly seaweed sheet, and one-inch discs are cut off and served in pairs. Then we return to the abalone motif, but this time the resilient sinew has been tamed by boiling and made succulent with a sauce that is thick and brown, like warm chocolate—your server explains informatively that it is "special sauce." And if you have been swallowing everything placed before you without making a face, you qualify for some Japanese eel—it is salted and smoked in Japan, and it is behind the counter window in a little wooden box, and you will like it if you like smoked, rubbery, jellied salt.

Of course, you needn't go the whole route.

Having warmed up on seafood, you proceed to meat, which will, if you wish, be served to you at the sushi bar. And while you are waiting for it, you may observe an egg loaf, deep-yellow, lightly browned, being sliced behind the bar for delivery to some of the Japanese customers. Get a slice—it is steamy and sweet and firm, a rolled Japanese omelet, made in clear oil.

Now your Katsu Don arrives—thin slices of breaded pork, made in an eggy batter, served with onions and mushrooms, atop a bowl of rice. Or else your Gyu Don—beef that is barely steamed, very tender, with delicate slivers of sweet onion, on rice. Of course there are good versions of teriyaki and yakitori, and so on, but as the principal attraction of the place is the products of the sushi bar, a properly gluttonous approach to that may dictate a restrained one toward meat. You have to watch out for the man behind the bar. As you are about to wipe your lips for the last time, he hits you with some charcoaled tuna stomach, hot and sweet (you really do well here sampling what the knowing Orientals have made for them), and it is very hard to resist the oily fish with the sharp accent of the charred parts.

At the real end, someone will bring you a nice hot glass tea.

★★ SWISS PAVILION

4 West 49th Street
LUNCH, MONDAY TO FRIDAY; DINNER, MONDAY TO SATURDAY.
Closed Sunday.
Reservations, 247–6545.
Credit cards: AE, CB, DC, MC.
Expensive.

This has always been potentially one of the best restaurants in New York. But there has always been one thing or another.

The food at the Swiss Pavilion is not only good but authentic. Even that is not necessarily a virtue, but this authenticity is more than just a matter of the right ingredients in the correct proportions; one has the feeling here that the food is prepared by people who grew up with it, people who care about its tasting the way it tasted in the original, who provide not just the technical quality called authenticity, but also authority grounded in tradition.

But the Swiss Pavilion seems to compromise itself, once it gets past the actual preparation of the food, by catering to certain popular tastes. The disproportionate number of flambés on the menu is one thing, of fondues another.

A third is the horseshoe bar, a before-dinner drink at which may lead you to suspect you have chanced into one of the many restaurant/dives in the neighborhood that make most of their money on the torrents of booze that pass over the bar during the cocktail hour. The customers, instead of the proprietors, run the place. It has become theirs, and it is noisy and sloppy, with empty bottles, messy-looking pots of cheese dip, stirrers, napkins and other assorted junk strewn about. You could overlook it, but sometimes the boys get a notion to have dinner here (not often), and when they do, they do not lower their voices.

In the handsome dining room, its walls hung with pennants, you are seated at settings of solid and graceful brown ware on soft, putty-colored linen. The service is not as professional as it once was (the dining room is no longer staffed by Swiss-trained Swiss, but by friendly and willing but still-learning South Americans of various nationalities). In the old days, for example, it would have been unthinkable for a captain to wave you back to the hatcheck room (if you got past it undetected and, thereby, got past the hostess); he would simply have seated you himself, or asked you to please wait while *he* went for the hostess.

But once the food starts coming, you are OK. You may begin with something called Ramequins—little quiches made with superior cheese and bits of meat and perfectly browned crusts; they are hot and aromatic, and they are delicious with cool red wine. Or you may start with Surprise au Céleri—a surprising and perfectly successful combination of poached apple, a delicate liver pâté, and crisp celery root, acidic, tasting almost raw, in a thick mayonnaise. If that does not seem ridiculous, take note that the dish is served with Cumberland sauce—lingonberries and orange—and that the sauce is delicious on these diverse ingredients.

The soups here are all very good, from the cold apricot soup to the hearty Basler Mehlsuppe, a beef-stock broth cooked with excellent strong-tasting flour. There is also one soup made on a base of chicken stock—it is called Schoppa Da Giuotta, and it is eggy, laden with big kernels of barley and bits of ham, and redolent of chicken fat—it is almost as thick as mayonnaise.

Among the flambés is one gaily entitled "Hühnerbrüstchen mit Orangen, flambiert." The chicken arrives at the serving stand already cooked—it is a chicken breast, stuffed with veal, nuts and honey. Your server combines this with orange, and he cooks it some more; he adds grapes and cooks it further, he tosses in some raisins and cooks and stirs again. Then he flames the event in Curaçao (after a couple of tries). The stuffing within the chicken breast is a little like a sausage, and the fruit-and-brandy sauce is very nice on the spicy meat. The dish is served with very good spinach, loud and salty.

The Tournedo aux Morilles is not invariably fashioned from a perfect slice of beef, but the sweet, crinkly mushrooms (morels) are spectacular, and the dish is served in a very good cream sauce made slightly sharp with a touch of brandy. The best things on the plate, however, are the almost unbelievable noodles—they are firm yet soft, the flavor of eggs is vivid without being in the least "eggy," and the butter they are moistened with is all they need—probably the best noodles in New York.

One very simple and good dessert: Öpfelchuechli. These (that's a plural) are apple rings that are deep-fried in beer batter right before your eyes (or under your nose, if you wish) and sprinkled with cinnamon and sugar. The inside is sweet and soft, the outside sweet and crisp—good stuff. The rhubarb pie is something else. It is quite tart, only slightly sweetened, and the excellent crust and good firm quality of the fruit notwithstanding, the dish requires learning to like.

★★VAŠATA

339 East 75th Street
LUNCH, SUNDAY; DINNER, DAILY.
Reservations, 650–1686.
Credit cards: AE, MC.
Medium-priced.

This lovely restaurant has an immaculate glow to it; it is a comfortable place for a comfortable Middle European burgher to bring his well-fed family. The ivory walls are hung with pretty Czechoslovakian pottery and modest and simply framed photographs of Prague between the unvarnished dark wooden beams. There are comfortable chairs, and the soft banquettes are upholstered in panels of amber and blue leather.

One is presented with a basket of crusty rye bread (studded with the caraway seeds that are a staple in Czechoslovakian cooking), croissant-shaped salt sticks, rolls, an amplitude of sweet butter, and a menu which is a defiant triumph of tradition. The dishes are mostly the mainstays of Central European cooking in their pristine, Platonic form—as Plato's mother made them.

The food here is so determinedly Middle European, with emphasis on the Middle, that no seafood (or, for that matter, fresh-water fish) is served, except for herring appetizers—sweet matjes herring, and a silvery, tart marinated herring. But these can be had in restaurants of many nationalities around New York, in equally good versions, and some of the other first courses here are much more typically Czechoslovakian, and much less readily available. One may start one's dinner with tlacenka, called "Head

Cheese" on the menu, but just as accurately described as a sausage. A cross section of it looks like a red stone wall: fibrous, tender morsels of meat with a cement of cool, firm jelly. The famous ham of Prague is available here (unfortunately it is now virtually unobtainable in Prague). This ham is dark pink, extremely tender, slightly smoky, and surrounded by soft, white fat—it would be a crime to make a sandwich of it. Suvorov, a salad of minced meat, pickles and vegetables, in homemade mayonnaise, is the right first course for the hungry. It is especially good with the superb light Pilsner beer served here at, unfortunately, $1.30 per bottle. The pickled calf's brains on toast are wonderfully marinated, and if you are a brain freak, this simple, bald presentation will seem perfect to you—otherwise skip it. And all the first courses here are presented with elegance and taste—the ham, for instance, rolled into a long, pink cylinder; the garnishes on all the dishes, of radishes, tomatoes, or what have you, are of good color, and are fluted, petaled and arranged to make each platter a decorative, jewel-like piece.

There are good soups (brought in silver serving cups, and poured into large soup plates), but they are heavy stuff. The tripe soup is notable for the tenderness of the tripe and the intensity of flavor that comes of cooking with huge quantities of good paprika.

Vašata is deservedly famous for its schnitzels. The Wiener schnitzel is, like all the veal dishes here, made of the choicest, most tender, white veal, which easily absorbs the flavor of the lemon marinade. The breaded crust is so perfectly formed that it stands away from the veal in large domes, and is crisp and dry. The dish is so ridiculously tender that it can easily be eaten with a wooden spoon. There is a dish of fried liver sausages which seems frightening when it arrives—two giant wursts, steaming, the color of heavily tarnished silver, in crackling casings. But they are surprisingly light, the first will go down easily, and the second just as easily if assisted by a couple of bottles of good beer. The roast duckling and chicken paprika are good here, as you would expect—the former crisp and moist; the chicken not so distinctly inundated in sour cream as in the Hungarian restaurants in this neighborhood. Vašata is rather amazing in that the listed potatoes and vegetables are all usually available—among them a sauerkraut that is not acidic (lots of caraway seeds), good simple pickled beets (only slightly vinegary), fluffy dumplings (you'll get a pitcher of gravy if your main course does not provide it), home fried potatoes (brown, with crisp edges).

The blushing Czechoslovakian busboy, who is learning to be a waiter by serving desserts, explains, in a charming accent, that except for the palacinky (thin pancakes coated with apricot preserves or strong, bittersweet chocolate), the pastries are much like French pastries. But he points to a hefty tube (explaining that in his country it is known as "curls") which turns out to be an extremely light, flaky crust filled with pure, fresh whipped cream. What could be bad?

The customers are long sitters and talkers—a Pan-Slavic (and beyond) assortment of Zsa Zsas, Landowskas, Sonja Henies, Rudolf Bings and Titos, who have made of this place their home away from Europe.

ONE MAN'S MEAT

—⟨◦⟩—

Most restaurants exist in one tradition or another, and we automatically judge them by the standards of that tradition: in steakhouses we expect small perfections and large servings; in French bistros, honest food; in Italian places, emotional food.

But every once in a while someone—an original—comes along and makes a restaurant that is like art: personal, idiosyncratic, governed by its own rules. It takes a stubborn and independent personality to pull this off successfully. Therefore, it's not surprising that the proprietors of these restaurants don't knock themselves out in search of your commerce; and when they get it anyway, they are not servilely solicitous of your favor. The message is, if you don't like my restaurant exactly the way it is, you may express yourself by not returning. A little proprietary arrogance is heartwarming when it freezes the yokels at the next table, but when it's turned on you . . .

These places all have their excellences.

★ BALLATO

55 East Houston Street (near Mott Street)
LUNCH AND DINNER.
Closed Sunday.
Reservations required at dinner, CA 6–9683.
No credit cards.
Beer and wine.
Medium-priced.

The proprietor claims that he opened this restaurant to prove a point—that location is nothing, that if you sell good food, people will seek you out. So he opened it, back in 1957, in a neighborhood that is not even a neighborhood. This is certainly not Greenwich Village, nor is it Little Italy, nor the East Village (the Lower East Side, as it was known then). It may qualify as SoHo, but we can't blame him for that, as there was no SoHo in those days.

The customers have certainly sought out Ballato, but whether it's because of good food or because of an indefinable quality that sometimes makes an improbable restaurant successful is debatable, since there are restaurants as good as this one and restaurants better than this one that would gladly sacrifice their locations for the loyal following that keeps Ballato going.

Which is not to say that this is not an honest place. Ballato consists of eleven tables in two rows, in a small, neat, oblong room. The walls are earth colors (earth, earth-green, earth-orange, earth-ochre), with a few prints and photographs. The problem of a swinging door between the kitchen and the customers has been eliminated by removal of the door, and the clean-looking kitchen is visible to almost all parts of the dining room through a large portal at the rear. The floor is staffed by the portly proprietor, looking like the help in a cotton jacket of the kind supplied by commercial laundries; a waiter in a formal, white dinner jacket, looking like the proprietor; and on busy nights, the fifth wheel, a hireling waiter who answers that the Bardolino is $7.50 (actual price: $5.50); that there is really no difference between the manicotti and the cannelloni; that, yes, you may have some celery (but you give up your olives in the process); and that, no, there isn't any cheese (the proprietor produces three varieties in good condition). It helps to know the ropes.

One of the ropes: ask for celery and olives when you sit down. The celery is green, crisp and clean, and the olives are black, flaccid and loud, having been marinated in oil, garlic, parsley and bay.

Another rope: the first courses are uninteresting. The stuffed things are either stuffed with a dull seasoned-veal mixture which, despite its blandness, reduces mushrooms, eggplant and zucchini to indistinguishable identity; or with an ordinary breading (in the mussels, clams and artichokes) which at least succeeds in permitting the flavor of the principal ingredient to predominate.

Begin, rather, with half portions of pasta: either firm green noodles in a thick sauce of cheese and cream, graced with a dollop of tomato sauce on top—a flawless dish, and you may prefer a full portion; linguine with white clam sauce, the sauce clear and briny, the clams fresh minced cherrystones, and lots of fresh parsley; or the Spaghetti Marinara, in which the tomato has been reduced to a strong, heavy paste, and the garlic sautéed until it tastes blackened.

Proceed to Home Made Sausage Pizzaiola with Peppers—crackling sausage skins, partially blackened, stuffed with a textured filling that includes hunks of meat as well as ground meat, all buried in a thick, garlicky tomato sauce with heavily oiled, sautéed green peppers and mushrooms. Or to Polpo Affogate—tender lengths of octopus in a creamy tomato sauce that tastes of strong meat stock, black pepper and herbs. Dishes that are not dominated by tomato sauces, however, are less successful. Chicken Ballato, of which one might, from the name, expect great things, is an uninspired combination of sautéed chicken, sautéed mushrooms and ham, in a bland wine sauce. The Veal Valdostana consists of a veal chop, a slice of boiled ham and bland cheese—a bit of tomato sauce redeems it.

The green salads are fresh, and the dressing is tart, garlicky and well flavored with oregano; chunks of bread, soaked in the delicious dressing, come buried under the arugula, watercress, lettuce or whatever. When there is cheese, it is at room temperature and fresh. The cheese cake is made with ricotta, not cream cheese; it is accented with candied fruit, and it is moist, almost wet.

Your host is a dignified, vandyked presence who enjoys very much his reputation of being quite a character. On occasion he will sit at your table to discuss the menu with you, but his instincts are sure and if you're not interested in camaraderie right now, thank you, he will not make a mistake. On a slow night he'll tell you of his Sicilian past back in the thirties when certain impotent groups entertained Utopian visions for the Europe of the future; and of his World War II days, when his earlier underground experiences provided priceless contacts and saved thousands of lives for the Allied forces. If you keep listening, you'll hear that the missus spends entirely too much time in church, but that that is her right; that the Church (and here his beady eyes become positively black, and he can barely remain in his seat) has been a force for regression in our lifetime; and that the help (what's this?) you get nowadays doesn't respect the value of the boss's dollar. Ballato is nonunion. He has his less passionate side, however —he kisses the hands of the new women customers and nuzzles the more familiar ones. He waddles behind a departing cashmered beauty, his beard in her ear. She takes note: *"Ça va?"*

A quite good restaurant if you stick to the pasta and the tomato-sauce dishes. The customers arrive in their large cars from some of the fanciest neighborhoods in town, and they wait patiently at the front (magazines are provided) for their tables. They make phone calls from the telephone in the kitchen. The comfort of the place cannot be denied.

★★★ BOX TREE

242 East 50th Street
LUNCH, MONDAY TO FRIDAY; DINNER, DAILY.
Reservations essential, PL 8–8320.
No credit cards.
Wine.
Very expensive.

Hardly more than a right turn and a left beyond the tiny vestibule, and you have seen the scene. The Box Tree is a little gem of a place, a tiny free-form bauble of dark glinting stones in which eight tables, twenty-one chairs and pretty things have been lovingly assembled, with an impeccable eye for ornament; it is a jewel bejeweled, the dabs of bright color here and there like high-class ice strewn on dusky velvet.

There are two small adjacent dining areas, the larger of the two holding four tables and thirteen chairs. The choice table is at the front window—not much to see through the lace curtain that filters your view of East 50th Street, so you turn your eyes to your immediate surroundings. The deep-green walls are spotted with small sconces, two tiny red lampshades per bracket. To supplement them, pale lamps of fluted glass hang from the high ceiling and glow weakly, white candles in turned copper candlesticks throw off one candlepower per table. The walls are adorned with polished pewter and framed prints, the tables carry brilliant arrays of fresh flowers in china vases. In the front room the period-piece tables are shown off without cloths, but in the back room things are different. It is hardly a room at all, rather a cubicle the size of a second-class stateroom on a second-class steamer. But the little area has been shrewdly exploited—four oblong tables arranged in the shape of a U, two as the base, one as each side; seating is on the colorful high-backed banquette that rims three sides of the room. Here the tables are linened, and one assumes that the need for furniture tailored snugly to the space precluded the use of antiques. This is intimate dining for eight people who know one another. By the evening's end, eight strangers will be at least acquainted. For privacy, specify a front-room table when you make your reservation.

There seem to be more employees than customers. The young men in tuxedoes are everywhere, the chef/owner, in his kitchen whites, is almost everywhere, and boys in white are everywhere else. The help is amateurish and a little bumbling—despite their numbers there may be a bit of a wait. Withal, the place is comfortable and relaxed. One has the feeling that the customers come for leisurely dinners, that there is no hurry, that speedy service would be off key.

The menu is printed up daily. It is brief, there are a few changes from day to day. The cost of complete dinners depends on which entrée you choose—the range is around $17 to $20. That may seem a bit steep, but there are more courses to a Box Tree dinner than in any of the other *haute cuisine* restaurants in town: hors d'oeuvre, soup, main course, salad, cheese, dessert, coffee. If you are unhappy at less-than-larcenous prices, not to worry: you can be taken for a very long ride on some of the wines—$32 for a Latour of *1968*, for example—but there are a handful of quite drinkable inexpensive wines that are just as alcoholic. No matter what wine you order, you will drink it from huge Burgundy glasses.

One of the boys in white will keep you supplied with warm bread. If your bread-and-butter plate is bare, he will decorate it with a slice. You will want that bread and butter for the Terrine de Foie de Canard—a buttery and creamy mousse of duck liver that is served in a ramekin, a thin layer of cool jelly and a sliver of truffle over its top. This satiny terrine seems to have a spot of cognac in it, which at once intensifies and mellows the strong flavor of duck liver. Something billed as Croustade de Crevettes consists of a handful of shrimp in a flaky well-browned pastry, served with a polished white sauce made slightly pink with wine—these shrimp have a clarity of flavor that comes of their being fresh and not overcooked. If you are fortunate enough to come on one of the nights when the chef chooses to make snails, you will be able to sample a startling preparation. The snails are not served in their shells, but instead in what may as well be called a snail plate, a circular piece of pottery with six snail-size concavities, into each of which a snail is fitted with hot butter flavored with Pernod. Across the top, grated cheese has been spread and browned during the final baking. You probably would not have dreamed up the unlikely combination of snails, Pernod and cheese, but it works very well, particularly with the plump tender snails you get here.

The soups are good, if not consistent. The cold cucumber soup, which has been a summertime cliché in New York restaurants for more than a decade, is here made in a version that is distinguished from the others by a powerful overriding flavor of vividly fresh dill. But on one occasion the cucumber and yogurt flavors were lost, though another time, when the cucumber was in sizable crisp chunks, all the tastes were clear. A far greater tragedy is the fact that the Crème de Fenouille is not invariably what it can be. At its best, this thick soup of fennel and potato in a chicken-stock base has a quality of primal nourishment, as of the flavors of the earth. Sounds pretty good? Well, on another occasion it had been puréed too far, its slightly grainy quality gone, a thin smoothness (as of too long in the blender) in its place. That slight change kills the whole thing.

You order the Carré d'Agneau à la Menthe Fraîche, and you specify that you would like it rare. The owner/chef makes one of his frequent trips to the dining room to inform you that the lamb has been roasted to medium and that there is no more lamb in the house with which to start over. At any rate, it is good lamb, presumably even better when it is cooked to order, and it is served with a dollop of a deep-green sauce that is essence of fresh mint, lightly moistened and seasoned—just a bit of it livens up the overcooked lamb and would even improve rarer meat.

With so brief a menu, the management displays an admirable audacity by listing liver among the handful of main courses, particularly as this preparation is not liver in disguise, but rather, liver that retains its smooth texture and flavor, even though it is moistened with the winy deep-brown sauce studded with bits of black truffle—a spectacular dish.

There must be better ways to exploit the chef's talents than with Filet de Boeuf Sauce Fine Champagne. This is perfectly good beef and all that, but like most filets, it is relatively bland. This quality can be offset somewhat by grilling at high heat to form a crust, or by wrapping the rim of the filet in bacon before grilling, to impart the flavor of fat to a meat that has little of its own. Unfortunately, the filet here is grilled gently, and though it is sauced very nicely, in the same sauce that went on the liver (sans truffles), that does not rescue the steak.

Bass is served a number of ways, including a rendition with a cream sauce based on fish stock to which sautéed vegetables have been added for flavor and to which fresh lime juice is added just before serving. The fish is fresh, sweet and cooked to the right point, and the sauce transforms it into a startlingly piquant dish.

Salad. Three leaves of endive are set on a plate like three canoes, with a dollop in each hull of thick dressing made with a grainy mustard. Leaves of lettuce and sprigs of watercress surround the endive. The menu does not so state, but you are offered cheese with your salad, different ones on different nights, and they are excellent.

The Vacherin Box Tree is one of the greatest desserts in town. This vacherin consists of a crown of hazelnut-flavored meringue filled with alternating layers of whipped cream and raspberries. On occasion, before slicing it up, your waiter will parade the whole thing through the dining room. It is worthy of at least one bow of the head. Plump liquored strawberries are also available, with a thick silken cream very akin to a French *crème fraîche*. The dish is called Fraises Romanoff, but if that is a dish you have come to know in New York restaurants, be assured this is to the usual thing what Escoffier is to the Good Humor man.

The place has its inanities. Females receive menus without prices (if there is a male in the party). There is background music (especially preposterous in a small crowded restaurant that is noisy enough with customer conversation and the sounds from the kitchen). Though the waiters never walk more than ten feet from the kitchen to a table, they sometimes emerge with three or four plates piled on one arm; they perform the feat with such awkwardness that you hold your breath until the plates are safely put down.

Your check arrives on a plate with a rose. Of the two, the rose is prettier.

★★★ CASA BRASIL

406 East 85th Street
DINNER.
Closed Sunday.
Reservations essential, 288–5284.
No credit cards.
No liquor.
Expensive.

These are the rules, as stated by a sage gastronomist thirty years ago:

> [Good] restaurant keepers . . . provide only good wines. They do not crowd their guests together like sardines, or furnish the place so expensively that a prohibitive increase of prices is inevitable. They set no store by luxurious interiors lighted with excessive brilliance, where a few solitary individuals dine lugubriously and groups of unoccupied waiters stand about. . . .
>
> In a good restaurant the tables are well placed, the service is simple and the bill of fare consists of a few dishes only—but the preparation of each dish must be a labour of love, executed with care and patience. No orchestra disturbs the quiet of the place. The head waiter does not insist on your ordering what he himself fancies; the proprietor comes to ask your opinion of the Armagnac and kirsch served to you. And a delightful surprise awaits you—the bill is moderate. The result is that you leave the restaurant having dined well, your mind at ease, your heart at peace with the world.

In New York, Casa Brasil comes closer to meeting this set of guidelines than any other eating place.

Madame Helma, the proprietress, does not provide good wine (the customer brings his own), and her restaurant is fairly crowded when filled, but in every other respect, she approaches or reaches this ideal. This is especially to be praised because she maintains this level of performance for a clientele composed mostly of leather palates and stainless-steel gastrointestinal systems. Lancer's rosé and Chilean Riesling are the wines brought in most often, to "wash down" the food. Especially for the second sitting, and more especially on weekends, many customers arrive with the air of gin.

Originally a six-table, twenty-seat restaurant a couple of blocks from the present site, Casa Brasil was successful enough to move to these larger quarters—a brownstone with two dining rooms on the ground floor, and seats for about fifty. The tables are set with immaculately fresh, flower-printed cloths, good china and flatware, and excellent wine glasses—large and thin—for the wine you bring. There are always fresh flowers, in good condition, on every table.

There is no printed menu. The first appetizer is set, and the second is a choice of two;

there are three or four main courses to choose from (except on Wednesdays); and four or five desserts. On Wednesdays the main course is feijoada, the national dish of Brazil. (More accurately, it is the Brazilian way of eating meats. It can include pork, beef and beef tongue; fresh, smoked or dried, or all three; and sausages.)

The first course has often been hearts of palm in a pungent cheese sauce flavored with ham, pepper and hard-boiled eggs, and garnished with a couple of black olives. The dish is extremely vigorous and, at the same time, very light. It stimulates your appetite, without beginning to satisfy it.

The second appetizer is a choice of crabmeat in seasoned mayonnaise and sour cream (it comes on a few lettuce leaves which are in better shape than the lettuce in most restaurant salads) or melon and prosciutto—a rather bland prosciutto, but the Persian melon, served cut from its shell, is perfectly ripe, and extremely sweet and juicy. This course is accompanied by a basket of bread equal to the best in New York (the recent introduction of Interbaco notwithstanding). The basket contains croissants of such an airy and buttery quality that almost none of the little rolls return to the kitchen. They always arrive warm—never hot, never cool. Wisely, they are not served from the start of the meal. They are as easy to eat as it is to breathe, and they could displace several courses.

At this point—the wrong point—a good salad is served. The break following two appetizers is a good spot for a freshener—a light salad or a sherbet—but if only one such course is to be served, it should follow the main course and precede the dessert, where it is needed in a long dinner. That aside, the salad is fine—not a speck of brown on the fresh Boston lettuce in a lemon-and-oil dressing flavored with puréed garlic, onion and parsley. The dressing is made up daily, probably just before mealtime, because the flavor of raw onion is especially fugitive once an onion has been sliced, chopped or puréed, and the onion flavor in this dressing is absolutely pristine.

Among the main courses, Casa Brasil offers a Beef Wellington which, it appears, is on the menu because there is a demand for it, or because it is expected in this kind of restaurant. Beef Wellington is really a silly dish—filet mignon wrapped in pâté and pastry, and served in a brown sauce flavored with a deglazing of the beef. Filet mignon is the most delicately flavored of all beef, and pâté overpowers it, so its flavor must somehow be built up, or get lost. Moreover, pastry and meat do not cook the same way, so separate preparations of each are required before they are combined. Trouble is no argument, if a dish is worth it, but these ingredients do not long for each other, do not get along when wed, and all the ooh-ing and ah-ing is at the *sight* of the complex thing. These problems are recognized at Casa Brasil, and there is just a hint of pâté, but there is a clear lack of enthusiasm in the preparation; even the sauce, which *can* save it, is cursory, and the whole thing is tasteless. But the customers love it.

The roast duck is another matter, served *without a sauce!* If you know how to roast a duck, you can get away with that. Here it is crisp, moist, done to the bone, but not stringy.

The scallops of veal in a winy cream sauce are very good. The chanterelles are not fresh, but very well handled. Most important, the veal is *white,* and delicate, able to pick up the flavors it is cooked with, which is the whole idea of veal.

Bowls of four or five vegetables are served. Better to serve two or three, if the peas and artichoke hearts are to come from packages. A puréed squash, with lots of butter and nutmeg, is excellent; there is some very good rice, flavored, oddly, with sage; and an excellent warm compote of stewed apricot, pear and pineapple.

The Wednesday-night feijoada is a completely different world of food. Ordinarily it is a coarse dish, but the version served here is a slight deflection toward something more delicate, without any loss of character. The ingredients (each in its own bowl or plate) include rice cooked in stock and flavored with hot pepper; and the black beans, cooked with Portuguese sausages, and flavored with garlic and pepper. These two, combined, are the starch of the dinner. Two kinds of meats are served at Casa Brasil, both beef: one fried very rare with onions, in a pan gravy thick with blood; the other a fricassee —sautéed beef braised in wine. There are garnishes of fresh orange, very ripe bananas fried in butter and brown sugar (for these the only word is succulent), and a farina of the yuca plant, used as a zest, like salt and pepper. The food is heavy, but difficult to stop eating. It is one of the most distinctive meals in New York.

Of the good desserts, one is singular and stunning—tapioca poached in wine, covered with a crème Anglaise. The tapioca takes on the appearance of purple berries, and the flavor of concentrated wine, the alcohol removed. The other desserts include strawberries in a raspberry glaze; raspberries (better ones do not grow) with whipped cream; and an excellent nut cake, extremely moist, made with walnuts, almonds, pecans and dates, also covered with fresh whipped cream. The coffee, as you would expect, is perfect.

There are a few shortcomings in the management of this place, including the proprietress/chef's short fuse. As a rule she is grand and gracious, which suits her position and talent. But her occasional pique at a customer, though understandable, is audible and visible enough to discomfit others. She terminates the early sitting by abruptly turning up the lights (the rooms are small enough for an announcement to be audible). The waiters—food carriers really—don't know the answers to simple questions about the food, though the menu hardly varies. But in some ways, they're well trained: if you bring two kinds of wine, they change your glasses when you switch. Signed testimonials on the walls—from André Kostelanetz, Joan Crawford, etc.—are superfluous and not decorative. This sort of thing puts a restaurant in doubt, as if it needs something beyond its own performance to persuade the public of its quality.

• THE DUCK JOINT

1382 First Avenue (near 73rd Street)
DINNER.
Closed Monday.
Reservations, 861-1102.
Credit cards: AE, MC.
Medium-priced.

This was a good idea for a restaurant when it opened, and it is still a good idea, but unless you know what to order, the idea will be superior to your dinner.

The menu is built around ducks and geese, and nothing is thrown away but the feathers. "How about a treat for your pet!" says the table card. "We have fresh goose and duck gizzards cooked in natural gravy, quick frozen and conveniently packed in 1 lb. containers 45¢." The other side reads: "Did you ever try to cook with goose fat?? or dip a piece of crisp bread in it? it is incredibly goooood! Handy containers of pure rendered goose fat 85¢ lb."

The appetizer of potted goose livers is an example of Middle European cooking for which one must have a taste. The potted livers are stuck with whole cloves and served cold, buried in pure goose fat. The idea is to eat the livers with bread spread with the fat. Unfortunately, this restaurant seems to buy only day-old bread, which they make into garlic bread. Bizarre, particularly with this wonderful dish on the menu; garlic bread is simply wrong with clove-flavored livers and goose fat. Of the other appetizers there is a delicate and creamy Duck Liver Mousse en Gelée, an excellent Russian Egg on Ham Salad, a Smokehouse Selection (a good sausage and a bad one), and Various Pâtés (two again, both mediocre).

The regular menu lists only three main courses—roast goose, roast duck, and braised duck with grapes—but a supplemental menu ("For our friends who do not like Duck or Goose") lists "Wiener Schnitzel as Only the Viennese Can Do It," which is fair warning, since the management here is Czech; Bauernschmaus—a Middle European choucroute—made with excellent sauerkraut, but with only moderately good pork and with sausages which, even without chemical analysis, are food for Ralph Nader's anti-hot-dog campaign; and roast baby lamb, served with huge slices of dumpling and a good sauce of wine, rosemary and garlic.

To get back to the main menu, braising is an excellent method of preparing duck or goose—the bird remains moist, gives up most of its fat and picks up the flavors of the braising liquid. But if you braise a duck and then serve it with seedy, sour grapes, you get sour customers. Who wants sour customers? The roast duck and roast goose are much better, though not invariably perfect. They are served with little pitchers of natural gravy and a brandied cherry sauce, and a delicious stewed cabbage flavored with caraway is served with all main courses.

For dessert there is a very well made apple strudel which, unbelievably, is served at refrigerator temperature instead of at room temperature (which is better) or a little warmer (which is best). The Sacher Torte is rich and covered with Schlag. The fresh strawberries, on occasion, have been fresh for an unnaturally long time. A couple of good cheeses can usually be found on the board, but they must be eaten with crackers, as fresh bread is not available. The fruits that accompany the cheese may well be in bad condition, except perhaps for the orange, but an orange is, of course, an absolutely wrong fruit with cheese and wine. Well, dessert is not The Duck Joint's strength.

This is a handsome restaurant, with the atmosphere of a European inn. The tables are large and well spaced, and the service is friendly, if amateurish. One senses that the management could do much better but doesn't have to. A look at the tables around you offers a clue: most of the customers are drinking the house carafe wine, which is undrinkable—which tells you where their palates, as they say, are at.

If you stick to the simple duck and goose items, a salad and then Sacher Torte for dessert, you'll get a pretty good dinner.

★★★ MADAME ROMAINE DE LYON

32 East 61st Street
LUNCH.
Closed Sunday.
Reservations accepted for five or more, 758-2422.
No credit cards.
Beer and wine.
Medium-priced.

Hatpin handicapping is a race track system for the selection of horses. One purchases a program of the day's races, and without opening the booklet, pierces it at an arbitrary point on the front cover, through to the back cover, with a hatpin. The hatpin is removed, returned to its hat, and the program opened. The selections for the day's races are the horses whose allotted spaces on each page are perforated.

This system is indispensable at Madame Romaine de Lyon. It's impossible to decide that one omelette is preferable to 519 others, and as the 520 omelettes offered here are listed on 16 pages, a hatpin reduces the problem by 97 percent, from 520 to 16. The patron is still faced with a dilemma, but one of human proportions.

A selection of 520 omelettes is such a wonderful gimmick that a restaurant could succeed even if the omelettes were bad. Madame Romaine produces omelettes that are the equal of the best on earth. Not only are the eggs fresh, the butter sweet, the pan hot, the preparation rapid, and the delivery instantaneous (omelettes go bad in just a few minutes), but the ingredients—the beef, brains, mushrooms, chicken livers, etc.— are pre-cooked superbly: the beef is sautéed, the brains marinated, the bacon fried (but not to a crisp) by an expert who could have stopped right there and still delivered an excellent dish.

There is a palpable pleasure in simply reviewing the names and ingredients of some of these fabulous concoctions: Rochambeau (spinach, sausages, mushrooms, cheese); Jourdan (caviar, ham, bacon, onions, mushrooms, cheese); Maxim's (beef, foie gras, mushrooms, spinach, tomatoes, walnuts, Courvoisier sauce); Suprême (chestnuts, chocolate sauce).

No main courses except omelettes are served, but brioches, croissants and rolls are available, as well as a salad of good greens and a light, refreshing dressing. Desserts are a huge assortment of pastries, a chocolate mousse of the heavy, black, you-can't-be-hungry-after-this variety, and a macédoine of fruits which the menu happily defines as "all kinds of fruits mixed."

The worst thing about Madame Romaine de Lyon is that it is open from 11:30 A.M. to 3 P.M., that is, for lunch. Who wants to go back to the office after a lunch with a bottle of wine at this incredible restaurant? It should be open for dinner. And it should be open for breakfast, because an omelette makes an excellent breakfast. And it should be open on Sundays, because people eat on Sundays. It should always be available. What a marvelous 3 A.M. alternative to bed or the Brasserie.

Assuming that the hours are lengthened, and that one eats three meals a day here, seven days a week, it would require twenty-four weeks, five days and a breakfast to consume one of each omelette. If the schedule is not changed (notwithstanding that, after thirty years it's time for a change), one can eat two omelettes a day here—a late breakfast at 11:30, and a late lunch at 3. (A nap is recommended in between.) This *régime* would stretch the project to forty-three weeks and four days. The omelette cost of either plan is $2,297.65. Money well spent.

The décor is dreadful, the service simple and polite. White Bordeaux are, as a rule, the best omelette wines.

• MR. & MRS. FOSTER'S PLACE

242 East 81st Street
DINNER.
Closed Sunday and Monday.
Reservations essential, LE 5–1234.
No credit cards.
Wine and beer.
Expensive.

After overcharging twenty-five patrons twice a night, six nights a week, for a number of years, Mrs. Foster, the sole proprietor, apparently still can't afford larger quarters for her establishment, or the elimination of a couple of tables so that the remaining diners could eat comfortably. At one dinner a gentleman facing west was locking elbows with a man facing east at another table, while a couple of feet away, on a skimpy banquette, the third guest at a table too small for two had the options of (1) not facing his food, (2) eating sideways or (3) standing up.

"This is a jacket-and-tie place," Mrs. Foster informs you over the telephone, after accepting your reservation and food order (the latter required in advance), but she neglects to mention that the place is for Hobbits.

The odium of comparison will be noted more by Mrs. Foster than by Madame Helma (of Casa Brasil). The comparison is unavoidable because, superficially, the two restaurants resemble each other. Perhaps this place should shut down for a few months while Mrs. Foster, who obviously knows how to cook, serves an apprenticeship in other aspects of restaurant management at her neighbor's place only a few blocks away.

Dinner at Mr. and Mrs. Foster's Place begins with a minuscule ramequin of chicken livers sautéed in butter and madeira, and served with buttered toast. The livers are superb, and the toast would seem excellent at the counter of a hotel coffee shop. The next course is a small, excellent blini stuffed (well, almost filled) with red caviar and sour cream, and served with lemon and watercress. These are so delicious that it's a crime to serve only one, but a thread of sadism seems to run through this place.

Then comes your tiny corn bread, made in a corn-shaped mold, and very crispy. It is meant to accompany the soup, but that arrives later still. Negotiations for more bread may be undertaken and concluded satisfactorily, but the second piece never actually arrives. The soups include an excellent cold apple, made with white wine and served with sour cream; a tepid mushroom consommé; and a good lentil soup flavored with parsnip and nutmeg, and served with lemon and sour cream.

At this wrong juncture the vegetable salad arrives, composed of cold, parboiled broccoli, string beans and carrots; tomato, blanched to remove the skin; and lettuce; all moistened with a good French dressing.

After your waiter returns your fork to the table from your salad plate, you're ready for the main course. Mrs. Foster serves Beef Wellington made without pâté, and if she eliminated the pastry as well, we would really be getting places. Beef Wellington (whatever one may think of the pretentious dish) without pâté is the equivalent of ham and eggs without eggs. Whatever you call it, the dish is excellent here—served with a well-flavored madeira sauce. It is available only when ordered for two.

Something called Burgundy Beef is sautéed beef and sautéed végetables (celery, carrots, white beans and onions) in a sauce made with a strong stock, a little wine and a heavy enrichment of butter.

The shellfish dishes are all good, including a very large lobster (at an immense price) stuffed with crabmeat and shrimp; and crayfish flavored with parsley and dill.

The desserts are disappointing: a dismal mousse made, it seems, with milk chocolate; a vanilla pudding named "Snow" but reminiscent of junket; a dull cherry torte; and a chocolate cheese cake which seems to have been coagulated rather than baked.

When asked what this or that dish is flavored with, Mrs. Foster caresses the back of her hair, giggles girlishly and announces that she never gives her secrets away. Her best-kept secret is how she gets the customers to come back.

Your check arrives when the waiter decides it's time. This is the same genius who, besides his corn-bread and salad-fork ploys, can't remember which of two soups is for which of two people, never fills an empty water glass unless he is asked, and grandly decides for you that the wine is OK, simply plunking the bottle down on the table. (If you want your white wine kept cool in a bucket, you must so plead.)

Most of the food is good. Almost everything else is not. Pay, and pick your way out carefully.

The Restaurant Associates Thing

Restaurant Associates has done more for the New York restaurant scene than any other single force since Henri Soulé opened Le Pavilion and thereby engendered, through a series of defections from his kitchen and dining room, almost all of the more pretentious of New York's French restaurants.

R.A. is most notable for two kinds of restaurants: romanticized versions of the familiar—Charley O's is the sleekest and coziest Irish saloon in town, The Ground Floor is the ultimate drugstore; and unprofitable fantasies—The Four Seasons, here included, is a superbly rendered dream, the Forum, not included, a perfect nightmare. The last two were sold to former R.A. employees, and the latter is now defunct.

Even R.A.'s failures have style, which is accomplished by attention to detail: the printed menu, the flatware and china, the furnishings, the waiters' and waitresses' uniforms are always right for their particular place. This does not mean that the place will be right for you. Style is not quality, and R.A. restaurants, for all their graces, are guilty of mundane food and clumsy service about as frequently as their more orthodox competitors.

★ BRASSERIE

100 East 53rd Street
NEVER CLOSES.
Reservations accepted for dinner, 751–4840.
Credit cards: AE, BA, CB, DC, MC.
Medium-priced.

Presumably we must be grateful to the Brasserie. It is the only decent non-Oriental restaurant in the city open twenty-four hours a day, every day of the year. Anyone with the appetite can get good French and Alsatian food at any hour, and a drink, wine or beer at legal hours, in pleasant surroundings.

The Brasserie is a huge, very popular restaurant, occupying three rooms below ground level on the north side of the Seagram Building. There are tables for about 100 in the smaller back rooms, for about 125 more in the main front room, plus a comfortable 30-seat counter, at which the service is much better than at the tables.

During its busier hours (lunch and after the theater) the floor is badly understaffed, and you must have your order ready at once because the waiter may not be back for fifteen or twenty minutes. The hosts—they have the demeanor of department-store floorwalkers—are very, very bored, and the dining room succeeds in being at once inflexible and disorganized.

Yet the Brasserie is still liked and patronized by thousands, and with good reason. The food is hearty, a sense of gaiety seems to have been built into the place, and the frequently changed decorations and restrained use of wall posters add to the feeling of well-being. Some prices are still fair, some low, and the menu is not bound to mealtimes but lists good sandwiches and cold plates, salads, quiches (not soggy), good egg dishes, and desserts through most of the day. The customers come to eat informally, which may explain why they accept the casual service.

The restaurant's reputation is based largely on its off-hours availability, heterogeneous clientele and snacky menu. It does offer inexpensive table d'hôte dinners ample enough for a lumberjack. Of the appetizers, Poitrine de Veau Farcie Froide—a spicy terrine of ham, pork and veal—is gigantic; and the clams are very fresh, served with the usual cocktail sauce. There is a good onion soup, made with strong stock, thoroughly browned onions, a substantial slice of melted Gruyère cheese on a crouton of French bread, after which you will have completed the equivalent of a substantial lunch. This is perhaps just as well, because the main courses are undistinguished, though acceptable—one fish, one duck, one pork, etc., with some of the dishes changed every few months. Insurance against your walking out hungry is Gâteau Côte de Chevreuil (literally "cake side of venison"), a pretty good description for this haunch of chocolate cake in a chocolate hide with almond antlers. Ice cream, mousse and tarts are also available.

The à la carte menu, available most of the day, is more interesting, including some of the dishes the Brasserie served when it first opened—choucroute (now diminished in the breadth of its charcuterie), pfannkuchen (a delicious, heavy meat-and-tomato sauce flavored with rosemary, wrapped in a pancake, and bizarrely served with rice), Veal Cordon Bleu, tripe, steaks. If you can bring yourself to say "fromageburger," you can get a good cheeseburger, with ratatouille and potato salad. The waiter may ask how you want it, but the kitchen knows only medium.

★★CHARLEY O'S BAR & GRILL & BAR

33 West 48th Street
LUNCH AND DINNER.
Reservations, 582-7141.
Credit cards: AE, BA, CB, DC, MC.
Medium-priced.

"I only drink to make other people interesting."

—George Jean Nathan

"A gourmet who thinks of calories is like a tart who looks at her watch."

—James Beard

"New York is a catastrophe, but it is a magnificent catastrophe."

—Le Corbusier

These photograph captions (there are dozens more) and the establishment's motto, "Solid drink and good food. That's my theory," set the tone—pre-lib masculine with stand-up lunch: hefty sandwiches; shrimps, clams and oysters sold by the piece, to people who know just what they want. "I'll have four shrimp, two clams, an oyster, a CB on rye, a Harp's on draft, and a small Guinness for color" is the ultimate lunch order, to be eaten, of course, by a 6-foot 2-inch, 185-pound advertising killer, who ruins the effect by tossing a Master Charge card on the bar instead of a ten-dollar bill, and signing his name with exaggerated loops.

But don't laugh. That lunch was delicious. The oyster and the clams were opened a few minutes before they were eaten, the huge shrimp were cold and not overcooked, and the spicy corned beef arrived on two slabs of crusty rye bread. When you're in the mood for body contact, have lunch at Charley O's. Clear a place for your food by sweeping your arm over a square yard of counter, remove your raincoat and eat.

Or come at dinnertime (not cocktail time, when the lunch mob has either returned or not yet left), when the place is metamorphosed into an elegant eating house, with crisp linen, polite, competent waiters and good food.

There is a wonderful assortment of appetizers, including a huge serving of pâté which is strong and coarse, pigs' knuckles in a gamy jelly, soused shrimp (marinated in lemon, oil and raw onions), and the same good clams and oysters.

It's not unusual for one of the seven daily specials to be out by seven-thirty, but it's assuredly irritating. The best of these are a roast duck with a sauce of chestnuts and peaches, and a sirloin of beef braised in cider. The regular menu offers the inevitable corned beef and cabbage, good steaks, an excellent lamb stew, and fried prawns in beer batter. Whatever you have, have the Irish fried potatoes—diced, par-boiled potatoes, fried to a luscious dark brown in grease, with salt and pepper. It's difficult to believe that anything this good is obtainable in Ireland, where the reputed high level of serious drinking is due to the fact that the best-tasting stuff in the country comes out of a bottle.

The strawberries and cream are usually good here. The whiskey cream pie is literally intoxicating, but the hot apple pie is not. It is an individual little pie, in a crust simulated of Melba toast, and it tastes awful. Calling it apple pie is a misrepresentation—if not technically, then morally.

A good, inexpensive wine list.

★ CHARLIE BROWN'S ALE & CHOPHOUSE

200 Park Avenue (Pan Am Building)
LUNCH, MONDAY TO SATURDAY; DINNER, MONDAY TO FRIDAY.
Closed Sunday.
Reservations, MO 1–2520.
Credit cards: AE, BA, CB, DC, MC.
Medium-priced.

Charlie Brown's is a handsome place—brick walls, stocky brick pillars, beamed ceiling, red tiled floor in a brickwork pattern, a bustling open kitchen, spacious booths along the walls, good-sized tables with captain's chairs, and handsome pewter table settings.

The food is, for the most part, Improved English and variations thereof, including, among the first courses, a refreshing dish of mussels in a cold, sharp curry cream, sprinkled with chives; the herring, which has always been superb; a salty Scotch egg (a hard-cooked egg wrapped in spiced meat). The egg comes with a tangy sweet-and-tart relish of red pepper and pickles, which is desperately needed—the leaden dish itself is something only a Briton could love.

Among the main courses there is a pretty good beefsteak, kidney and mushroom pie. Technically this is a difficult dish to make. The stewed filling must cook under the crust, and the steam from the boiling concoction should not prevent the pastry from becoming crisp and brown; at the same time, the vapors from the stew add flavor to the pastry. Here the whole issue is sidestepped. The meat is prepared in one place, the pastry is baked in another part of the oven, and they meet on your plate. This simplifies things in the kitchen and assures a good flaky pastry, but it tastes rather French.

There is excellent roast beef here, served with the aforementioned horseradish sauce. But the so-called Yorkshire pudding that comes with it is flat, heavy, and to judge from its flavor, not made in suet or beef drippings—not Yorkshire pudding at all, just a popover. The filet mignon in a crust is a small triumph. Grilled with dough over it and stuck under the broiler to brown the crust, it is served with a good sauce Bordelaise, including a slice of the marrowbone fat with which it is made. The sauce permeates the crust (this dish is also more French than English), and no one is complaining.

Pretty good fish and chips—the fish crisp and flaky, but the potatoes, like all the French fries here, rather limp; here authenticity would serve well.

Deep-dish Sour Cherry Pie is really sour, and the crust is a real lard crust—a sprinkling of coarse sugar provides just the right accent. Strawberries are served with that mellifluous, vaguely chalky, tender stuff called Devonshire cream.

The bar is usually packed, jam-packed, or, especially on Friday evenings, packed to paralysis. This presents a problem, because one must pass through the bar to reach the dining room. No suggestions.

★★★ THE FOUR SEASONS

99 East 52nd Street
LUNCH AND DINNER.
Closed Sunday.
Reservations, 754–9494.
Credit cards: AE, BA, CB, DC, MC.
Very expensive.

The Four Seasons gets a lot of criticism, usually on the grounds that it is not Lutèce or La Caravelle, or something. In fact, it is itself—singular, imaginative, in some ways beautiful, almost breath-taking, and a better restaurant today than it has been before. Accordingly, it's often easy to get a table for dinner, and on most days you can walk in off the street in the middle of the dinner hour, even on a Friday or Saturday evening, and as long as you have your clothes on, you will be received like royalty and seated at once, if not in the main dining room (called, in the absence of so much as a yard of green felt, the Pool Room), then in the less formal grill-less Grille Room, just behind the big handsome square bar.

The effect of the place is at once grand and monastic. The ceilings are around twenty-five feet high, and the windows, from the floor to the top, are hung with countless arcs of copper-colored chain. The walls are of dark wood or plain ivory-colored panels. In the Pool Room the relief to this spare interior consists mainly of one pool: square, centered, cool, softly illuminated, quietly bubbling, framed in white marble, with a somber potted tree at each corner, like an oasis. At night the room is quite dark, though lights set deep in the ceiling illuminate the tables. At lunchtime the place has a warm, golden glow. Lunch or dinner, the room is comfortable. Perhaps it's the huge tables, covered with soft beige linen, and the deep armchairs.

The Grille Room is more human—the same tall windows and the same walls, but there is the famous two-part Lippold sculpture of hanging brass rods, the larger section over the bar, and the small one over the raised dining area on the east side of the room. There are many potted plants, placed informally, and the semicircular black leather booths are cozier than the pearly banquettes in the main room.

One is received here with perfect cordiality, and though the service is not always immediately available, it is polite, intelligent and helpful.

Its reputation for the far-out notwithstanding, there are actually a number of dishes here that are simple little things, like the small clams with chopped green onions and truffles, served on cracked ice in a huge deep silver plate. This is not an inspired dish, but the clams are sparklingly fresh. The Four Seasons has the sense, when serving littlenecks, to give you nine of them, and the onions and truffles do add a touch of interest. And there is a no-kidding-around Country Terrine, principally of liver, pistachio nuts and lardons of pork fat, garnished with a cool jelly. This is so rich and strong that it's almost impossible to eat it without bread (preferably the small flaky croissants that help fill the plain silver breadbasket) and wine.

Some of the warm appetizers are more original, and one of the most successful of them is the Crisped Shrimp Filled with Mustard Fruits. The name just about describes the dish, though it must be stated that the seemingly disparate elements—very firm deep-fried shrimp, a mustard-flavored white sauce and sweet stewed fruits—come together perfectly. The Crabmeat Crêpes Impériale are made with *fresh* crabmeat, and a spicy brown sauce with pimentos and crisp parsley added at the last moment, all in a tender pancake. There is also a Marrow Soufflé, a moist little cake that is a sort of ninth cousin of Yorkshire Pudding. It is slightly heavy, and it has the strong basic taste of all soufflés (eggs, milk, browned flour), overlaid with just a touch of the rather coarse flavor of beef marrow. For some reason, garlic is not permitted in the kitchen of this restaurant, so an effort has been made to contrive a snail dish without garlic. No dice.

The gazpacho is as close as you will get to a Spanish gazpacho in New York. It is slightly grainy, the tomato flavor is concentrated, not tomato-juicy, the spice is fresh red pepper, and the waiter spoons croutons and chopped vegetables over the cold soup just before you eat it—a wonderful interlude between a hot appetizer and the main course. So is the Tomato Madrilène with Sour cream and Red Caviar—none of the elements of this cold soup is singular, but the combination is, and the crunchy caviar, jellied broth and the thick sour cream are a spectrum of flavors and textures that are almost adjacent, but distinct, and slightly contrasted with each other.

One of the big deals here is Whole Striped Bass on Flaming Fennel. This is a variant of a dish native to Provence, in which the Mediterranean fish called *loup* is actually cooked, not just flamed, over burning fennel. That preparation imparts an extraordinary anise flavor to the fish. Here, instead, the already cooked fish is flamed in Pernod during the brief fennel conflagration, which is not the same thing but very good, and made better by a house invention called sauce Grégoire, a fish-stock and white-wine velouté combined with a heavily tarragoned Béarnaise—fabulous stuff. Paupiettes of Salmon with Mousse of Trout sounds terribly refined, but it is in fact a hearty dish: three tubes of salmon, filled with trout and covered with a sauce flavored with sorrel —a very strong green.

The Peppered Duckling is not only peppered with copious black pepper but accompanied by sautéed green peppers—almost invariably the bird has been perfectly roasted and flavored. There is a Beef Stroganoff here which earns the name by the inclusion in the dish of beef and sour cream. Otherwise this is simply a delicious house invention. The beef used is filet mignon, it is cut in slabs rather than slivers, it is browned in butter and paprika, and a reduction of sherry, cognac, beef stock and lemon juice is prepared in the pan before the sour cream is added. This makes a rather splendid sauce for the rare, tender beef, and if there is more of it than the beef calls for, you eat it with the barley that accompanies the meat. The à la carte vegetables are nothing special—the rösti potatoes, for example, are simply a crust, lacking a soft potato interior, and spoiled further by what tastes like Cheddar cheese.

Generally the desserts don't deserve their reputation. The coffee cup soufflé tastes like instant coffee and ice cream, which are, in fact, two of the ingredients. The chocolate cake is simply melted chocolate. There is a cool Bavarian cream wrapped in chocolate—it tastes Bavarian, if not Lüchovian, and it has a graham-cracker crust. The fruit tarts are on a doughy pastry. By the end of a complete dinner here the best choice is probably the excellent sherbets, made of fresh fruit, that are prepared daily.

Certain things about The Four Seasons are stunning: pitchers, bowls, serving plates and baskets of solid, gleaming sheet silver; the beautifully printed wine list, the broad range of wines, and their reasonable prices; the expertness of the captains—a duck is carved in sixty seconds, with hardly an ounce of meat left on the carcass; the pungent, oily little olives from Nice that come in the dish of *crudités* at the start of your meal;

the handsome gleaming crystal and china; even the cool politesse with which tourists are served their Cokes and ketchup. You will not often get a meal that is completely unforgettable, but it will always cost a young fortune. Nevertheless, there is nothing else like The Four Seasons, and it must be visited.

★ MA BELLS

218 West 45th Street
LUNCH AND DINNER
Reservations, VO 9–0110.
Credit cards: AE, BA, CB, DC, MC.
Medium-priced.

Ma Bells is a spacious, airy, relaxed saloon. It is Original Joe's and Charley O's; O'Neals' Baloon without the vulgarity; a sprawling frontier tavern with a plate-glass revolving door. It is perfect New York; the little gift we didn't know we wanted until we got it. We would cherish it more if the food were better.

Ma Bell, as you know, is Wall Street's name for AT&T, and if you get a table along the wall, you get a table with a telephone on it—please, only local calls. The old-fashioned, stand-up instrument is made by Norelco.

The green-and-white tiled floor does not have sawdust on it, thank you, but it looks like the kind that usually does. The tables are of handsome dark wood. There is a bar, eighty feet long, we are told, and if there is a burst of thirst during a coincidence of intermissions here in the theater district, no bar nearby can accommodate as many shoes on the brass rail as this one. If you want something longer and more confidential than a quick one to help you through Act II, there are enclosed booths along one side —no drawn curtain, the portal is open, but they are excellent for long, serious drinking, interrupted now and again by a sandwich or two to renew the capacity. Find a friend with a despair commensurate with one of your own, settle in and spend the day. The service is good enough to keep the frights away, and for further distraction you can watch the slowly spinning ceiling lamps. Real saloons—that is to say, saloons that seem to be where they are out of some inevitability of place and community—are usually festooned with devices of the day and of earlier days. To fill this perceived gap we are given large and very large photos, mainly of motion-picture celebrities in scenes from old movies, telephone in hand, with fanciful captions that are meant to be amusing. Mostly they are not, but Barry Goldwater saying "Hello, 19th Century Fox?" into a telephone speaker has a certain ring. Another device is the TV—everyone watches the afternoon ball game.

There is a lunch menu, a dinner menu and a supper menu, and they are pretty much the same, each a rearrangement of the other. What's good is the Crock of Onion Soup with Calvados. The dish is filled almost entirely with cheese and onions, what there is of the broth is thick and sweet, the cheese is gummy and strong, and you can taste a bit of brandy and a slight accent of burnt onions. What's not so good are the shrimp —either in the cocktail (with a better-than-everyday cocktail sauce) or in the Shrimp Salad Louis (with a very good Green Garden Sauce: mayonnaise and vinegar, and enough puréed parsley to make the thing green). But the shrimp, good grief, are past their prime.

What else is good is the steak, and you know what a fairly good steak is like. But what else is not so good is the French fries—gross oblongs of Idaho potato that are soggy and limp. The hash is satisfying—abundant, spicy and heavy, and served with poached eggs that run all over the hash when you break into them. Tell them to hold the sauce (an unpleasant Worcestershire-and-tomato mess) and bring the ketchup (ketchup has its place). The sandwiches are thick. The so-called Green Salad is made of iceberg, tomatoes, cucumbers and crunchy but tasteless croutons; the Roquefort dressing is of real Roquefort.

Cheese cake made of cream cheese is inherently bad food. But if you disagree, you may disagree more when you taste the version served here—there is a layer of caramel between the filling and the crust, which jazzes up this otherwise excessive dessert. If you and your friend both want to try it, order only one, which is quite enough of this extremely sweet substance. The chocolate cake is called Chocolate-Chocolate Cake, and as you might have guessed, it is very chocolaty.

During the day there are peanuts on the bar; at cocktail time, crocks of cheese and plates of crackers. There is no free lunch.

★ PROMENADE CAFÉ

Lower Plaza in Rockefeller Center (near 50th Street and Fifth Avenue)
LUNCH AND DINNER.
Reservations, PL 7–5731.
Credit cards: AE, BA, CB, DC, MC.
Medium-priced.

This is the place where they skate in winter and eat year around. And wherever you skate, you will not find a terrine of duckling like the one served here. Dishes of similar name are served in many places around town, but they usually taste like just another pâté. Here the terrine tastes like duck, with the duck fat not wrung out. It is studded with pistachio nuts, and served with an excellent Cumberland sauce—that spicy, sweet and tart mixture of currant jelly and orange rind. If that is the furthest thing from what you want, the taramasalata may be the nearest—there is a very good version at the Promenade of the Greek roe dish. The gazpacho is grainy, made hot with cayenne, and dominated by the flavor of tomato and green pepper.

If you're really hungry, you can start with an individual, five-inch bacon quiche, or if you're merely passing the time, that can be your entire meal—it comes with a nice green salad. The cold roast chicken is not really cold, but is served, as it should be, at room or outdoor temperature. You get half a chicken, very nicely roasted, and fresh string beans, lightly cooked and dressed with vinaigrette and a sprinkling of raw onions. The cold salmon steak is flaky and firm, served with dill-flavored mayonnaise and a nice cucumber salad.

The chef's salad at this restaurant is awful—a platter of julienne ham, chicken (so far, so good), shredded lettuce and domestic "Swiss" (an execrable cheese), garnished with canned artichoke hearts. This mess is served with one's choice of good, but wasted, dressings.

There are omelettes and several other hot main courses, but this is hardly the place for, say, baked cannelloni, or for bratwurst with spaetzle—after all, it is not air-conditioned, and that kind of eating can make the blood flow. If you must, there is a chopped steak "au poivre." The pepper is hard to detect, but the ground meat is good. It is grilled the way you order it, and it comes with pretty nice French fries.

The most popular dessert here seems to be the Summer Sundae—a giant portion of vanilla, with raspberries and whipped cream, and it is quite good. But the hazelnut cake —a light sponge cake sprinkled with crunchy hazelnuts—is really an excellent sweet with coffee.

Because of its location, the Promenade attracts a lot of visitors from out of town. Perhaps, under the circumstances, the management is to be commended for maintaining even its present level of quality. After all, most of these folks won't be back soon.

It was a wonderful idea someone had a few years back, to roll out a green carpet where the Rockefeller Center skating rink is during the winter, fill the space with umbrella-shaded tables, and serve good food near the soothing sound of the fountains. The tables are well covered by their broad sunshades, but if you lean back you can look up at an expanse of open sky, the sleek skyscrapers of Rockefeller Center on all sides. At night, changing colored lights are played on the fountains and on the huge, golden statue of Prometheus delivering the stolen fire.

• TRATTORIA

200 Park Avenue (Pan Am Building)
LUNCH AND DINNER.
Closed Saturday and Sunday.
Reservations, MO 1–3090.
Credit cards: AE, BA, CB, DC, MC.
Medium-priced.

The Trattoria is a great big flashy place—a drinking bar at the west end, near the entrance from the Pan Am Building (it gets some of the overflow from Charlie Brown's); a great, circular serving counter where food is displayed with pride that is only occasionally justified; rows of handsome leather-upholstered booths; tables with garish but pleasing orange-and-chrome chairs; a wall of black-and-white photo posters of the swinging world we're lucky enough to live in; gleaming candy-striped hanging lamps; deep-blue walls; red pillars; shiny floors—contrast, glare, action! The service, on the other hand, is sluggish; the food, save for the pizza, an occasional pasta and the desserts, is very ordinary, and some of the waiters are simply dumb:

"We'll have one baked clams and one Pizza Trattoria, and after that one spaghetti with oil and garlic, and a Veal Francese."

"The clams take fifteen minutes."

"Then bring the pizza first."

"The pizza takes fifteen minutes too."

The clams are not bad (they come in about two minutes)—whole cherrystones, a bit overcooked sometimes, but with a nice, simple breading moistened with oil and flavored with garlic. Your individual eight-inch Pizza Trattoria is of the thin bread type, easy on the cheese and tomato sauce, with sautéed fresh mushrooms, strong fennel-flavored sausages and green peppers—very tasty. But the pasta dishes here are utterly unpredictable, though sometimes you can get one that is wonderful. On one day a fettuccine is not only *al dente* but brittle; another day you order spaghetti with oil and garlic, and the simple sauce is just perfect, with its slightly browned garlic and about half a fistful of fresh green parsley to a portion, but the pasta itself is limp and glutinous; another time your Spaghetti al Pesto is so devoid of sauce that to have any taste at all it must be rescued with three heaping spoons of the good grated Parmesan cheese served here.

Nevertheless, on balance, those are the kinds of dishes to have here—hot appetizers, pizzas, pastas, sandwiches, omelettes. The main courses of meat or chicken are simply lifeless, like photographs of food—ordorless and tasteless, but perfectly prepared. The green salad is of crisp romaine lettuce, with oregano and a strong wine-vinegar dressing.

The desserts are incredible. This place serves the most intensely chocolate-flavored ice cream in creation, and then they have the splendid audacity not merely to bury it in fresh whipped cream but to roll the thing in thick shavings of pure, black chocolate —this is called Tartufo. Something called Nugatina is a scoop of vanilla and a scoop of chocolate, covered with whipped cream and pine nuts, over which chocolate sauce has been poured—all topped with a hazelnut meringue. Of course if mere heavenly sweets bore you, there is a Zuppa Inglese here that is, it is true, sweet, but also soaked in rum, studded with candied fruit and with lumps of chocolate the size of golf balls, all covered with a lightly browned, soft and moist meringue. You get the idea about the desserts—none of them are subtle, but they are of brilliant ingredients in elegantly exaggerated combinations.

The clever waiter brings your check before you ask for it, and looks over your shoulder as you write in his tip.

Hangouts

Theatrical and musical types, the jet set (poor things, they learned about food on airplanes), hard-headed newspaper guys, one-night-standers on the make; businessmen, as well as subgroups, such as garment men, as well as sub-subgroups, such as (a) old-style garment men (bald, silver ties), and (b) new-style (long-haired, turtlenecks); writers and their agents, poets and peasants; the lonely in search of company, the gregarious in search of more. In these restaurants only the trappings are of the dining room, for these are living rooms away from home. (The bedroom away from home is not yet built into restaurants.) Eating at these restaurants can be OK, but like the art at openings, it is the ostensible, not the real, order of business. The order of business is business, or news, or to gossip, or to feel at home. Outsiders make the regulars feel uncomfortable; they figure there is someone here they don't know whom they *should* know.

• ALGONQUIN HOTEL

59 West 44th Street
LUNCH AND DINNER.
Closed Sunday night.
Reservations, 687–4400.
Credit cards: AE, BA, CB, DC.
Medium-priced.

You arrive for late supper and you are instructed to check your coat. Fine. But the hatcheck hag informs you that she's going home at midnight and she's not hanging around for one or two coats, so if you want to check it, OK, but ya better be ready to pick it up at midnight or she won't be responsible, in fact she'll just hang it here outside the hatcheck room and you can get it when you want it. You point out that you have been *instructed* to check it, that outside the hatcheck room the coat is insufficiently protected from unprincipled coat collectors, and that you insist on either keeping the coat with you or putting it in the safekeeping of the Algonquin staff. She moans, groans, accepts the coat, and informs you that she will deliver it to your table at midnight, and you do not enter into a discussion with her of the idiocy of compulsory checking of coats to assure neatness of the dining room if neatness does not count after midnight.

Or you arrive at nine for the dinner that supposedly is served until nine-thirty, and you are informed that dinner is over and that supper has begun—that, in fact, the hours have been changed, which is not true, but you let it go. You are given the supper menu. Fine. The supper menu lists Our Chef's Chafing Dish for Tonight, and you ask what it is, and you are informed that, yes, it's true, it's too late to order dinner, but it's also too early to order hot supper, perhaps you would like a sandwich or some cold cuts, and you demur, pointing out that the supper menu itself states that dinner is served until nine-thirty, and you will settle only for some of the famous hot roast beef, certainly it is not made to order, but the kitchen refuses the waiter.

Try lunch, and try informing your waiter that you want your salad after your main course, and he places the already dressed salad on the far corner of your table so that you can easily reach it later. If you actually settle for that cold supper, you will find that the waiter may politely ask whether you want cole slaw or potato salad with your Assorted Cold Meats, apparently for the purpose of bringing the one you did not want; that to get the Apple, Walnut and Raisin Salad that ostensibly accompanies the Tongue and Swiss Cheese platter you simply have to get lucky; and to get mustard with any of these things, you must stand and wave your arms.

Whatever you try, your check arrives unrequested. And if that is not enough to unseat you, there is always plenty of closing-up activity at the end of lunch or supper to make the idea of a brandy and coffee unthinkable—the lights are turned up, tables are stripped, yawning waiters bid each other goodbye.

This is the famous Hotel Algonquin, with its handsome wood-paneled Oak Room, much like the dining room of an ancient men's club, where the lunchtime talk is business, business, business, where half the customers are known by name, and where the peculiar eating habits of many are catered to without so much as a double take (cornflakes and milk for this one, Melba toast and raw vegetables for that one). And there is the ornate, pillared pink Rose Room, where the gay after-theater crowd tumbles in at around ten o'clock to tipple and nibble. But most of all, of course, there is the literary lobby lounge, with its Victorian sofas and deep armchairs, to which one-half the editorial staff of *The New Yorker* repairs at four o'clock in the afternoon (three on Friday) to check up on who is leaving the office early, where the food is peanuts and the wine is whiskey, and where there are bells on the low cocktail tables to summon the waiter for another round.

Some of the food here is dreadful, some is good, and a few items are superb; and the inconsistency among items is almost matched by the inconstancy of any given dish. On one day, for example, your Steak Tartare, Garni, is made with far too much mustard, no oil, anchovies that are sliced in half, at best in thirds, rather than reduced to a paste, or left out and served as a garnish; on another day the balance is better. The meat is always good, apparently ground to order, but the waiters simply do not know the dish, and you should insist on mixing it yourself or not order it. Sometimes there is bouillabaisse, and since it is made to order, the fish is not overcooked. The ingredients are not the world's finest (mackerel, a few shrimp, and a recently frozen crayfish from another continent), but the broth is fairly well garlicked, there is actually saffron in the preparation, and the whole thing is a decent plate of food. The roast beef is thick, pink and tender, and the calf's liver is expertly grilled, so that the flavor is brought out without eliminating the moistness of the thin slices. There are decent steaks, French and Italian dishes that are available in better versions in French and Italian restaurants, good egg dishes, and good salads if you avoid those that are basically green salads. The Apple, Walnut and Raisin Salad, for example, is made with crisp apples, crunchy walnuts, fresh celery and soft black raisins, all in a thin mayonnaise, garnished with currant jelly.

The lunch and dinner menus are very much alike, and the supper menu is a simplification of those, eliminating all items that require a staff in the kitchen except for a couple of hot items that are kept in chafing dishes at the buffet setup at the back of the lounge. You order from the menu, and the waiter orders from the gent behind the buffet. Sometimes there is curried seafood, but it is made with canned crabmeat, scallops and packaged curry powder. Sometimes there is Beef Stroganoff, but it is not made with sour cream, if you can imagine such a thing. The best supper here is a cold supper, and if you must have something hot, the onion soup is not bad. The base is consommé rather than good, strong stock, but it is an acceptable bowl of hot soup. The cold cuts and cheese are in good condition, as are the cole slaw, potato salad, pickles and olives that are the usual garnishes.

The best food at the Algonquin is the desserts. The mocha mousse layer cake is vibrant with its strong flavor of fresh coffee; the so-called apricot tart is more than that, consisting as it does of a layer of cake that is a kind of date-nut bread on which apricot preserves are spread, all of which is then buried in whipped cream and almonds. Regular coffees and fancy coffees.

The Algonquin is one of those institutions which are not exactly run, but permitted to chug along. Some of the waiters are so incompetent that they arouse your sympathy before they outrage you. When the customers fill the place, their comfort in these familiar surroundings adds more to your feeling of well-being than anything the house undertakes.

• ELAINE'S

1703 Second Avenue (near 88th Street)
LUNCH AND DINNER.
Reservations, TE 1–9558.
No credit cards.
Medium-priced.

Elaine's (the restaurant) is famous for Elaine's (the proprietress's) icy or, at best, cool reception of any customer she does not know. On her own territory Elaine is the boss, and she wants everyone to realize it. For this endearing trait (and, it appears, for this alone) the literati have made Elaine's their restaurant and Elaine their Buddha. But is there another Elaine? Under that tough veneer, is there another veneer? Does this coarse exterior conceal a heart? And if so, what is it made of?

Being the darling of any fashionable set sure can get you into trouble. The set may not realize that the darling is not so darling off her turf; on neutral ground Elaine has trouble—after all, it's tough to throw someone out when he's not in your restaurant. Elaine gets invited to parties, and when the company is sophisticated, suave and unruffled—when, in short, they are not begging for a table at Elaine's—Elaine sits in a corner, going forth frequently, but only to replenish her plate, New York's most popular wallflower preserving her figure.

"To understand all makes us very indulgent," quoth Madame de Staël, so we overlook the symptoms of Elaine's pathology in search of pleasure in her restaurant. We must also, it is true, disregard the reflected malady sometimes seen in the waiters, but their crust is seamed, and if their witless brevity is countered with glazed indifference, they relent and struggle to gain favor. The food is decent, sometimes good, the customers picturesque, each sex in its way, and to the extent possible within the restrictions of literary etiquette, the mood is relaxed, even a little gay. (The etiquette, by the way, is a simple one. You speak only to those at your own table. To stride across the room, hand outstretched, to "Hi-Charlie" Charlie is an act of such abject gaucherie that ripples of empathic, nauseated embarrassment cause customers to close their eyes and cringe at the opposite end of the room. But there is heat beneath the cool, and if you walk in confident and unknown, and act, generally, as if Elaine's is your oyster, you will be warmed by curious glances.)

Elaine's consists of two long, narrow adjacent stores. The place is dim, the walls are dark and vaguely muraled, the tables are well spaced (no two are adjacent). The waiters strike odd poses—this one wanders down the aisle as he removes the cork from a bottle of wine; that one delivers a pot of espresso while clutching a rolled-up tablecloth under his arm. When there is nothing to do, they protrude their stomachs for the purpose of making a place to rest their crossed arms. There is a bar near the front, at the end of which Elaine takes her post until she sits herself down to eat late in the evening. When most of the customers have gone home, the cloths are removed from the black-topped tables and a core of regulars hangs on for a few more hours, for a bit of serious drinking.

There is a menu. It does not, for example, list the squid salad, the best appetizer in the place. It's hard to figure out why it is called squid salad instead of seafood salad, when it also includes shrimp and mussels, but it is made of fresh-tasting ingredients, including string beans, onions, capers and parsley as well as the seafood, all in a fresh vinaigrette. The steamed mussels (not on the menu, not invariably available) are carefully prepared, fresh and tender. The steaming liquid is a bit of lemon and the liquid from the mussels, and the result is a very pure dish. On occasion there are pretty fair stuffed mushrooms (stuffed with bread crumbs, chopped mushroom stems and parsley, blanketed with a thin slice of cheese and stuck under the broiler), and sometimes there is a simple shrimp salad (shrimp, chopped celery, mayonnaise) in half an avocado—the shrimp are firm and the avocado is soft and ripe.

We slip a bit when we come to pasta and meat. The Fettuccine Alfredo arrives suspiciously soon after it is ordered, and sure enough, it is gummy, as if it has been waiting for you. Something called Chicken Toscana, described by the waiter as "chicken with brown sauce," whatever that means, turns out to be sautéed chicken, sautéed not enough, in a sauce which, it's true, is brown, but tasteless. The Veal Parmigiana is better—the veal is pale and tender, there is flavor in the tomato sauce, and the cheese is a decent mozzarella. You're much better off with a broiled steak (tender, seared, accurately cooked), or with the Mixed Seafood (steamed clams and mussels, shrimp, and unfortunately, a tasteless lobster tail, all in a thick, garlicky marinara sauce of the most fundamental, aggressive and delicious character).

Avoid the chocolate mousse—it is a misnamed chocolate pudding. The pecan tart is a small pecan pie of no particular distinction. When there is cold zabaglione and strawberries, have that—the zabaglione is thick and heavily flavored with Marsala, and the strawberries are ripe.

Take your time about ordering. Wait until two or three waiters have approached and told you what is available—their versions will vary, one from the other, but a pretty fair outline can be put together if you get more than one set of clues.

• LA GOULUE

28 East 70th Street
LUNCH AND DINNER.
Closed Sunday.
Reservations, 988–8169.
Credit cards: AE, BA, DC.
Expensive.

The so-called beautiful people, the beauty of whose bank books cannot be denied, have a new home, and they gladly suffer the indignities of cramped dining on mediocre food at excessive cost, albeit in handsome rooms, to be seen, to have it known they know where to be seen, to be hard by the ultimate destinations of these rendezvous.

The place is good-looking—connecting rooms, a small bar and a few cocktail tables in one of them, dark wood-paneled walls with large mirrors set in, Art Nouveau sconces, brown leather banquettes all around. The tables are set with snowy linen, heavy tableware, gleaming china, and thin glass vases holding a few long-stemmed flowers. But they are so closely abutted that to sit down at or to leave a table along the banquette straightaway requires that the table be moved to the center of the floor; at the tight corner tables the cooperation of both adjacent parties must be enlisted.

To dispense with the worst first, La Goulue honors only one dish on the menu with the name of the house. Salade de Crabe "Goulue" is a drugstore-crabmeat fiasco of the worst kind of canned, shredded crabmeat, in mayonnaise, flavored with a little commercial curry powder, served in an ice-cold avocado, all made pretty with a shake of paprika. This is also the most expensive first course. They could use frozen crabmeat instead of canned. They could have their avocados at room temperature. They could dress the thing in vinaigrette. They could at least serve a slice of lemon. They could, of course, remove it from the menu. Terrible.

From the worst to the best: the cold bass is listed as "Bar sauce vinaigrette," but the waiter brings, instead, the sauce Mignonette that is meant for the oysters. This is a fairly happy idea. The bass has been carefully poached, it is moist and flaky, and the tart Mignonette sauce, with its slightly marinated onions, scallions, green peppers and coarse black pepper is a stimulating if slightly too strong accompaniment to the delicate fish. The Bayonne ham is the genuine smoky article, but it should come with sweeter melon than the poorly selected tasteless one you are likely to get.

Barely acceptable versions of standard New York French menu items. The Boeuf Bourguignon is made with a good stock, but the preparation is careless. The beef has not been thoroughly browned to start, so it is a little bland; this causes the gravy to suffer too, and it tastes raw and soupy rather than like a solid sauce; and the onions and mushrooms are allowed to sit around in the stuff, so they are a part of the stew rather than what they are supposed to be—garnishes that have been partially married to the main dish. The Poularde à l'Estragon is a decent chicken, but the sauce is obviously and excessively thickened with starch, and the powerful flavor of tarragon is the powerful flavor of dried tarragon. Escalope de Veau à la Crème is made with very good veal, but the sauce, of cream, white wine and stock, is not finished off with any polish; it is just an OK sauce to moisten the nice thick noodles that accompany this dish. The Steak au Poivre is probably the best main course in the place—good beef studded with coarse pepper, accurately grilled, and served with that rarest of rarities, thin French fried potatoes that are beautifully browned and soft and slightly moist inside.

The cheeses are at room temperature, and they are pretty good. As for the desserts, the Orange au Grand Marnier consists of sliced oranges in Grand Marnier, with a little shredded orange rind, which is nice. However, if the combination is permitted to amalgamate for a while, this can be a terrific dessert; here it tastes as if it is thrown together by the bartender when you order it. The strawberries are not particularly luscious examples. Good coffee.

The list of bottled wines is dull and vastly overpriced.

★ JOE ALLEN

326 West 46th Street
LUNCH AND DINNER.
Reservations, 581–6464.
Credit cards: MC.
Medium-priced.

If you don't work in the theater, you may feel out of place here. Of the fifteen or so restaurants in this block, Joe Allen is one of the two or three that do any business to speak of after the local curtains go up. It appears that everyone who has nothing to do on stage is here, wishing they had.

The world's most unconcerned host leads you through what seems like Central Casting to a table from which he removes the "Reserved" sign (there is such a sign on every table, reserved or not), and you are thereupon seated at a fairly recently laundered red gingham cloth, a bottle of ketchup, a sheaf of paper napkins, and a bowl of packets of "natural unbleached sugar in the raw."

Joe Allen is an example of the classic two-room-restaurant-and-bar. The bar itself is in the entrance room (with a handful of tables) and most of the eating is done in the back room, at the rear of which is the kitchen, for all to see, looking like a clean, cute little installation at a small prison: dreary, pale-green tiles, gray duct work, and for color, a red fire extinguisher. The barroom and the dining room are separated by a brick wall with arched, unpaned windows, and most of the rest of the interior is brick too, hung with sporting and nautical photographs, theatrical posters, plus, in the dining room, large slates on which are chalked the available dishes—shrimp cocktail (not bad), chopped liver (bland), Caesar salad (made with powdered garlic—yuk!), strong, heavy chili, good steaks and chops, broiled fish, shish kebab (in an excess of Middle Eastern-ism, it is sprinkled with crushed wheat), shrimp in ale batter (five large, moist shrimp, served with sliced tomatoes), chicken pot pie, ham and other burgers, and standard desserts, including a very tasty and crunchy pecan pie. The food is solid stuff, reliable, uninspired and rarely disappointing. It is best accompanied by beer (Bass Ale on tap), and one's enjoyment of it varies directly with the intensity of one's hunger, perhaps even more directly with the degree of diversity and activity at nearby tables.

The people here seem to be permanently in costume. At one table a plump strabismic has equal billing with a spit-curled soubrette and a bun-headed mother-in-law. At another, Tarzan holds hands with Isadora Duncan. Some are boisterous eater-drinker-talkers, others intimate nibbler-sippers, but at either end of the gustatorial and conver-sational spectrum, the subject matter is the same:

"Darling, you il*lu*minated the part. She [sneer] milked it."

"He took one look at her you-know-whats, and the other tryouts were just a formal-ity."

The waiters make their contributions too:

"I'm sorry this is late. I forgot all about it." Not surprising; half the help here hug and kiss half the arriving customers—the misemployed consoling the unemployed.

★ MAXWELL'S PLUM

1181 First Avenue (at 64th Street)
LUNCH AND DINNER.
Reservations, 628–2100.
Credit cards: AE, BA, CB, DC, MC.
Expensive.

Maxwell's Plum suffers for its singles' bar reputation. That is not to say that its business suffers—as the prices go up, the intensity of the demand for tables seems to go up—but no one quite takes the Plum seriously as an eating place. It's true that in this three-ring circus, the center ring, between the elevated, ornate back room and the informal, street-level café, is a densely populated horseshoe bar at which the day's ration of, say, 1,000 customers buys precisely 1,000 drinks for the privilege of commencing conversations with strangers on territory where that is socially condoned. But the food in the outer rings is pretty good, in some instances original; the wine list is extensive and sanely priced; the seervice is available and pleasant; and the surroundings are a sight to see.

You arrive for your back-room reservation as part of an endlessly entering throng (something like the four-abreast Chinese who are somewhere perpetually throwing themselves off a cliff), most of which is heading headlong for the sexual gold mine at stage center ("If we can't make out here, we might as well give up"). You give your name to the gent behind the book, and he informs you that coats are checked downstairs, and that when you return, Van will show you to your table. "Van?" Your gaze is directed to a waiting figure who closes his eyes gently, smiles thinly, bows slightly and all in all makes it quite clear that he will wait patiently for your return from the hatcheck factory on the lower level. Or you show up for your café reservation, and your table is not ready, so you are instructed to keep your eye on the flashing lights over the entranceway, and when your number comes up, you're a winner.

Maxwell's Plum makes the Sign of the Dove look like a monastery. The ceiling is of molded plaster in many places, painted to look like hammered copper; that is, except for the ceiling in the back room, which is an acre of glowing stained glass illuminating a room papered in pointillist pink nudes against a pointillist blue-green ground. There are flickering gas lamps, ornate mirrors, statuary, velvet banquettes, flowers on all the tables. Here, when someone orders one of what the wine list refers to as "Rare and Extraordinary Wines," a busboy holds a candle while, by the light of it, a captain decants and examines the precious fluid. The café tables are covered with cloths of chrome-yellow gingham, there are hundreds of ceramic animals hanging from the canopy over the sidewalk section, hanging plants at the windows, banks of flowering shrubbery, and pillars of painted brick.

Slightly different listings and pricings of dishes are available in the two sections of the huge place, with prices a little lower in the café.

The Hors d'Oeuvres Variés include a few interesting items, such as a rather mild guacamole made with good, ripe avocado; marinated fish that is flaky and lemony; well-garlicked cold ratatouille; Russian eggs, with a powerful dressing; and so on. For a more luxuriant assortment you may begin with a platter of Scottish salmon, smoked trout and smoked sturgeon. Admittedly, the quality of these foods is no tribute to the kitchen, but they are obtained from good sources and brought to the table in good condition—at room temperature, but with no sign of drying out—and they are served with a sparkling whipped-cream-and-horseradish sauce. The lobster bisque is made with lots of lobster, and it is thick and creamy.

You can get what they call Roast Wild Boar here, but though it may be roasted, it seems to have been battered and then sautéed. The meat is sweet, and it is served with slivered apples (they are slightly acid, which is good with this rich meat). Or you can have a cassoulet, here made with gamy meats and sausages, cooked until they have lightly burnt edges, all buried in crunchy white beans. Such a complex dish as Salmon en Croûte with Sorrel doesn't come off as well, although it *looks* lovely. The waiter expertly peals back the crust to cover the fish with a puréed mushroom sauce, but the sorrel stuffing has lost its sourness, the fish is overcooked, and the very good mushroom sauce can't really save tasteless fish, tasteless stuffing and tasteless pastry. If you want fish, order something simple, like grilled red snapper—the fish is perfectly cooked and lightly browned, and it is served with a delicate mustard sauce.

The pies and cakes are all good: a Black Forest cake that is part chocolate cake and part light chocolate mousse; good pecan pie that is loaded with nuts and cinnamon; banana fritters that are made with very ripe bananas, so that the crisp, deep-fried crust contrasts nicely with the sweet mushy center—this is served with a sauce of honey and cinnamon.

Sandwiches are available in the café.

★ PEARL'S

38 West 48th Street
LUNCH, MONDAY TO FRIDAY; DINNER, SUNDAY TO FRIDAY.
Closed Saturday.
Reservations, 586–1060.
No credit cards.
Medium-priced.

This is the *new* Pearl's, but with the same jokes on the menu—under "American" we have Chicken Chow Mein, Chicken Chop Suey, Pepper Steak, etc., just like in the old days at the old place. This is a system whereby the house can sell the stuff and still be above that sort of thing.

The old Pearl's was nondescript, the new one is anything but. The long narrow room is sleek, silvery, mirrored and sterile, which is appropriate to the traditionally icy service and to Miss Pearl's glacial demeanor. Surrounded by throngs of customers, she has a way of absent-mindedly straightening a place setting which suggests a search for tasks that will distract her from contact with the clientele. The customers do not mind. Pearl's is in the great tradition of Toots Shor's, Elaine's, and of course, Pearl's itself, those restaurants famous for their contemptuous owners, to which the rich and famous repair to demonstrate, we must conclude, that they are not held in contempt by the contemptuous owners and, therefore, that they must be rich and famous. Aspirers follow.

Each of these places garners its celebrities from a different world. The Pearl's world is the moneyed side of the media—TV, slick publishing. (The aspirers are from Seventh Avenue.) How different these journalists and hangers-on are from the four-eyed, hirsute intellectuals at Elaine's. Here you see *blazers*! And *crew cuts*! And sculptured, metallicized hair, and perfect teeth in perfect smiles, and suntans. Many are actually ringers for manicured dogs. At hangouts the food is not the thing, generally, but in this regard Pearl's is better than the others. Lots of humdrum stuff served here, but also some dishes that are terrific, so you can come here to ogle and also eat well, if you know your way around the bill of fare.

Look around, and what do you see? Everybody starts off with Yook Soong (you'll recognize it right away). You get a dish of lettuce leaves (crisp iceberg), a dish of hoisin sauce (thick, sweet and spicy), a dish of the stuff itself (an oily mixture of pork and crisp water chestnuts), and on request, a set of instructions from the waiter ("quarter teaspoon sauce, some pork, wrap in lettuce, eat with fingers"). The combination of cool greens, the succulent meat mixture, the sharp sweet sauce and a few bits of strong scallion make for an extraordinary first course. This place is also big on dumplings, and for something homier than the Yook Soong, the Har Gow is coarsely ground shrimp, slightly oiled, wrapped in a tender noodle bundle.

Among the best of the big-deal dishes is Pork with Black Bean and Garlic Sauce and Mustard Greens (to put it exactly as it is put on the menu). This is a hearty stewlike dish, made with large chunks of slightly fibrous and slightly chewy pork, heavily peppered, served in an oily sauce with two-inch lengths of scallions—winter food. Among the least of the big-deal dishes, albeit one of the most famous, is the Lemon Chicken. The appeal of this dish must be its peculiarity—it is composed of slivers of chicken (hardly identifiable as such from their taste), strands of lemon rind, and bits of shredded lettuce, all fused together in a cloyingly sweet flavor of lemon. The Poached Sea Bass with Pickled Cucumber and Scallions is also a sweet dish, but a much better one. It is made with fresh fish, and the vegetables are a nice contrast to the almost caramelized thick sauce.

There is little of interest among the desserts—lichees, preserved mixed fruits, kumquats, all from cans; an excellent sweet and tart lime sherbet.

On Sunday evenings there are three sittings—at five, seven-thirty, and at ten. The last of these is the fashionable one, with lots of big names and famous faces.

• P. J. CLARKE'S

915 Third Avenue (at 55th Street)
LUNCH AND DINNER.
Reservations, PL 9–1650.
No credit cards.
Medium-priced.

P. J. Clarke's is a saloon with a back room. A gigantic skyscraper was designed around it. Famous people eat in its little dining rooms.

In the front room the mirror behind the ancient, sagging bar has lost almost all its silver, and your image in it looks like an old photograph of a corpse, under a flag of the Irish Free State. The floor is of barbershop tiles, and the grandfather's clock gives the correct time twice a day. The juke box fails to drown out the beery middle-management pencil pushers who loudly exchange virile improvements on their pasts, ignored by the good-sport secretaries who accept liquid favors from dandy ad execs.

The back dining room is much like the front room, complete with bar, here used only for waiter service, and there are lots of little red-checked tables, and it is dark and clubby. The menu is chalked on a slate at the rear, and the white-shirted, long-aproned waiters (two generations—old, portly, red-nosed; young, thin, pink-nosed) move around a lot, exchange *macho* humor, and manage, finally, to get food and drink to the tables. And what does that consist of? Simple stuff, mostly, with a few anomalies: the ham in the ham-and-melon appetizer is sliced thick, spread on a plate and strewn with chunks of fairly ripe melon; the watercress soup, on a coarse potato base, has an honest, leafy taste (served with individual, cellophane-wrapped package of saltines); the really sparkling mushroom-and-spinach salad, usually eaten as an appetizer, has an accent of minced scallions and a nice lemony dressing.

The main courses include a perfectly good steak at $6.75, and a perfectly odd one called Steak Diane, which turns out to be tender sliced beef in warm Worcestershire sauce. (Yes, Virginia, there is a Steak Diane but this isn't it, which is all right, but this isn't anything, which isn't.) The Steak Tartare is of good, freshly ground beef, with capers and onions, and so on, but no oil or mustard. (Yes, Virginia, there is a Steak Tartare, etc.) You can have something called "smothered" for 50 cents—it consists of fried mushrooms and onions, it is delicious, and you can put it on anything.

The chef's salad is made up of lots of large chunks of moist, white chicken, hard-boiled eggs, tomatoes, onions, radishes and lettuce, all in good condition, and in a powerful blue-cheese dressing—good with beer. The very nice hamburgers are delivered on toasted, buttered buns. The vegetables are overcooked, the potatoes are OK.

There is a bouncer here who would frighten a whale, and a strutting host named Franky who walks on his heels, sucks up to the famous, and makes a federal case out of the most elementary responsibilities of his job. He looks around a lot as he walks, now behind him over his left shoulder, now over his right, as if to catch out by surprise waiter and customer derelictions of decorum. He finds nothing, invariably, shoots his cuffs and struts some more. An odious presence.

★★★ RUSSIAN TEA ROOM

150 West 57th Street
LUNCH AND DINNER.
Reservations, CO 5–0947.
Credit cards: AE, BA, CB, DC, MC.
Expensive.

The Russian Tea Room is not merely cheerful, it is extraordinarily happy. The room is happy, the customers are happy, the waiters seem happy, the food is mostly happy. Many famous musicians and theater people eat here, and even the unfamous look famous—it's the feeling of well-being and the look of success that come of being properly fed and cared for.

The customers? Priests and soubrettes mingle with dress manufacturers and publicity agents. Seventy-year-old ladies smoke Luckies thoughtfully and deeply, as if they were Havana cigars. (O yesteryear.) Enter nervous, impatient, shifty-eyed, minked, high-polished lionesses. They end up with roving forks (Your blini look marvelous, I wish I'd ordered that . . . oh, very good!) or fingers (May I dip my bread in your eggplant?).

The long room is dim, the pink-clothed tables rather crowded together, and as everyone knows, the Christmas decorations never come down, not even for the Holidays. A skillfully placed strip of mirror that runs the length of the room above the banquettes enables those who face the wall to scan the room.

The food is all tasty, ample and in good condition. A chopped-liver appetizer served at midnight does not have the dried crust found on this dish in other restaurants an hour or two into the dinner schedule. Of the other appetizers, the Eggplant Orientale is overwhelmingly delicious—baked chopped eggplant, made into a paste with garlic and oil. One eats it with bread.

There is a superb maatjes herring—sweet, sour, salty, soft, firm—and good borscht, hot or cold.

Among the severest penalties of poverty is having to drink, say, Chablis with your caviar, when the people at the next table are having champagne with theirs. But all life is struggle. Carry on. RTR serves caviar with blini (thin buckwheat pancakes) and sour cream.

There are many other good main courses, including Luli Kebab (very simple, broiled lamb patties), Chicken Kiev, Eggplant à la Russe (baked au gratin), and Pelmeny (beef and veal dumplings), which are served at Wednesday lunch.

For dessert, halvah is available, good French pastries, a baba au rhum (it is only a cut above coffeeshop Danish), and blackberry-wine Jell-O. Perhaps it is best to sate one's self before dessert.

One evening ten "girls" from the offices of International Cable & Slab, or some such, came to the Russian Tea Room for a snack after their annual evening out to a Broadway musical. They were treated like queens, with a host at each end of their long table carefully noting down the idiosyncratic preferences each had for her pink or yellow drink. Questions about the food were carefully answered, sandwiches were subdivided, pastry fillings described before selections were made. Van Cliburn at a nearby table received no better treatment. And at around one in the morning the party was gaily discussing the advisability of doing this more often.

Many of the waiters are Old New York Jewish, the men whose hands tremble only when they are carrying soup. And a number of more rough-hewn young fellows who joined the staff a few years back are now mellowing. They no longer curse small tips; they know they all average out in the end. The European busboys do their job as though it were the most important work in the world, seriously and rapidly.

At suppertime there are excellent open sandwiches and egg dishes at reasonable prices.

• "21" CLUB

21 West 52nd Street
LUNCH AND DINNER.
Closed Sunday.
Reservations, JU 2–7200.
Credit cards: AE, CB, DC, MC.
Very expensive.

Jack and Charlie's, as the cognoscenti like to call it, is probably the most successful culinary sleight-of-hand ever carried out. It has been going on since Prohibition, and the flow of customers is inexhaustible. Yet anyone who attends this place once, and then voluntarily does it again, has got to have been fooled by the reputation, the glittering clientele or the intensely masculine interior, because the food, frantically tended flames at the serving tables notwithstanding, is nothing but Stouffer's at three times the price, from the Pâté of Chicken Livers "21" (an airless mousse much like peanut butter) through the Terrapin Maryland (turtle à la king) to the Kersen Aardbeien en ys Van Urk (berries, including white strawberries, with pineapple and raspberry sherbet, in tutti-frutti sauce).

To the credit of the place, the ingredients are of decent quality, but the preparation of the food is so uniformly lackluster, and its service so pedestrian, that the only thing to be admired here, in fact to be wondered at in awe, is the list, lengthy and starry, of gourmets, epicures, columnists, dining-out authorities, travel books and restaurant guides that not only take "21" seriously but treat it with a respect usually reserved for the central figures in the world's religions.

Everyone "knows" that it's very difficult to get into "21." In fact, there is nothing to it: make a reservation and show up. It's true that the man at the desk will greet you coolly if he doesn't know you; that the coat-room attendant, if she sizes you up for a dodo, will give you your ticket and say "Don't lose it"; that you may be ignored for a while before you are transferred to one of the host's underlings; that the latter may be hard to follow as he leads you, without looking back, to a table through a thick crowd of black-jacketed captains (from whom he is impossible to distinguish); and that your captain will take your order willingly enough, but may well answer your questions, if any, with a degree of impatience that is only partly the result of his ignorance of the menu; but all that must be weighed against the security that comes of the certain knowledge that the food at "21," though tasteless, is harmless. This is a clean place.

It's best to pass up the more ambitious dishes for simpler food, though this is no guarantee of results. There is no faulting the clams or oysters, but the ratatouille appetizer, for example, is little more than a dish of poached vegetables, whereas, on the other hand, the clam-juice cocktail ($1.75) is certain not to disappoint. The Blue Lake Bean Salad tastes like cold overcooked beans, but the Bismarck herring is firm and tart. At $3.25 you can actually get unripe avocado. There is much Caesar salad eaten here as an appetizer. To call it Caesar salad is to take a liberty; to serve it at all is to take license—decent greens in an eggless, overly sour dressing. The cold Sénéga-laise soup is served here in a bloodless version (imagine a few grains of curry powder combined with sour cream and minced chicken) that would be a big hit at Patricia Murphy's. Like much of the food here it is wholesome, but prepared for eaters whose idea of perfection is Mama's mashed potatoes.

You can get good roast beef here; and the sautéed brook trout with capers is fresh and flaky, if not inspired. But "21" is supposed to be a big deal for game. If you order partridge, pheasant and quail, you can be certain that they will be given an all-American roasting to the point of stringy dryness of flesh within, limp dejection of skin without. The pitchers of currant jelly (Ann Page?) and white sauce (Wondra and milk) are actually welcome.

There is a "21" Burger listed as a *Spécialité.* (Your waiter may allow as how it is the most popular dish in the place.) This is the final triumph—the world's most ordinary dish, a hamburger, prepared without any imagination, served with a sheaf of hangdog string beans and peddled as a specialty of one of the most expensive restaurants on earth, for which board chairmen, pols, celebrities of stage, screen and tube point the noses of their liveried chauffeurs toward West 52nd Street.

The Eggplant Orientale consists of nothing but stewed eggplant and onions in a thin tomato broth. The so-called Pommes Anna are made in grease, not clarified butter, and should be called by another name, or better, dropped. The chestnut purée, of fresh chestnuts, is thick, slightly sweet and delicious.

You are cordially warned that soufflés take an hour. So you order the Crêpes Soufflées "21," which take only thirty minutes, except that they take an hour. (How long would the soufflé take? Is the rule to double, or to add, thirty minutes?) The Crêpes Soufflées turn out to be a bit of brandied soufflé filling in pancakes (so far not bad), served with a congealed crème Anglaise that lacks utterly the sharp flavor of cooked milk but tastes, rather, like an ulcer patient's custard. The apple pancake is better—the same pancake, filled with pretty good stewed apples.

The wine list is not exorbitant—there are decent wines at $8, and some nineteenth-century wines at many times that amount.

There is a low-ceilinged barroom on the main floor, with a number of tables nearby —this is the informal part of "21." Upstairs there are wood-paneled·walls, red linen, red leather chairs and banquettes, silver urns and plates on shelves and on the walls, sporting prints, horsy wallpaper—the effect is of a hunting lodge in the form of a mansion. Where else can you see, at a table for six, six gray suits? If money is beside the point, you might drop in sometime (reserve) to see what all the fuss is about. A steak lunch or a cold-salmon dinner will be quite all right. And nothing will taste actually vile.

Lincoln Center

In the beginning many feared that the architectural blemish called Lincoln Center—a quadrangle of bleached, bulbous mausolea in a clearing near the intersection of Columbus Avenue and Broadway—was the single rotten eyesore that could be the seed of the Big Apple's final cultural decay, irrespective of the quality of the music-making within. No faith. New York can swallow several Lincoln Centers before breakfast, with no dyspepsia beyond a slowing of automotive peristalsis in the major arteries at concert times.

Lincoln Center has been taken up by New Yorkers as a poor, ugly-duckling relation is clasped to the bosom of a happy and generous family. We rain attentions on it, and of course, we circle it with restaurants. Most of these eating places are nothing more than crass exploiters of the commercial opportunities created by this concentration of culture, but a few exist in a restaurant tradition as well as in a financial one, and in the better of the Lincoln Center establishments both the food and the customers are treated with respect.

★ AUNT FISH

Lincoln Plaza (Broadway at 63rd Street)
LUNCH AND DINNER.
Reservations, 799-7200.
Credit cards: AE, BA, CB, DC, MC.
Expensive.

This enterprise is the combined undertaking of the O'Neal boys (Ginger Man, O'Neals' Baloon, Landmark) and a surviving interest of the late and mourned Lobster, of West 45th Street. It would be hot stuff to report that the establishment combines the best of both worlds. No can do.

As the ghastly name is already right there at the head, one may as well proceed with the other inanities. You wait ten minutes for your small glass of 95-cent draft beer, and during the interval you piddle very briefly with a "bread" basket of sesame sticks, cellophane packets of tasteless things called Nabisco Dandy Soup and Oyster Crackers, and some clay models of hot biscuits, cold. It may be that the delivery of the beer was delayed as your waiter first committed to memory the sounds of your instructions and then repeated them to the house translator somewhere in the back. In full recognition that even the non-English-speaking must work, it is suggested that waiting on tables is not the occupation of choice for those so handicapped, unless the house translator accompanies them on their rounds; it is no help for the waiter to repeat ever more loudly that the special fish of the day (the menu suggests that you "Ask Your Waiter What's Available Today") is Breed Steed. Or perhaps it was Steed Breed. (At any rate, he *can* be quick, and later on he tucks your check right under your dessert dish while you are eating from it. Of course he offsets this undue haste by disappearing for fifteen minutes just when you have decided it is time to pay it and leave.)

Now here comes a group of four of moderate means. They seat themselves, consider the menu while they unfold their napkins, sip their water and sample the stale crackers; they decide to repair to the much improved Teacher's restaurant farther up Broadway, to save their solvency. They leave. The busboy carefully refolds the napkins (late in the departeds' laps) for the next guests.

The words "Aunt Fish Serves Fresh Fish" are in quotes not only here but as printed on the menu. There is a theory that if an advertising slogan is in quotation marks, the advertiser, if challenged, need not prove its accuracy, only that someone once said it. The slogan is probably technically correct, if by "fish" you mean the things with the gills that swim. Aunt Fish's Deviled Crabs, for example, taste as if they were, it is true, once fresh, but that then they were frozen, shipped, thawed, seasoned, baked, frozen, thawed, heated, served. And partially eaten. Just enough to report that the brown substance that arrives packed into clam shells is stringy, crusted over with a breading that is spicy-hot but tasteless. Only the bits of cartilage prove that some of the stuff is crabmeat. Aunt Fish's Shrimp Sauté, it should be noted, is a far, far better thing—very nice shrimp, crunchy and not excessively cooked in the butter, white wine, parsley and a bit of garlic, though the sauce this yields is a bit off. The oysters and clams *are* fresh. The New England clam chowder is a satisfying plate of soup, strongly flavored with corn and celery, heavy in the dull way that suggests thickening with starch, and short on clams. N.E. chowder is the kind of soup that causes arguments—everyone knows how it *should* taste—and this one in particular will probably please no one, though if you simply approach it as a plate of food, you will find that it is not bad.

They claim the fish is fresh, but they do not assert that the lobsters are "live." Whatever they are, they are not long from the water—they are accurately broiled to the point where they are hot, moist and sweet—but anything short of a fresh-killed lobster loses something of the bright brininess you hope for. This is a good lobster, better than what you will get in most places in New York, including some where they are "live."

Eight dollars for a slab of broiled striped bass. But this *is* fresh, soft and flaky and juicy and slightly grained, harmlessly colored with a storm of paprika, glistening with butter. Even the accompanying tartar sauce has a fresh sparkle to it and the crunchy quality of freshly minced pickles—on occasion the stuff has been colored green, however, which gives it a frightening cast.

Sautéed Bay Scallops, Parsley Butter, is $8.75, though once again the quality of the dish is impeccable. Bay scallops they are, not the huge ocean scallops or circlets cut from a halibut, and they are lightly floured before they are sautéed in butter, just to the point where the plump little bodies are warm, moist and not yet toughened, and the coating of flour crisped and browned.

Aunt Fish's Fish Fry at almost $9 is yet another O'Neal steal, and at these à la carte prices it will not require much business for this new place to succeed. This is not a bad deep-fry of scallops, shrimps, clams and what the menu identifies as "filet of sole," which is perfectly fresh but nondescript. The elements are dipped in a thick batter, deep-fried in hot fat, and served. The batter could be crisped to a slightly more brittle point, but the dish is ample and satisfying in a pleasant junk-food kind of way.

No baked potatoes. Your waiter explains that they had them for a while, couldn't get them to "come out right" and gave up. That's the spirit. If, as sometimes happens, your waiter asks whether you want hearts of lettuce or coleslaw and then brings neither, don't despair. The heads of lettuce are quartered early in the day and apparently stored over the radiator. The coleslaw, with caraway seeds, is cool, crisp and otherwise unexceptional. The vegetables that accompany the main courses are kept in a steam table. They may be OK at the crack of noon.

Your waiter inquires if you would like dessert. Yes, you would. He informs you, "We ga ripe putty, caramallacassa, and caracay." Out of curiosity you order one of each and ask that they be brought at once. The ripe putty is more like a pebbly rice pudding than anything else, and the caramallacassa would have you persuaded, if you didn't know better, that it is nothing more than a bland caramel custard. But the caracay, ah, the caracay. You decipher and decipher, even after it has arrived and you have looked at it and even tasted it. You call for a copy of the printed menu. Could it be? Could it be that the listed "Carrot Cake" bears some relationship to the exotic dish before you? Perhaps. In any event, either the carrot cake or the caracay is the most delicious anomaly in the restaurant—a huge chunk of dark cake, honeyed and moist, cloved and cinnamoned, with a dark crust and a copious topping of something related to whipped cream. A miracle. Where, you wonder, do they get it?

This is a pleasant enough place, retaining none of the appointments of the previous tenants—La Grande Cuisine de France and La Quiche. The tables are on two levels; many of them afford glorious views of West 63rd Street, and, by turns in the room and partitions, much of the place has been given a coziness that belies the restaurant's spaciousness. The decorators aimed for the spare, lean look of Gloucester House—there is a nautical cleanness to the ivory walls and to the wooden floors, there are nautical prints here and there, the ample tables are crisp-looking and slightly softened by fresh flowers in little glass vases. The small bar at the left is of copper, which is nice, but the hangers-about are members of the O'Neal crowd, and their audible, inelegant conversation may lead you to believe you are before or after the performance at Madison Square Garden on fight night, not at Lincoln Center.

★★CAFÉ DES ARTISTES

1 West 67th Street
LUNCH AND DINNER.
Reservations, TR 7–3500.
Credit cards: AE, BA, DC, MC.
Medium-priced.

Ah, the past, recaptured and preserved as in an old movie, the place so redolent of the thirties that you automatically look down to see if the snappy clientele is wearing spats or silver slippers.

This is no relation to the egregious restaurant of the same name that occupied these premises in recent years, though the portly former host, the old cud-chewing waddler who once so discourteously mishandled all but the tottering regulars (whose private reliquary this place was) is still in evidence, presumably to help retain some of the slow action that kept this place from slipping the one last rung below what seemed like perpetual moribundity. Now he is as much the wandering duck as ever, but his present function is merely hereness, and he carries it out perfectly.

Very little in the way of renovation has been imposed on the Café except for some felt on once dingy walls, and artfully lowered lighting. But that is all it took to accentuate the jewel-like quality of these small rooms, the semidarkness brightened here and there by cavorting peachy nudes, the subjects of the famous Howard Chandler Christy murals. In the pretty barroom the mirrors are still present, and there are black-and-white prints hung on the new tan felt. Throughout there are tables, quite cheek-to-cheek along the banquettes, and in the barroom there are a few booths wherein one may appreciate a bit of privacy. Avoid tables near the front door—on icy days there are chilling blasts.

Two speeds of service—slow and halt. Everyone is polite, you understand, even glad to see you when they get back to you, but then again, it's been very long time no see. And then there is the supervision of the floor—two different parties promised the same table, and the race is most assuredly to the swift who run for it as soon as it is set up, without benefit of escort.

You are at last seated, and you inquire of your waiter, what, please, may the red carafe wine be? Burgundy, says your servant. You inform him that there is Burgundy and Burgundy, and you suggest, further, that such inexpensive carafe wine is probably neither. He assures you that it is Burgundy. He is right, of course, in the way that a White Owl is a cigar, and you opt for a review of what the menu refers to as "Good Wines from the Café's Cellar 6.00 by the bottle" (capitalization and punctuation theirs), and you are brought a couple of metal baskets for your inspection, in which are standing a handful of wines—not bad stuff at all, and the Moulin à Vent at $6 is a bargain.

The printed menu is a matrix of printed categories (chilled soup, veal, etc.) and some always-available dishes (gravlax salmon, gazpacho, etc.) onto which are dittoed, in purple ink, a couple of dozen additional items available the day of your visit. Among these are Oysters or, at a 25-cent premium, Oysters Saucisse. As these mollusks are not invariably the morning's catch (though they are certainly not over the hill), set aside the notion of having them with just a squeeze of lemon and a couple of turns of the pepper mill. Surely any slight incorrectness of taste will be obscured by the cocktail sauce, but it is firmly recommended that you try the Saucisse version, in which the circle of raw oysters surrounds a little ramekin of tomato-flavored beef broth and chopped sausages, into which you dip the oysters before eating them. For some strange reason this hefty sauce does well with the oysters, and if there is a hint of off taste, the sauce eliminates it while permitting the sweet taste of fresh oysters to show through—a good dish. The aforementioned gravlax is billed as Gravlax Salmon, Dill Marinated. This is the famous Scandinavian dish of raw salmon that has been marinated in salt and pepper, sugar and dill, served, traditionally, with a sweetened dill-and-mustard sauce. The Café's version is quite terrific, several slices of the deep-red tender and sweet fish sprinkled with coarsely ground pepper and served with a strong and sparkling version of the mustard sauce.

Each day a pasta dish is listed. One of these is Spinach Noodles with Mussels in Cream, and it is a semisuccessful essay. In re the noodles, instead of long, even strands we have shreds, as if these are the result of a first try on an at-home noodle-making machine; they are not overcooked, and they retain a subtle spinach flavor, but it's frustrating to eat the slippery slivers with a fork. As to the mussels in their cream sauce, the thickened cream is perfectly nice, but the quite fresh mussels are not quite perfectly rinsed—a single grain of sand in every single mussel. Your waiter brings what looks like a pencil sharpener, in which there are chunks of Parmesan cheese—a few turns of the handle liven the dish.

Unusual preparations of snails are becoming fashionable around town, and the Café is right there with Garlic Snails Sautéed with Prosciutto & Onions. These are snails without shells, tossed in an oily pan with the ham, onions and tomato and served on a layer of what seems to be sautéed garlic. The snails are at once metallic, oily and briny —sea-gamy—and the slivers of ham are an excellent foil to the rich snails.

Young Duckling with Pear in Williamin Brandy—the duck itself will give you a good notion of how to roast a bird. This one is crisp and moist, and the listing "Young" duckling is apparently true, for it is juicy and tender. The pear-and-pear-brandy treat-ment, however, yields a sauce so delicately flavored as to be overpowered by the rich bird.

That New York is not a pork city is the only conclusion that can be drawn from pork's almost universal absence from New York menus. And in fact it is not regularly listed here, which is a pity, for the Tenderloin of Pork, purpled in under "spit-roast," and served in a brown, gravylike sauce, arrives, surprisingly, as several slices of meat and one chop, and it has the sweet, fatty succulence that makes pork the richest of meats. The pork is surrounded by garnishes—nicely browned and creamy scalloped potatoes and a buttery purée of broccoli.

Escallopine of Veal, Gypsy Style, does not flaunt its Romany origins. The dish is made with perfect pale, buttery meat, but the sautéing is carried out at too low a temperature, and the cutlets are not properly browned. They are surmounted by strands of tongue, the whole thing served in a creamy sauce—an excellent dish that would be even better if the meat were more carefully cooked.

Olive Cured Mozzarella is the regularly available house cheese. It is queer stuff, fibrous and permeated with olive-sourness—pickled cheese. But sometimes other cheeses are available, and some of them can be just as odd, including something called Crème de Gruyère, which tastes like candied cheese, while some others can be quite normal, such as a good, strong French Roquefort.

Pass up the temptingly named Strawberry Collage, a three-container ensemble of (1) merely decent berries, some of them unripe, (2) sticks of sponge cake, most of them a little dried out, and (3) whipped cream which is of real cream, but "whipped" by a machine, so that it lacks the buttery quality of the real thing—it is only light. Opt, rather, for the pumpkin pie, when it is available—it is brightly spiced with cinnamon and cloves; or for the chocolate tart, an almost black cake under an equally dark icing, crushed nuts in every bite.

• FIORELLO'S

1900 Broadway (near 63rd Street)
LUNCH AND DINNER.
Reservations, 595-5330.
Credit cards: AE, BA.
Medium-priced.

A snappy, snacky place for after a performance at Lincoln Center; an utterly disastrous one for a pre-concert dinner.

This is a garish place, offshoot of a well-known Roman trattoria. The tabletops, for example, are of *copper.* Over the opening in the rear wall, through which one may view the gleaming kitchen, is the name of the restaurant, in soft-glowing green neon—*inside.* The walls are of sweeping diagonal lines of dark mirror and stone-colored rough masonry. Low-hanging factory lights, modern blond captain's chairs, red tile columns, an old-style Wurlitzer juke box, complete with the tenor voice of Mario Lanza, the strings of Percy Faith, and the less easily identified instruments of more recent lights. You reach the facilities through the kitchen—all is clean.

But the dinner hour is a joke. Every table is taken, the kitchen is of limited capacity, the dining room is understaffed and short on civility under the circumstances. A waiter tells you, "Your waiter will be with you soon." Turns out he's your waiter, but in the meantime you desisted from trying to interrupt him in his flights. When you are handed the menu, you are not told what is out, and fifteen minutes later, when you order, you discover that out are the things you want. Finally you get some OK baked clams and good, nicely toasted garlic bread. *A moment later* you get your Tortellini Fiorello and Veal Marsala. You protest that now the service is too rapid, and the waiter in a grand display of exasperation, which he shares with your neighbors, allows as how some customers apparently don't eat out very often. The veal is unexceptional, with wilted mushrooms and a vague memory of Marsala, but the tortellini are good, in a thick creamy sauce studded with peas and bits of tomato.

Post-concert dining is staggered, and there is less of it. People start their suppers by sharing the big bowl of slightly bizarre "Caesar" salad—it includes chickpeas and

Parmesan cheese, not a great deal of garlic, and plenty of oregano in the wine-vinegar dressing. They proceed to the Paglia e Fieno alla Romano, a mixture of white and green noodles in a pleasantly heavy sauce livened up with peas, mushrooms and bits of sausage—the pasta, however, is on occasion gummy.

No pizza during dinner, but you can have it at other times. The crust is thick and tasteless, and to certain partisans, that is the only correct pizza crust, and the ingredients you may choose—sausages, pepperoni, meatballs, mushrooms, green peppers—are oily and strong.

Rather excessive Italian desserts. Something called, modestly, Zeppole Straordinario, are those street-fair fritters, available with brandied apricot preserves that are low on brandy and the flavor of apricot, but high on sugar. The Crêpe Italienne is a tender crêpe, filled and topped with whipped cream and touched with the same apricot preserves. The Chocolate Nut Pie is a bad pecan pie with chocolate and whipped cream.

A pretty awful place, but if you come in for pizza or pasta when things are slow, you will not be badly used.

★ FLEUR DE LIS

141 West 69th Street
LUNCH AND DINNER.
Reservations, 874–9060.
Credit cards: AE, BA, CB, DC, MC.
Medium-priced.

Frequented in large measure by old-time West Siders—semiradical intellectual entrepreneurs, music teachers, Viennese reminiscers and small-time diamond traders—supplemented by an admixture of new West Siders—Juilliard students, young unmarrieds and boutique operators—this straightforward restaurant sometimes fails to please lovers of *haute cuisine* because of the vigorous quality of its definitely unsubtle food and service.

The menu here is startlingly elaborate, but then, this place does a very steady level of very good business. Of more than twenty-five appetizers, several are of genuine interest. The gallantine of pork is, in fact, a hearty headcheese, heavily weighted toward tongue. It is bound in a strong jelly, and tastes great with bread, strong mustard and white wine. The Bismarck herring is as good as Zabar's best, which is saying a great deal. It is served with pickled raw onions, and it is firm, shiny, spicy and brilliantly sour—not exactly French, but a superb appetizer. One first-course oddity is the Salad Niçoise, which in this country is usually thought of as a complete lunch. This is a small Niçoise, with the usual tuna, tomato, hard-boiled eggs and anchovies. But a sprinkling of slivers of superb green olives, raw onions and green peppers, and a dressing of a good, mustardy vinaigrette, help to convert it into a stimulating first course.

The pâté is a simple, garlicky country version, and the garlic sausage is a savory chain of discs of powerful charcuterie laid over a mountain of delicious potato salad—very oily, well-peppered, loaded with parsley and lightly flavored with onion.

This is not exactly a restaurant for fancy food. Not that there is anything wrong with the Seafood Cardinale or even with the Lobster Thermidore; rather, better versions are available elsewhere and Fleur de Lis is more adept at, for example, grilled fresh salmon, with butter and parsley, which is bright pink, flaky and strong, or grilled halibut, a fish which is almost invariably ruined by cooks determined to eliminate its oiliness and thereby end up with something that seems to have been woven. Be assured, the halibut here is oily.

Game in season is often available, and the venison stew (Civet of Venison au Beaujolais) is gamy, tender and authoritative—the sauce is a deep mahogany; the meat, which is thoroughly browned, keeps its shape through long cooking; and as is usual here, one's portion is enough for one's family. The stew is inundated with sautéed onions and mushrooms.

Fleur de Lis, if it is famous at all, is famous for its cassoulet. Unfortunately, in one respect it is not what it once was—that is to say, it is no longer enough for three stevedores after a twelve-hour shift in December. It can only be concluded that the former portions were left unfinished so frequently that the management felt justified in reducing their scope. This is to be deplored, because cassoulet is a dish which must be copious to be itself. A small serving of cassoulet is like a little bit of love. The dish, as served, is still redolent of pork, mutton, sausage, beans, herbs, garlic and white wine, and, therefore, it is still delicious, and there is no restriction against ordering a second portion.

Salmis is a rare but marvelous cooking method in which a bird is roasted for about two thirds of its cooking time, and braised in a sauce, with vegetables, for the remaining third. This yields a more tender, juicier bird than roasting permits, and a heartier texture and taste of skin than is possible in a fricassee, even when the bird is thoroughly browned beforehand. The Salmis of Pheasant is one of the best dishes at Fleur de Lis —it tastes like a roasted bird, and also like a stewed bird, and the thick sauce in which the pheasant is finished is strongly flavored of Chablis, onions, mushrooms and pork. There are few dishes like this available in New York, and if one is to make a single visit to this restaurant, this is the dish to try.

The green salads are large, the cheeses, unfortunately, are refrigerated, and the desserts are something of a comedown. The pastries are only OK; better strawberries are available in other parts of town than one usually gets here; the rum cake is yellow and tastes sort of yellow.

Fleur de Lis has always had a slightly more interesting and more reasonably priced wine list than other restaurants in its class, but the choice is far from extensive. Normandy cider is also available, and it is very good with the powerful Tripes à la mode de Caen.

★ GENGHIZ KHAN'S BICYCLE

197 Columbus Avenue (at 69th Street)
LUNCH AND DINNER.
Reservations, 595–2138.
Credit cards: AE, BA, DC.
Medium-priced.

You can play backgammon (or, presumably, anything else) in the gallery, one flight up; you can watch the passing people (the gender[s] of your choice) through the circular windows of the walled-in sidewalk café; you can lose yourself in Eastern fantasies to the amplified strains of a wailing oud plucker; you can speculate on the derivation of the name of the place—as six centuries intervened between the demise of the conqueror and the birth of the bike, this will take a bit of imagination.

The host—he greets you with a cigarette and in his spare time nuzzles a reluctant waitress who must balance her uninterest against her interest—a job's a job; the hangers-about at the bar—management's cronies, they are not ornamental; the Nubian in the Turkish toweling and turban who serves the Turkish coffee and asks if you would like your fortune read—she is simply a false note among these mostly unaffected West Siders in this modernistic setting. The place is spiffy white and brown and mirrored and all geometrically laid out, and the customers, colorful and hirsute, comport themselves gaily in the hard-edged surroundings.

The steamy kitchen is slightly visible, and you spot your first note of what looks like Turkish authenticity—a bulbous chap with heavy eyelids, thick lips and a drooping mustache is apparently in charge of the food, and sure enough, his exertions are not wasted—you can eat well here, and the secret of eating *very* well is to order nothing but appetizers.

_ The Bicycle serves what may be the best homus in town. This dish of ground chickpeas, with garlic, sesame oil and herbs, has an exceptionally rich and grainy texture, and most of the oil is poured over rather than mixed in, which is like a cool, mellifluous relief to the pungent paste. Moreover, the dish seems to be very freshly made, with not a trace of drying out—it has life, freshness, sparkle.

The menuese is (1) comic and (2) inaccurate. Midye Dolma is described as "Fresh mussels, nuts and rice all amicably tossed together." No matter the disposition of the assembler, he used littleneck clams, fresh and tender, tomato, onions that were cooked until sweet, a touch of hot spices. This is a terrific dish, the flavor of the clams sweet and briny, of the sauce sweet, tart and spicy. The cold liver appetizer is called Arnavut Cigeri, and it consists of chunks of breaded and browned liver, mildly spiced and pleasantly chewy—you squeeze lemon onto the meat to add moistness and tang. Pastirma is rhapsodized over as "Spiced dried beef sliced almost as thin as nothingness." Actually the little red slices are not particularly thin, but they are gamy and loud, fragrant and high, and a bit firm to the tooth—very delicious stuff. There are also good versions of imam bayildi, borek (the feta-cheese pastry made with meat or spinach, here described as "comfortably at rest between thin leaves of dough"), tarama (the spread of fish roe and bread), stuffed grape leaves, and more. The cold cucumber soup, made with yogurt and fresh dill, is OK, but would be much better if the dried mint were omitted entirely if fresh mint is not available.

The main courses are something of a comedown. The Tas Kebab is a rather ordinary stew of lamb in tomato sauce. The Guvec, on the other hand, is at least rich—chunks of lamb and eggplant, each of them somehow saturated with oil in a way that renders them succulent without being the least cloying, with a bit of tomato in the thick sauce. Much more interesting than either of these is the Izgaka Kofte, an exceptional version of beef patties. The little sausage-shaped items are flavored with hot spices and herbs, they are lightly blackened in the broiling, and they are served with raw onions and parsley. The meat is far from rare, in fact it is a bit dry, but this seems to create the right texture for this particular blend of fragrant flavorings and beef.

You are brought a tray on which are shown six desserts. Do not select any of them, except out of curiosity. There isn't anything wrong with the orange-flavored custard, or the baklava, or the rice pudding ("A Turkish rice pudding that is a nice rice Pudding"), and so on; it is, rather, that these excessively rich sweets will probably be insipid to the Western palate, as will the silly ritual of the Turkish-coffee maker as she boils your coffee before your very eyes, bored and impatient as she somnambulizes through the motions.

• THE GINGER MAN

51 West 64th Street
LUNCH AND DINNER.
Reservations, SC 4–7272.
Credit cards: AE, BA, CB, DC, MC.
Expensive.

Over the years The Ginger Man has managed to receive considerable notice in the local press. The place has always been treated *seriously,* as if it were a restaurant to be reckoned with, as if someone, having eaten there, would thereafter be ever so interested in any bit of news or comment about the place. Most recently The Ginger Man made the headlines because its latest chef is a *woman!* This should hardly be startling, particularly at The Ginger Man, where the very first chef was a woman— the late Dione Lucas. Having eaten some of the current food, one may safely conclude that the latest lady in the kitchen was hired for her publicity potential, not for any ability with a stove.

This is one of New York's first tries at a British-style pub. There are hideous oil paintings all around, by way of carefully chosen idiosyncrasy, and sure enough, the hidden spotlights are played on that very art. Dark wood, exposed brick, semidimness. The sidewalk café of half a dozen tables, is enclosed, and it is used the year around. And, as ever, the place sports its celebrities. Marilyn Horne, for one, has been seen stoking her furnace here—plenty of butter on plenty of bread, while waiting for the hot food to arrive.

The waiters are inept—that is, when they are available. You nab a wandering host and you explain to him that after obtaining some wine there has been no sign of a waiter for twenty minutes and that you wish to order immediately and receive food promptly thereafter, or you will leave and pay for nothing. "In that case," he says, "I'll take the order myself." *In that case.*

Eventually your waiter arrives, and after he addresses the usual question, you wonder why, if he asks "Who gets the coe-keel?" for coquille, he does not ask "Who gets the pate?" for pâté. Something to think about while you consider your food: a cool and spicy pâté, served with the lovely little sour pickles called cornichons; a decent coquille, actually made with bay scallops as well as tiny shrimps and mushrooms, all in a competent white sauce under a layer of bread crumbs—you squeeze on lemon to bring the dish to life. There are artichokes, and occasionally they are not overcooked —their dressing is made with an abundance of mustard. And there is onion soup, but because the onions are not cooked until brown, the result is simply beef stock with onions, and not a strong stock at that—the tasty melted cheese on top almost rescues the dish.

The Canard à l'Orange is almost blackened in the attempt at a crisp skin, and there are myriad mandarin orange sections in the thick but undistinguished sauce. At $10.95 your filet mignon should be of first-class beef—it is not; and the so-called sauce Béarnaise, which pours from the pitcher like lava, is predominantly salty, short on the flavor of tarragon.

Among the supper dishes, the steak sandwich, once a bargain, now mocks your money at $5.95, though the meat is tasty, particularly with a dab of mustard. This is where the Spinach Salad with Mushrooms & Bacon got its big start, and you still get a good one here—very fresh, well-cleaned spinach leaves, a couple of handfuls of slices of raw mushrooms, and a few strips of bacon—that undistinguished dressing that you had on your artichoke is, unfortunately, repeated here.

The fruit salad no longer has the shredded citrus rind that used to distinguish it from dozens of others. But the Austrian Nut Roll is as creamy, sugary and delicate as ever.

The Ginger Man's carafe wine is something pretty bad from California, so you are forced to drink bottled wine from an exorbitantly overpriced wine list.

★ LIBERTY CAFÉ

43 West 64th Street
LUNCH AND DINNER.
Reservations, 877–1119.
Credit cards: AE, BA, CB, DC, MC.
Medium-priced.

Formerly Liberty Ice Cream Concern, and they probably had a helluva backslappin' time coming up with that name. But the laughter froze with the cold weather (ice cream sales decline when the temperature does), and little time was wasted on another creative session—the specifics of the rechristening were settled on in consultation with the sign painter (he charges by the letter), and then there was the hasty call to the ad agency.

This would be a nostalgia scene if your neighborhood IRT station were not still in business. Walls of large ancient tiles, narrow stairways leading from one level to another, an enameled corrugated ceiling, children's art in place of graffiti. But as you are not going anywhere, there are also old-fashioned standing hat-and-coat racks, a handful of stools at the marble bar between you and the soda fountain downstairs, ice cream chairs at the glass-topped tables, and youngsters in T-shirts, *Liberty* emblazoned thereon, to bring you your food and refreshments and to return your fish fork to the table so you can eat your cake with it.

The printed menu consists of ice-cream-parlor and café stuff, and the blackboard menu adds a few items available from the kitchen of the Ginger Man, to which this place is connected in both a physical and fiduciary way.

If you are serious you may begin with a slice of quiche, a quite respectable version for one that is reheated, made with a custard that is heavily thickened with cheese and studded with bacon—grated cheese is sprinkled across the top and browned before the good-size slice is brought out. You can get the wonderful spinach salad here that is so popular at the Ginger Man—big floppy leaves of raw spinach and many slivers of raw mushroom, dressed with hot bacon fat and tossed with slices of the hot bacon itself. You may go no further than a sandwich afterward—the Grilled Cheese, Bacon & Tomato seems slim at $1.95, but the bread is a good caraway rye, and the cheese is a variety of American that has a bit of flavor.

Or you may overlook the snacky surroundings, and when they are on the board, have the Boeuf Bourguignonne (a potent stew, principally of chunks of well-browned beef, cooked long, until tender, in a virtual sea of limp onions, served with slippery, eggy noddles) or the Coquilles St. Jacques (little bay scallops and mushrooms in a gentle sauce, served with rice that has been cooked in broth).

You are clued in on the ice cream brands (the vanilla is Schrafft's, for example, the butter pecan Louis Sherry), and standard concoctions are available—banana splits, hot fudge sundaes—as well as a few house inventions—Huddled Masses, Sad-Eyed Lady. (They really worked at that creative session.) The whipped cream is the real thing, as is the hot fudge; if you ask for nuts you get a substantial dose of good walnuts. The only trouble is that the stuff costs ten times what it did when you first learned to like it.

○ MONK'S INN

35 West 64th Street
LUNCH AND DINNER.
Reservations, 874–2710.
Credit cards: AE, CB, DC, MC.
Medium-priced.

In restaurant journalism, eating places are often rated separately for different aspects of their operation. Thus, one place may be scored very high for food but very low for cleanliness, or good for "atmosphere" but bad for service—which raises certain questions. Should someone in search of dinner repair to, say, O. Henry's, with its mindless menu, vulgar service and dirty floors, to sample a portion of its ambience?

Among the restaurants in New York that trade (successfully) on one restaurant feature, giving indifferent attention to the others, is Monk's Inn, where interior design is all, and food, service and cleanliness (and you) are nothing. A local mag refers to its "monastic mood." It's the customers who must be in a monastic mood to tolerate the place, and apparently they are. Their saintly indifference to mistreatment and their Zen relish of discomfort are manifested daily. Hundreds of them, paralyzed to abject faith by the overwhelming air of the place, line up—wide-eyed masochists, grinning, eager to be playthings in the management's and waiters' sport.

The waiters are dressed in knee-length monk's habits—baggy pants and scruffy shoes protruding from the bottoms, shaggy heads from the tops. The restaurant itself is a huge brick-walled, street-level dungeon, dimly lit by tabletop candles, each set in a wine bottle. The candles are fast-burning, and new ones are installed at every table at almost every meal, a service attended to far more rigorously than the delivery of food and drink, or the removal of the detritus of previous courses. The drippings of the candles have accumulated pyramidally around their bases, and the encroachment of candle wax seriously compromises the serviceability of the already wee tabletops. In time, when the tables are completely useless, they will be removed, and the worshipers will eat from their laps with one hand, holding the candle-bottle in the other hand, and twice as many of the faithful will be accommodated (if that is the correct word).

The waiters are brinksman penance inflicters, always testing to see how far the devout will let them go before they cry "Enough!" (The management will let them go as far as their ingenuity carries them.)

When you sit down at your checkered, encrusted tablecloth, you will be presented with a couple of slabs of complimentary cheese. Leyden and smoky Wisconsin Cheddar are an odd appetizer, but this is the best part of the meal, so eat it when you can, which may be five minutes later when your sticky silverware arrives, or five after that, when the bread materializes (with a couple of apples), or if you are stubborn, later still, when the waiter, in his flight, drops off the butter.

The first courses are soups: Soupe Montagnarde, described as "Lumber Jack Style Soup," and undoubtedly, some lumberjacks eat vegetable soup, au college dormitory; Potage Esau—*Then Jacob gave Esau bread and pottage of lentiles; and he did eat and drink* (Gen. xxv. 34)—get it?; Gratinée des Halles "Onion Soup Halles Style," though one would have to look all over Paris, let alone in the district of Les Halles, to find an onion soup that can't stand up to a glass of tea. More interesting than comparing the soups with their descriptions is finding a place for them on the table, by now already overburdened; but the waiter moves your cheese plate to the left of your fork, places the breadbasket half over the edge of the table, snuggles the salt into the ashtray and forces the soups into position.

Now comes the main course, and you thought the waiter was going to remove the soup dishes, didn't you? They are piled one on top of the other, the ashtray (still with the salt in it) is lowered into the space you left in the breadbasket when you ate one of the apples (you couldn't eat the other, because it was resting in its own fermenting liquor), the wine and water glasses are forced against the base of Mount Candle, the cheese board (you remember the Leyden and Cheddar?) is placed atop the soup dishes, and you are served, say, La Raclette Valaisanne, "A Swiss Aged Bagne Cheese scraped from the Wheel at the Stove served with Potato and Assorted Relishes" (capitals theirs), which is tasteless cheese, melted directly on a very thin metal plate (which promptly gets cold, the cheese with it), decorated with Heinz pickles, gimlet onions, frozen kernel corn (golden yellow) and a cold, soggy boiled potato. Or else you may sample the Bratwurst aux Pommes Lyonnaises, which tastes like a hot dog—not at Nedick's, not at Nathan's, not at a Sabrett hot-dog stand, no, more like the rubber hose Harry Stevens serves to his captive clientele at the Big A. A call for mustard means the saltcellar must be removed from the ashtray (which, you will recall, is in the breadbasket) and placed between the stems of the adjacent water glasses so that this essential spice, brought in a saucer, can be placed on the ashtray.

Dessert? Well, that means you are through with your main courses, which simplifies everything. The large plates are placed one atop the other, the breadbasket atop these, and luxurious space is available for Crêpe aux Groseilles Flambées (an excess of lingonberries wrapped in suede, burned in kirsch), and *café*, which is mud in a cup in a pudding dish (the saucer is busy with the mustard).

This restaurant wasn't bad when it first opened—at least the food was edible. But now the chef, not content to be outdone by the dining-room staff, matches the penance they exact with forced fasting. The famous table of cheeses flaunts a Bel Paese with the telltale map of North and South America, and a Brie which not only runs but shouts. The wine list is a joke.

• O'NEALS' BALOON

48 West 63rd Street
LUNCH AND DINNER.
Reservations accepted for large parties, 765–5577.
No credit cards.
Medium-priced.

O'Neals' Baloon is an American brasserie. People come for just a drink, or for coffee and cake, or for three-course meals. The place is angular, sprawling, garish, noisy, active, and despite many kinds of illumination (clusters of brilliant, unfrosted bulbs at the ends of bent wands; red-and-white movie EXIT signs; pale chartreuse globes, Tiffany lamps; antique ceiling fixtures) it is dark and a little sinister because the walls and ceiling are an unrelieved black but for the glum paintings, posters, mirrors, ducts and pipes. The L-shaped sidewalk café is of a piece (dozens of little tables in rows, under a long green awning) but inside we have a jumble of rooms (up a few steps for this one, around this corner for that one), all of them filled with bare-topped, wooden tables (a bottle of Heinz on each), red chairs, coatracks, the sounds of the juke box, at the south end the competing sounds of the exposed kitchen, at the north end the lesser, guzzling noises of an active bar.

Everyone here is theatrical or musical, or at least a little bit exhibitionistic: Juilliard students; West Side semiprofessionals whose occasional theatrical earnings barely cover their Equity dues; members of the chorus and corps de ballet at the Met and the City Opera; and a few more-successful types, though most of these prefer The Ginger Man or Le Poulailler after an evening at Lincoln Center. The waiters, of course, are either *manqués* (gray-haired and wry) or aspirers (King Valiant hair and pimpled), all in red newsboy aprons.

No one has ever been heard to say "Let's go to the Baloon—I love their——." But if you know what to avoid, you can put together a decent little meal here if you select from:

O'Neals' Chili Con Carne: crunchy beans, chopped meat, a modicum of hot pepper, and if you wish, a garnish of chopped raw onions.

Chopped Chicken Livers—an apple-size ball of fresh, spicy liver, decorated with chopped hard-boiled egg, a few rings of red onion, and a garnish of more or less wilted marinated vegetables.

Avocado Vinaigrette—a ripe avocado, sliced, dressed with a good, thick, mustardy vinaigrette, and garnished with a few slices of pimento for color, and chopped raw onions for the hell of it.

Hamburgers, Cheeseburgers, Bacon-Burgers, Chili-Burgers, Cheese-Bacon-Burgers: good stuff.

Southern Fried Chicken, Shoestring Potatoes in Basket—the chicken is moist inside, crispy outside, and there is plenty of it. But the fries suffer from being shoved under the chicken, and they arrive wilted.

Fish & Chips in Basket—read the previous item and substitute fish (flounder) for chicken.

Spinach, Mushroom & Bacon Salad—the West Side staple, made with fresh spinach, crisp raw mushrooms, crumbled bacon and mustardy dressing.

Aunt Sylvie's Torte—layers of cheese cake, chocolate cake, marzipan, and a creamy chocolate frosting flavored with orange liqueur—a good, sweet dessert.

Good cheese cake, a pecan pie that has a buttery filling, and hot chocolate in the cold season.

Avoid conscientiously: Sliced Steak on French Bread with Olive Salad (tough, tasteless meat). Bratwurst & Potato Salad in Skillet (the potato salad is good, but the sausage tastes like brown soap). Freshly Ground Steak Tartare (the meat is ground fresh, but it is served to you with a little paper cup of dressing which, when added to the meat, simply does not make a steak tartare—it makes wet meat, which is something else). Curried Chicken & Pineapple with Tomato and Egg Wedges (cubes of cold chicken from a cold-chicken roll and cubes of pineapple from a can—in this sauce they look and taste alike).

★★★ LE POULAILLER

43 West 65th Street
LUNCH AND DINNER.
Closed Sunday.
Reservations, 799–7600.
Credit cards: AE, DC.
Expensive.

Think of it. After the opera, the hungry pass up the pleasure of seeing their favorites take extra bows in order to sprint across Lincoln Square and snatch a Ginger Man table before the waiting line forms. Unnecessary. One may applaud until gratitude is exhausted and then stroll one block farther north, where, for a lousy $20 more, two may sup in a spacious room at a well-laid table, be attended by professional waiters and captains, and eat food prepared by actual chefs, who demonstrate concern for its taste, texture and appearance.

One of the appetizers on the dinner menu is an excellent smoked ham, served simply as a blanket of thin slices on a large plate. It effectively quickens a dormant appetite. And there is a tangy seafood salad which leans heavily on smoked trout and marinated mackerel, flavored with fresh celery, green peppers and tomatoes, in a fine vinaigrette. If one's appetite is already keen, the pâté de campagne, redolent of gamy, blood-rich meat, will serve to quiet it until the main course comes along. The littlenecks and cherrystones are always fresh, and the smoked trout, when not part of the seafood salad, is served with a sparkling sauce of horseradish and mustard, which is the perfect accent for this slightly oily fish.

The main courses include a superb roast veal—dry, thin, porous, white as ivory, the most delicate veal available in this country—on which a rich brown sauce, powerfully flavored with fresh tarragon, is poured at the table. The veal becomes juicy, limp and irresistible. The various steaks are cut from beef aged to a point of outrageous tenderness, and they are served with an excellent Béarnaise—grassy, tart, sharp, buttery. "May I have some more Béarnaise?" "Madame, you may have all the Béarnaise in the world," quoth the gracious captain, and the lady breathed freely.

Frogs live and work in almost all parts of the temperate zone, but for some reason many of the frog's legs found in New York restaurants are frozen in Japan. Le Poulailler prepares their frog's legs perfectly—Provençale, breaded and fried crisp, and then covered with a strong sauce of tomatoes and garlic. The legs are delicious, but seem Oriental. Their flavor is light, and they are slightly mushy instead of slightly fibrous.

The vegetables which accompany main courses are particularly good, especially the creamed cauliflower, crisp and well seasoned with nutmeg, and the thin-sliced carrots, cooked slowly in butter and sugar, so that they produce their own limpid sauce.

A tart salad may be had before the cheese. Brie is usually available, but often it is not good. If you are being served by the right captain, he will confide its condition. Otherwise you will have to see for yourself.

Some of the desserts are unforgettable. There is a pancake filled with sweetened cream cheese, a superb Paris-Brest (a sort of cream puff with crisp chopped nuts and very light whipped cream), a good coffee mousse, and exceptional fruit tarts.

A quite acceptable California wine is available in carafes. You will find, however, that the food calls for good wine.

Le Poulailler is one of the most beautifully decorated restaurants in New York. The rooms are pervaded with an airy, golden glow, the tables are well spaced, and the banquettes comfortable.

★★SAKURA CHAYA

198 Columbus Avenue (at 69th Street)
LUNCH AND DINNER.
Reservations, 874–8536.
No credit cards.
No liquor.
Inexpensive.

The average age of the diners is twenty-six; the average income is below average; the average tab for two is $15, including beer, tax and tip; the average allocated floor space per diner is about two feet square; and the average attendance equals the total number of chairs plus 10 percent, except at the off-hours. But though the appeal is the low prices, at a sacrifice of commodiousness, the food is excellent, and this is certainly the best of the three Japanese restaurants that are neighbors on Columbus Avenue near 69th Street.

Japanese trappings are sprinkled about—bamboo screens, masks (one angry, one in ecstasy), paper parasols, fierce-face kites, paper lanterns (sans lamps), illustrated scrolls and painted screens—but the basic furnishings are domestic, including bare Formica tabletops, plastic-upholstered side chairs, and carpeting. There is a six-stool lunch counter, which may be the best place to sit. A genial gentleman (who likes his work and his customers), artfully, effortlessly and without the flashy display of talent that is found at the sushi bars in midtown Japanese restaurants, assembles lovely raw fish dishes—and these, sushi and sashimi, are made of perfectly fresh fish—better cannot be found in New York. They are variously delicate, sharp, tender, chewy, elusive or aggressive, but they are all near-perfect. For one visit the thing to order is the sushi-sashimi combination, for two reasons. Reason 1: you get to sample all the raw fish items; reason 2: if you are at a table rather than at the counter, the kimono-garbed waitress, who is all shy smiles and little bows, will startle you by ordering ONE COMBI! from the man behind the counter before she politely takes the remainder of your order.

Sushi, as everyone by now must know, is morsel-size combinations of fish (often raw) or vegetables and vinegared rice, sometimes wrapped in seaweed; and sashimi is strips of raw fish. They are served with soy sauce and with a powerful green horseradish paste, and with such garnishes as pickled ginger (served here in parchment-thin slices), cucumber and white radish. At this restaurant the seafoods that go into these dishes are raw tuna (it is the color of red beef when it is uncooked, but it is surprisingly delicate this way), squid and octopus, as well as varieties of local fish. This food is sparkling and stimulating, but subtle. Other cold fish dishes are served here, including a splendid salad of octopus, sesame seed, bean sprouts and cucumbers in a thin, tart dressing of vinegar and sesame oil.

Less common, and just as good in its way, is the raw beef served at Sakura Chaya. It is listed as Nama-Niku and consists of shredded beef, scallion greens and sesame seeds, dressed with soy sauce and garlic. It looks just like raw tuna, but it is strong and satisfying, and unlike the raw fish, which can be eaten endlessly, this stuff goes a long way.

There is an excellent tempura—shrimp and vegetables deep-fried in a very light batter, so that the resulting crusts are very delicate and crisp.

Sukiyaki, teriyaki, kushi-katsu and all the other familiar items are available here in good versions. None of the food is prepared at your table (no room), but this does not affect its quality. Included is a fish sukiyaki—a pungent fish stew made with octopus, tuna, clams, mussels, abalone, shrimp, mushrooms, bean sprouts and many other ingredients (including, unfortunately, a frozen, tough and tasteless lobster tail), in a strong fish broth. The varied ingredients retain their character, and each is modified in an interesting way by the powerful stuff it is cooked in. This is a wonderful dish, but some people may find it a bit too loud. The chicken teriyaki is of nicely browned chicken in a sweet thin sauce, with bean sprouts and lightly cooked carrots.

The desserts include ice cream, sherbet, fruit and yokan—a sweetened bean cake that may seem a little soapy if you're not used to it.

This is a good restaurant if you don't mind the mess-hall ambience.

Almost no one here uses anything but chopsticks, but you can get a fork if you ask.

East Side, West Side

Each weekday evening at around five o'clock New York comes to a boil. It cooks for the next couple of hours or so, during which time hundreds of thousands of its midtown and downtown office personnel are, like the most volatile substances in a bubbling retort, boiled away, to New Jersey, Westchester, Connecticut, Long Island. Left behind in the still are our proud and chauvinistic lees and dregs, the little island's only loyal citizens, those who in the morning assault midtown and Wall Street from behind the barricades that separate the densest concentrations of commerce from Manhattan's built-in bedroom communities, and who in the evening attack again, from the opposite side.

Such types live all over town, but the most extensive concentrations of them are along the strips of land between Central Park and the East and Hudson rivers, known, respectively, as the East Side and the West Side. Both settlements are relentlessly middle-class. The people on the East Side, however, have more money; those on the West, less fun. Neither side is restaurant-rich. These are some of their better local places.

• ADAM'S RIB

23 East 74th Street
LUNCH, MONDAY TO FRIDAY; DINNER DAILY.
Reservations, 535–2112.
Credit cards: AE, CB, DC, MC.
Medium-priced.

Adam's Rib reviews itself. This, then, is a review of a review.

"This is a simple restaurant. Run by one man, N. A. Nicholas. His Philosophy: serve the best. Always."

Very tricky, this Mr. Nicholas. Notice that he does not claim to serve the best always. He claims that that is his *philosophy*. He does not point out that it is also everybody's philosophy. Philosophy shmossify. How do you account for some of this less-than-best food, Nick?

"The menu, you will note, is limited. The reason is a belief in superb quality. One cannot prepare everything well."

More waffling. A *belief* in superb quality. Hah! Might just as well believe in the Ten Commandments, the Golden Rule, and the Surgeon General's Report while you blow smoke from a stolen cigarette in the face of an allergic asthmatic.

"The Non-Beef entrees, frankly, are a compromise. This is a roast beef house. Order one of the other menu items only if you are unable to enjoy roast beef. For you can enjoy such entrees, as good as ours, in several New York restaurants."

See how he gives himself away? Nick, baby, even as a hypocrite you're incompetent. Only two paragraphs ago you were talking about ". . . the best. Always," and now, *compromise*! Give us a chance, please, to dream a little before you return us to reality.

"The Prime Ribs of Beef are, however, unsurpassed. Their flavor, texture and juiciness are a result of many things. The corn and grain feeding of Prime Midwestern Cattle, the ageing of the standing roast before preparation and, of course, the roasting. These are among the things that N. A. Nicholas cares about most."

Bunk. This time, however, we got him. He comes right out and says "unsurpassed." You can get better roast beef at Pen & Pencil, at Cheshire Cheese, at Charlie Brown's, to name a few places. The beef here is tender, rare (if you want it that way) and pretty. But there is nothing special about its flavor, which is a little flat.

Nicholas carries on, with flat wit, about some other aspects of his roast beef dinner:

"FRESH BROILED MUSHROOMS. Kennet Square, Pa.'s contribution to the world."

This time he's right, even if he isn't saying anything. The mushrooms are those small-capped, long-stemmed tender ones, and they are exceptional.

"A YORKSHIRE PUDDING. Somehow this flavorful pastry puff sounds better than it tastes."

It does the way you make it, Nick. Your pastry has hardly puffed. It is sodden and greasy.

"A HORSERADISH SAUCE. Just a strong flavor for zip. It obscures the subtle flavor of the roast nicely."

Right on.

"IDAHO BAKED POTATO. Butter and/or chives in real sour cream."
Flawless.

"THE AUTHENTIC CAESAR SALAD. Romaine sans the distractions, with the turned on dressing Caesar Cardini invented 50 years ago."
Overdressed, wilted, gooey.

The best food in the house is something for which no claims are made. It is called Chocolate Pie Suisse—it is thick, creamy, cool, with a strong flavor of good Swiss chocolate. Something called Peach Combinage Bavarian Cream arrives with frozen strawberries not yet thawed.

No first courses. The other main courses, which Mr. Nicholas suggests can be found in equivalent versions in other restaurants, can, in fact, rarely be found in worse renditions. The Chicken Kiev, for example, spurts butter when you cut into it and all that, but it is almost inedibly tasteless.

This restaurant is situated in the Volney Hotel and it very much has the look of an old hotel dining room: high ceilings, dark wood-paneled walls, red carpeting, white linen. The place is popular, the clientele staid—crew cuts, narrow lapels, knee-length dresses, sensible shoes. With Adam's Rib a woman was made. Very little of that going on here.

"THE WINES. A brief list of those wines we find most compatible with our beef . . ."

Oh, yes, the wine. Can't you just see old Nick sitting down with a haunch of beef and about fifty wines to come up with this list, and then concluding that the "most compatible" include six items from Paul Masson, among them "champagne," one real champagne from France, and Mateus Rosé? You may bring your own wine.

★★ CARROUSEL

1307 Third Avenue (near 75th Street)
LUNCH, MONDAY TO FRIDAY; DINNER, MONDAY TO SATURDAY.
Closed Sunday.
Reservations, 744–4978.
Credit cards: AE, DC, MC.
Medium-priced.

For some reason, despite the phenomenal success French restaurants have enjoyed in New York, in particular the constantly thriving bistro-like places in the West Forties and West Fifties, the East Side has largely done without. Along come these pioneers, to break new ground. But these are timorous adventurers, undertaking to settle hardly more than a twenty-five-foot storefront, and sure enough, the place is no sooner in business than it is jammed, tables available by reservation only at dinner, a brief wait at lunch.

Carrousel is the quintessential theater-district French restaurant, transported piece by piece to this foreign ground. The walls are of a deep salmon pink that should age very well, and if you thought that the cluttered look of many French restaurants is a condition arrived at through years of aimless acquisition and installation, this place is a jumble from the start. There is a framed poster on every patch of wall; where the space to be filled is three-dimensionable, there is a green plant. A tiny vestibule is separated from the dining room by a partition of engraved glass, and through this minuscule space the diners come and the diners go, which is bad enough, but hooks on the wall must accommodate coats, and when there is chill or rain in the air, you walk through a jungle of cheviot, gabardine and poplin to reach your harried host.

If you have experience piling families of six into a subcompact, you have some idea of how the tables were inserted into this space. Well, you have all seen crowded restaurants before, but they are usually eschewed by the kinds of customers you find here. It appears that inflation and recession have caught up with even our moguls, and here they are, their male frames in tailor-made suits, female ones in one-of-a-kinds, supping at lower prices than once was their wont, now that the economies are just around the corner. Yes, this is a reasonably priced little place, but you can be certain the prices will get stiffer if this level of business continues; and, yes, it is a hectic one, but somehow it is all OK, once you are comfortably ensconced in your chair; the action and chatter all around you are like the rain and lightning outside your family-filled, sealed Volkswagen.

The menu is brief, and it follows, though not slavishly, the pattern of most French menus in town. Among the deviations is the Feuilleté au Roquefort—a hot first course of Roquefort cheese and custard baked in a pie. The strength of the cheese is heightened by heat, and it is offset by the creamy custard and by the browned and flaky pastry. Of the handful of appetizers on this menu, this is the best. But if strong cheese is not your meat, the Escargots are a bit above average in that the snails themselves are plump and tender, and the sauce, milder than many in its spare use of garlic, is well-balanced and herby—the snail butter is an excellent moistener for a few tufts of the good bread served here. Of course there is pâté, but this one is more like cold meat loaf, *too* cold, slablike, though its flavor is not bad.

Fish baked in a crust is becoming a familiar item in French restaurants around town. Here it is called Filet de "Bass" en croûte (someone is yet to do that study on the use of quotation marks in menus), and it is, in this version, a simple and very good dish —a section of impeccably fresh bass wrapped in a pastry envelope. The tender fish and a hot buttery sauce are sealed in the pastry, which is delicately browned. The magic of any sealed-in cooking is that moisture and flavor are kept where they belong, in the food, instead of in the air.

The ambiguously named Escalope de Veau is a cutlet of properly pale veal, browned in butter and served with browned fresh mushrooms in a delicately seasoned, creamy, wine sauce—your basic scallop of veal.

Inevitably there is Canard à l'Orange, and by this time you probably never order it. If you will think back, however, you may recall that this dish, when properly prepared, is something fabulous, which is how it got so popular in the first place. What you get here is the pristine thing—not only is the duck crisp and moist (with three slices of fresh orange as a garnish), but the mahogany-colored sauce is deep rather than sweet, brandied rather than candied. It is served with a mound of wild rice that is undiluted by white rice.

Not all is well. The Steak au Poivre Vert is of beef that is mild, as if it is too young; the green pepper is used sparingly, which is to say *too* sparingly, and the thin sauce makes little impression even against this pale steak.

Vegetable garnishes (mostly not bad) and salad (in a mustard vinaigrette) are, as the menu informs you, *inclus.*

Yes, there is mousse, and moreover, it need not be chocolate, if you prefer orange or coffee; all of them are good, none is spectacular. The best desserts are the fruit tarts

—blueberry, strawberry or apple, when those fresh fruits are available, and the flaky pastry and light custard are piled high with the plump berries, piled low with thin slivers of apple.

What is most surprising about this new place is the excellence of the waiters and the orderliness of the dining room in the face of this pace of business.

★★★ CHEZ PASCAL

151 East 82nd Street
DINNER.
Closed Sunday.
Reservations necessary, 249–1334.
Credit cards: AE.
Very expensive.

It is as if the people who start up French restaurants are slow to learn, but all-out once they grasp their lessons. The lesson for today, as it has been for decades, is "Go where the money grows." And all at once New York's East Side, where that paper crop flourishes, is sprinkled with French restaurants, to which the flower of the harvests (expendable income) is delivered, in return for something more edible. Among these places is Chez Pascal, wherein, the menu informs you, the *chef de cuisine* is one Pascal Chevillot, scion of a famed French family of wine merchants and innkeepers, a family which has already given us La Petite Ferme, the minuscule farmhouse-restaurant in Greenwich Village. Today's Chevillot, however, is not a miniaturist, and Chez Pascal is not the out-of-the-way little bistro; it is, rather, a highly stylized grotto, the secret chamber, the posh speak-easy behind an unmarked door on an anonymous block, the gaiety within insulated from the East Side's barren nighttime streets.

In carving out this place, the old plaster has been removed to reveal walls of rosy brick (warmer and softer than any paint, and, oh, so durable); the ancient stamped-tin ceiling has been silvered to a dark luster, as of burnished zinc; the floors are stripped to bare wood. Within these pristine planes, illuminated by the gentle glow of opaline chandeliers, the luxurious appointments seem to be in a warehouse, *en passant* between the maker and a posh apartment. Plump banquettes of gray suede opposite French period chairs in white and wicker, here a wall of wine bottles, there a display of appetizers and desserts, on the walls unobjectionable art, everywhere lovely flowers. And before each seat, white octagonal plates which will be decorated (once you are seated) with a slice of saucisson en croûte while you consider the wine list and the menu. That unexpected morsel is, happily, superb and of a quality that foretells excellences to come—the sausage at once sharp and fatty, the pastry that rims it moist and flaky, and the mustard that accompanies it the perfect sharp foil for the glistening and rich meat.

That wine list, by the way, consists of a paddle to which are affixed an assortment of wine labels, under glass. Included are a couple of house wines—white and red—at very reasonable prices for such eminently drinkable, if small, potions. Most of the other labels carry the name Chevillot, as shipper, usually a sign of a good bottle.

The waiters wear long aprons, the captains spiffy civvies, the clientele a spectrum of finery extending from Bond Street to Job's Lane; and this place has their numbers, perfectly. Some of these folk are more than the least bit stuffy (the last thing in the world they want believed), and Chez Pascal, with its armory air, helps them to feel that they are ever-so-slightly slumming, that the rose petal in the finger bowl is satiric rather than *riche,* the steep prices larky rather than *bourgeois.* Here on East 82nd Street, where $80 tabs for an intimate little supper for two are signed blind, those revelers, in their nostalgic fantasies, are courting in the neighborhood joint.

That is a tough revery to nurture if you order Pascal's Trois Terrines. (This dish is, by the way, a good introduction to the abundance with which plates are here laden—in contrast to the subsistence portions sold by the Chevillot of Greenwich Village.) Those terrines arrive as three slabs, each the size of a package of filter kings. A wooden spoon is dipped in a gallon jug, and you are garnished with those little French pickles called cornichons. These are good terrines, one porky, one livery, one studded with ham, and though you can easily praise their quality and distinguish them by their differences, they are simply in too narrow a range, and this appetizer ends up being too much of a good thing, unlike the similar dish of four pâtés at Lutèce, each one in startling contrast to each of the others. You will enjoy it more if you share it than if you tackle it alone. Another ambitious first course is something called La Salade Royale, also a prodigious item to undertake: a mound the size of a grapefruit, made up of crisp, barely cooked strands of stringbean; spears of fresh and perfectly poached asparagus, a bit too fibrous, having not been peeled before the boiling; hearts of fresh artichoke, cooked not a minute too long; chunks of crabmeat and shrimp; and a few spears of endive, all dressed in a vinaigrette that is strengthened with minced onions and mustard. This is a perfectly nice salad of better-than-average vegetables and sea-food, but the mélange has little character—you feel as if you have eaten good things, but not a good dish. Eschew all but the artichoke, by ordering Artichaut Vinaigrette, and this time you even get the leaves—one wishes the article were not so recently taken from the refrigerator. Each day Chez Pascal offers one or two fixed-price dinners at around $18, and occasionally the first course of these dinners is Moules Marinière, a common enough item on the menus of French restaurants in town, but rarely served so nicely. The mussels, in their half shells, are arranged on your plate as the petals of an opened flower. Within each shell, along with its fresh mussel, is a pool of the marinade—oil, wine, minced shallots and parsley; at the bottom of the plate, more of the same—the master pool, which you clean up with this restaurant's excellent bread.

If you come to Chez Pascal just once, you would do well to order Le Bass en Croûte Monloup. You are presented with a huge oval platter, its perimeter graced with string beans, braised endive, grilled tomatoes; its center occupied by a browned cross-hatched pastry in the shape of a fish, the pastry thus cueing you to its contents: a small bass that has been spread with a duxelles of mushrooms, which in itself sounds like a wonderful idea. The dish is completed when your waiter turns back a section of the crust and pours in a creamy sauce of fish stock, white wine, shallots and abundant butter. On occasion Chez Pascal offers a grilled lobster, a preparation not usually found in these parts, where one is either an adherent of boiling, steaming or broiling, or one is a fool. But careful grilling yields a lobster equal to any—to grill a lobster, it is immersed in boiling water for a couple of minutes, to make the meat firm, and then it is finished by turning it in a hot well-buttered pan until the meat is thoroughly cooked but not dried. They seem to do it perfectly Chez Pascal, bits of charring here and there, the lobster fresh and moist, the silken sauce that comes with it sweet and buttery.

Sometimes there is a pigeon offered whose meat is so rich you could mistake it for liver; it is surrounded by the usual little peas and the unusual slivers of black truffle.

The bird, browned and moist, is as good a pigeon as you will find in New York. And sometimes there is Gigot d'Agneau, the lamb slices showing bright pink centers and crusty browned edges. The gamy meat is surrounded by browned scalloped potatoes and a slightly sour grilled tomato that is plump, moist and generously herbed.

There is a simplicity of desserts, including a very refreshing lemon mousse; an orange tart of deeply darkened pastry, a smooth thin layer of custard, and discs of darkened fresh orange, sweet, tart and juicy; a cake, the principal ingredients of which are a purée of chestnuts and a mousse of chocolate, and the main qualities of which are a smooth airiness, somehow combined with solidity and richness; raspberries, soft and firm, in a Crème Chantilly, which, you should understand, is a lightly sweetened and vanilla-flavored whipped cream.

Study your bill to the accompaniment of some lovely petits fours.

★ CSARDA

1477 Second Avenue (at 77th Street)
LUNCH AND DINNER.
Reservations, 472–2892.
Credit cards: AE.
Medium-priced.

The advantage of a fire that totals a place is that you can start over from complete scratch. With the incineration of the original Tik Tak we lost a garishly appointed restaurant that served the best Hungarian food in town. With the installation of this one we have gained a pretty little place which claims to replicate the cookery of its predecessor.

Within what was probably a tight budget the premises have been simply fitted out. The walls are of rough, dead-white plaster, they are hung with sconces, a few paintings, and peasant pottery. At the front of the small room there are tall windows of clear glass, hung with loosely woven curtains; above there are large panels of translucent glass just under the high ceiling; all of which makes for a bright glow in the early evening hours. The dining room is rimmed with a dark banquette, the tables are surrounded by sturdy rustic chairs and are set with crisp white linen and red napkins folded to stand at each place. The place is immaculate without being antiseptic. The waitresses have their old jobs back under the new management, and they seem a little worried, because the level of business at Csarda has not yet equaled the former restaurant's hectic pace. They bustle around the tables doing a little more than needs to be done, which can be annoying. Who, for example, needs to be shown that on the little table before him there is not only salt and pepper, but also a cellar of paprika? Who wants to be asked approximately every five minutes if he would like some more cucumbers? Business will pick up, and they will, it is hoped, be kept busy with essentials.

Those cucumbers, by the way, which you are served before you order, taste the way they did at the old Tik Tak, and one is thereby given hope that nothing culinary has changed. The liquid is tart, the cucumbers crisp, and there is only a trace of sugar in the preparation.

The appetizer of brains and eggs is very much what it always was here—there are a few onions in the dish, the brains coarsely chopped, and the eggs cooked just a little past the point at which they begin to solidify, so the dish has texture. The Lecsos Kolbasz is a hot appetizer of sweet-and-sour stew, made with discs of strong sausage, green peppers and onions in a thick tomato sauce. For something cool in the coming hot weather Csarda offers a cold cherry soup. It is sweet, creamy, heavily flavored with cinnamon and crowded with pitted cherries—well, nine out of ten are pitted.

This is the roast stuffed chicken you will remember. For one thing, the stuffing is not in the cavity, but forced into an incision in the breast, which imparts some of flavor of the stuffing to the meat of the chicken and also tends to keep the chicken moist while it is being roasted to the point where the skin is deep mahogany and crisp.

There is an item here called Garlic Medallions of Veal, and it is a simple rendition of pale and tender veal, in which the meat has been transformed into an almost unbelievably strong expression of garlic and butter in a consommé sauce. The Roast Pork with Sauer Kraut may arrive without sauerkraut, but the three medallions of pork are just as happily coupled with roasted potatoes. The roasted meat, in a red-pepper gravy, is flavored with garlic, and its edges are browned and crusty from the roasting. Naturally there are paprikash dishes, including an interesting one of calf's liver, slivers of green pepper in among the slivers of meat, all in a thick and slightly oily sauce of cream and paprika, served with the gentle little bits of noodle called nockerl.

The famous onions are still here, the crisped rings of lightly battered onion weightless and high.

When you tire of palacsintas and strudels, and when the dessert of the day is chocolate cake, try that. The cake is moist and almost black, between the layers of cake thick and pully chocolate-flavored pastry cream, over the top of the cake a velvety layer of dark icing. If that is a bit much for you, you can always go back to the excellent palacsintas and strudels.

• NICKELS

227 East 67th Street
DINNER.
Reservations, 794–2331.
Credit cards: AE, BA, CB, DC, MC.
Very expensive.

This formula seems to work, and there are apparently plenty of people around with investment money to work it. Nickels is another seventies steakhouse, groovy and sleek, in the great tradition of Marty's Bum Steer and other bum steers. These places are packages rather than restaurants. The personnel in the kitchen could change every other week, perhaps does, and even habitual customers would never know about or care about the resulting differences, if any. If the mere depiction of a man on horseback can persuade a Marlboro smoker that he is a man on horseback, surely the actual separation from such a type of $11 for a steak will persuade him that he is prosperous and potent, particularly if the transaction is consummated in surroundings that are dark and clublike, providing, for anyone who makes a reservation and shows up, the impression that he has thereby been granted the privileges of the house of a secret society.

These joints borrow more than a little something from the Playboy formula. You notice it first when you check your coat. The walls of the cubicle are of bare rosy brick, softly lit; and perched on a high stool behind the half door a comely young attendant, paperback novel on her bare, crossed knee, is poised to spring smilingly to your assistance when you approach. (You get rid of your coat and head for your table; she turns off the smile and returns to her fantasies.)

The atmosphere (there is no other word) is one-third cigarette smoke and two-thirds cigar smoke. Dim bulbs in the dark ceiling pour down columns of soft-glowing amber light through the haze. You are surrounded by walls of glazed brick and dark mirrors. You are entertained (there must be another word) by a cocktail pianist. You are served by ceremonious waiters who seem to think they have graduated to the big time (conceivably this is the kind of place they frequent on their own nights off). They uncork and pour your wine with a flourish, they take a respectful step back as you taste, they bow slightly as you murmur your approval, with a smile that suggests they knew all along, as you yourself certainly knew, how precious was the fluid behind the Côtes du Rhône label. And you are mingling with the well-washed, well-fed, well-groomed—plaid pants and blazers, heavy make-up and heady scents.

Equally conventional is the menu and the preparation and quality of the dishes thereon. For a piddling $3.25 you get half a dozen (well, five) huge, tasteless, only slightly waterlogged shrimp with all the cocktail sauce you want! But you may suffer more cheaply through a so-called Chopped Liver that seems to lack butter, garlic, onions, salt, pepper, and for that matter, liver; the only guarantees of its existence are its visibility (there it is) and its temperature (frigid). As in many of these establishments, you are safest with the items to which the kitchen staff applies no more than a knife —raw clams, grapefruit, melon. And also as in many of these places, the beef is good —the giant rib of roast beef is rare, firm, tender, bloody and tasty; and the steaks, marbled with fat, are well-seared, juicy and fibrous. You can have them with some very nice hashed brown potatoes—a mound of little chunks of potato, some pale and soft, some leathery, some crisp, all soaked in grease and salt and pepper, and quite delicious. It is a mystery why these houses must have the house salad. Surely these creations do not convey the impression they are intended to make—that there is a strain of creativity somewhere in the background. This invention starts out creditably enough, with watercress and endive and lettuce, but then it is subjected to a dressing that includes some of the kind of oiled breading you encounter on stuffed clams. Gaga.

For dessert there are several flavors of cheese cake. The advantage of the chocolate-flavored one is that you know it is going to taste like linoleum before you taste it, because that's what it looks like. There are good fresh strawberries. And if, in safety, you began your dinner with half a grapefruit, you can conclude it with the other half —same price.

Very educational wine list. We are taught, for example, that Macon is pronounced "May-cong," and that the one served here is almost human in its virtue: "An elegant, gracious wine . . . Well-liked with sole, trout or an [sic] fine fish." Some of the data are for storing away for future use: Muscadet, we are informed, is "Excellent with oysters," but the house does not sell oysters. The list confesses that the sauterne has gone bad—it is described as "golden-brown."

★ O LAR

27 West 72nd Street
LUNCH AND DINNER.
Closed Sunday.
Reservations, 799–7331.
Credit cards: AE, CB, DC, MC.
Medium-priced.

A new, popular and bustling Spanish restaurant, situated in the quarters of a late catering establishment, where bar mitzvahs and weddings were marked. One must consider the room's new life a step up—those who come do so voluntarily, no accidents of time or place engender the proceedings, soon-to-be-longed-for pasts are not being bid adieu.

As in the way of such places, the space is vast, and, the glittering appointments notwithstanding, one has the impression of eating in a far-flung desert. A table near a wall is recommended to offset the free-floating feeling and to minimize the Cinerama effect of the broadly spaced chandeliers, silken draperies, mirrored columns. (The wall-to-wall carpeting is actually horizon-to-horizon.) But the scope of the surroundings fails to defeat the comfort of the establishment, because the air of the place is set by the Central Park West–and-environs middle-class families that have happily found themselves a new nearby restaurant, one to which they can even bring the brood—the prices are not forbidding, and there is no intimacy to be destroyed by the breakaway waifs wandering among the tables. It really does not matter whether they wander near or far because the enameled ceiling is formed in a series of long arches, like gigantic pipes sliced in half lengthwise; it reflects talk from across the room right into your lap, and your own brilliant wit mingles democratically with the pedestrian preoccupations of your fellow feeders: "Did we lose Johnny?" "I don't know. Did we bring him?"

Your Shrimp Ajillo arrives in a covered pot, and your waiter spoons the dozen crunchy shrimp onto your plate, the oil still bubbling, the bits of garlic just browned and sizzling and fragrant, lots of strong pepper making the sauce deep-red, lots of fresh parsley accomplishing little in this company. This is almost a main course, and at $2.50 per, you can spend $5 for a double, which is definitely a main course, and it competes well with the official ones. For something cooler, there is a pretty good Salpicon—fish and shellfish marinated in lemon, oil, herbs and seasoning; this is good, but it lacks the sparkle this kind of dish can have, as if it has been waiting for you awhile since it was removed from its marinade, and has grown weary.

The "Chick Peas Soup" definitely contains plural chickpeas—this is a simple, buttery broth, red-peppered, but not intensely, with lots of crisp peas, some floating, some sunken. Good gazpacho, seemingly made by hand-whipping instead of blender-whipping, which yields a nice, slightly grainy texture in which you can detect the tomato and oil as separate ingredients. You are offered chopped onions, chopped cucumbers, and croutons as garnishes, and they could be crisper.

Presumably, as relativists all, we judge Spanish preparations of veal within the context of Spanish veal-preparation. Very difficult to be so fair-minded. Veal is delicate stuff, and Spanish cooking rarely respects this quality. An item called Veal Gardener, described by the rather muddle-headed but quite cordial host/captain as veal sautéed with vegetables, turns out to be two substantial cutlets in a breading that is like a bread crust, garnished with two thumbs of carrot. Between the shell and the veal there is a thick white sauce, which takes a bit of doing to avoid leakage. This is perfectly executed heavy food. The question is, should it be executed at all? For solid stuff that has an indisputable right to be solid, there is Tripe Casserole, Andaluza Style—a thick, almost gummy stew with chickpeas and strong Spanish sausages and slices of smoky ham in among the tripe, the sauce between the solids a thickened, spicy oil—the dish is not only substantial, but well balanced.

The dessert cart is a frightening display of gleaming cheeses, polished fruits and sculptured cakes. Everything appears to be made of wax. You shudder, and the waiter suggests Angel's Bite and Filloas, which are not on the cart, are hot, come from the kitchen. You take a chance. The former is breaded custard in caramel—crisp outside, soft within, liquored, heavy, sweet; the latter are crêpes filled with an orange-flavored custard, in caramel. Both are pretty good.

The service, as in most Spanish restaurants, is sweet.

The new management has not abandoned the catering side. A section of the dining room is partitioned off, and on occasion, the regular dinner noises are augmented by amplified toasts and speeches.

★ PARIOLI, ROMANISSIMO

1466 First Avenue (near 76th Street)
DINNER.
Closed Sunday and Monday.
Reservations required, 288–2391.
Credit cards: AE, CB, DC.
Very expensive.

After a lifetime of raking it in and shelling it out, you may feel the need for rewards in the old age. And if your minuend has not been completely wiped by the household subtrahend, you may be tempted to siphon a little of the remainder into secret accounts, from which certain forms of solace are funded. That's what supports this place. It is the quintessential romantic hideaway, where the ages of the well-looked-after ladies can be subtracted from those of their escorts with several decades to spare. In these arrangements, as they are played out here, the exchanges of value are pure and simple. There are drinks. There is wine. She can have whatever she likes. If she doesn't like what she likes, she can send it back and like something else instead. If she wants to talk, she can talk. You don't have to talk. Think of it, *you don't have to talk.* You can if you want, but you don't have to. Usually she wants to talk. Tonight is tonight, but what about the future, which is tomorrow, or next weekend, or possibly the winter when, if she hasn't a tan to sport to prove she's been where you get them, she won't be able to go out. So you can see why she usually wants to talk. "I loved that place you took me to with the fountain in the middle and the waiters in silk tuxedoes. Can we go again sometime?" "We'll see." "I don't like the Plaza. It's too old. Can't I stay at the Park Lane?" "We'll see." "Are we going to Cozumel this year? You promised." "I didn't promise. We'll see." The driver's seat.

These intimacies are exchanged in an intimate setting—glazed brick that glistens dimly by the light of feeble lanterns, spots of light from the tiny lamps on the snowy tables, black ironwork to divide the room into cozy corners. Everything fits: the white china is rimmed with gold; your waiter ensconces even the most trivial wine in a straw basket, keeps it somewhere out of your reach, and pours for you unobtrusively when your glass is nearly empty; much whispering and fussing at the serving stand. The works.

Nowhere is it written, however, that the sinful in their shady retreats must eat ill. (Well, maybe it's written, but it's wrong.) The food in this lair is better than fair, and you can even come with your spouse.

On occasion the house serves a delicious appetizer of deep-fried squid; the squid are tender (*slightly* rubbery, which is how they should be), coated with a well-crisped batter, and served with fresh lemon, which brings the whole dish alive. The item is not listed on the menu, but ask for it. The other first courses are decent versions of standard stuff, but the squid are something special. There are a handful of pasta dishes offered, including Tortellini Bolognese—little crescent-shaped packages of chicken and cheese, quite firm, in a chunky meat sauce heavily flavored and fragrant with bay.

The Scampi alla Romana are not the best item in the house; they arrive prettily enough, in a circle, in a pool of butter and oil, their tails poked in the air, under a sprinkling of bits of fresh garlic, but the shrimp themselves may be a little overcooked, a little fibrous, and the heavy garlic-and-oil treatment needs rather desparately the relief of some fresh lemon.

A specialty here is something called Chicken al Cognac, which, it is true, is vaguely Cognacked, but is most noticeably an expertly sautéed breast of chicken, with browned mushrooms and garlic, in a very thick and creamy white sauce—very rich, and very good with Italian red wine. Naturally, there is Veal Parmigiana, and its presentation is dramatic: a moon of melted cheese and an aureole of red sauce. You trust, correctly, that underneath there is a cutlet of veal. The thing is well done, but not satisfactory, because the creamy cheese is much too mild for the strong, almost sour tomato sauce. The good veal that is concealed below can be had in a much more satisfactory Scalloppini Pizzaiola, in which the strong tomato sauce is augmented with huge slices of red and green peppers. This is one of the best dishes in the house. The delicious spinach is like a thick spinach-garlic-butter pie.

Your waiter suggests a salad of arugula and endive, which turns out to be a good combination. The salads here are carefully turned out—crisp greens, colorfully garnished with minced pimentoes, dressed in a very tart oil-and-vinegar.

Good cheese cake (made with ricotta cheese, slightly grainy, moist, vaguely sour); good rum cake (flooded with alcohol, flecked with almonds, and covered with rich whipped cream); and a terrible, unlisted suggestion of the waiter—a crêpe (tough, stuffed with heavy Italian custard, decorated with stewed cherries and uselessly flamed in cherry brandy).

★★P.S. 77

355 Amsterdam Avenue (at 77th Street)
DINNER.
Reservations, 873–6930.
Credit cards: AE, BA, MC.
Expensive.

This spot is much improved and, but for a couple of Chinese places on Broadway, it is now the best restaurant north of the Lincoln Center area on the West Side.

You enter to a snug brick-and-wood barroom and you are greeted, silently, by a coatrack, whereon, during bad weather and/or good business, are hung approximately twice as many coats as the fixture can comfortably accommodate. The customers' bodies, on the other hand, are somewhat more commodiously parked—at one of the several rows of white-linened tables, these in a prettily decorated room. Overhead the beamed ceiling; on the cream-white walls, children's art (New Yorkers will recognize this as a visual pun—P.S. 77, if it weren't a restaurant, would be a grade school—Public School 77), behind glass and neatly framed, like huge postage stamps; hanging and standing here and there, greenery; at the back of the dining room, a gleaming espresso station, a display fridge of desserts, and through a portal, a glimpse of a gleaming white kitchen. Along two sides of the dining room there are huge plate-glass windows, through which you have a panoramic view of the Texaco station on Amsterdam Avenue or the school playground on 77th—of course, you will probably prefer the look of your company because the playground is deserted during the dinner hour, and you may not wish to be reminded of the cost of gas.

The establishment is frequented by youngish West Side couples, some married—here a bit of hand-holding, there some spatting. She: "Why do you need another bottle of wine?" He: "Why do I need you?" Let's hope they don't have children.

Invariably on the menu are Escargots aux Champignons, three snails on three mushroom caps. These are quite lovely snails, plump and tender, the mushroom caps in which they are ensconced rather nicely sautéed, so that they retain most of the crunch of raw mushrooms while picking up that dark and smoky flavor mushrooms get when they are browned in butter and oil. On occasion there is available a simple avocado vinaigrette, and it is all you can ask for—the avocado perfectly ripe (pale pea-green and nary a hard spot) without being overripe at all (not a speck of brown). Within the hemispheric declivity formed by removal of the stone, you will find a pond of dressing—much clear-tasting oil, a faint echo of vinegar, and a distinct noticeability of sharp mustard—all very good.

The man who makes the sauces likes to make sauce Choron, for it is served with one fish one day, another another. Now, Class, what is sauce Choron? Right you are, it is sauce Béarnaise to which a bit of tomato has been added, and on occasion it is served with Quenelles de Saumon—little pink dumplings which are formed of puréed salmon, seasoning, egg white and cream, and then delicately poached. These have the required airy lightness, but the flavor of the fish itself is not perfectly clear and fresh; rather, it is just a bit fishy, as if the dumplings were made of fish which was half a day too old, and that is just enough to cause the flavor of the dumplings to overpower the sauce.

It is a good sauce, thick and pink, rather easy on the tarragon and heavy on the shallots and parsley, but you will be able to appreciate it fully if you have it with a more delicate fish.

Then there is a Suprême de Volaille Zingara. A "Suprême de Volaille," as you know, is the breast meat of chicken, removed from its bones and usually pounded down to a thin cutlet. In this dish the cutlet is sautéed very artfully—the chicken is thoroughly cooked, but it has lost none of its moistness (in sautéeing thin suprêmes of chicken, if you cook for a minute too many, the meat is dried out and ruined), and it is dressed with a dark and spicy sauce heavily populated with slivers of tasty ham. The vegetable garnishes are not bad either—diced eggplant under a white sauce which has been fortified with melted cheese, rice comingled with bits of sweet, sautéed onion.

P.S. 77 includes a small salad in the cost of your main course. It is eminently decent —fresh greens and the sharp dressing you appreciated so much with your avocado. It is listed on the menu and served *after* the main course (unless, of course, you ask to have it sooner)—Upper West Side self-conscious sophistication.

There is Brandy Alexander Pie, an old *New York Times* recipe which was so popular that it can be found not only in the recipe folders of thousands of housewifes (and househusbands) but also on the menus of around half a dozen New York restaurants. As a few of you may already have guessed, this is a pie with the flavor of a Brandy Alexander, which is to say, a chocolate milk shake with cognac in it—if you think you will like it, you probably will. The Linzertorte is a lovely little tart—crumbly almond-flavored crust under a thick Damson plum jelly.

★★ SZECHUAN

2536 Broadway (at 95th Street)
LUNCH AND DINNER.
Reservations, 663–8150.
Credit cards: AE.
Inexpensive.

This place lacks geographic appeal (the Broadway desperadoes up here make you wish you had eyes in the back of your head), atmospheric appeal (a large, garish room, a ceiling of acoustical tiles, long rows of tables and chairs) or service appeal (waiters who lounge against the cash register, hands in their pockets, sniffling—they come alive at around nine-thirty, when it is their turn to sup. They congregate around a couple of the large tables at the rear of the restaurant to eat, drink beer and exchange boisterous stories).

But for far-out taste appeal, this may be the place. Some of the dishes here are singular (for New York), and most of them are very well made.

The cold pickled cabbage that in some Chinese restaurants is provided free of charge will set you back half a dollar in this one, but it's worth it. The crisp shredded cabbage is mixed with carrots, celery and fresh ginger, and the vegetables are marinated in vinegar and the hot red peppers that separate the manly food of Szechuan from the boyish delicacies eaten in the other provinces. The peppers are easy to distinguish from the other elements of the dish—they are deep-purple, and if you neglect to separate them out by color, they will separate your gums from your teeth.

Ask for the Bean Curd Mixed with Preserved Egg. Chances are you will be informed that it is "out." Insist. The waiter will inquire if you have ever eaten it. He will intimate that most customers do not like it. Tell him you like it. In fact, you may *not* like it, but the only way to find out is to eat it. This extraordinary cold dish is composed of squared chunks of bean curd, firm green eggs in jelly (chopped), scallion greens and soy sauce. It looks hideous. But the nutlike quality of the soft bean curd, the intensified flavor of the eggs, and the sharp accents of the scallions and soy sauce combine into a robust, if slightly terrifying, plate of food.

Among the hot dishes there is something called Shredded Beef Dry-Sautéed, Szechuan Style. In the preparation of this dish, the thin strands of beef are rendered black and ropy by being cooked at high heat with almost no liquid, and you'll be at a disadvantage if you're not equipped with your natural teeth. But of course this texture is intentional: each individual piece of beef is small in itself; your occasional encounter with a bamboo shoot or a strand of carrot will renew confidence in your masticatory prowess; the spicy, blackened oil that moistens and flavors the entire dish lubricates the grinding process somewhat; and the fiery flavor and mixed textures are ingeniously well balanced.

For very little money you can have Noodles with Braised Beef—a huge bowl of dark, spicy broth (the braising liquid), in which you'll find a mound of noodles, a few peas, and chunks of coarse beef that have been cooked to tenderness in the liquid. This is an inelegant but satisfying dish.

The Diced Chicken with Hot Pepper Sauce is just that, with the chicken very thoroughly browned, and one-inch lengths of scallion to add a crunchy texture to the soft chicken. If you want strong flavor instead of fire, the Sliced Prawns with Garlic Sauce are made with plenty of fresh garlic, slices of crisp water chestnut, and that tender, leafy, mushroomlike fungus with a smoky flavor called "cloud ear."

Here you'll find Columbia University professors; Greenwich Village expatriate writers; young, second-generation locals emulating the cultural adventurousness of their collegiate peers; their collegiate peers emulating the primal pleasure-seeking of the young second-generation locals.

The management of the dining rooms is cursory, and the service ranges from casual friendly to casual lousy, but the food redeems the place.

• VICTOR'S CAFÉ

240 Columbus Avenue (at 71st Street)
LUNCH AND DINNER.
No reservations (TR 7–7988).
Credit cards: AE, DC.
Beer and wine.
Medium-priced.

When Victor's first established itself on this out-of-the-way corner, it was immediately accepted as the best Cuban restaurant in New York, though, admittedly, the best of only a few. And for a number of years a visit to Victor's, say, semiannually, provided sufficient culinary novelty to offset the rather crass quality of the food.

But now that Cuban food is a familiar commodity in New York, an evening at

Victor's can be a disappointing experience. The place is still jammed, it is still a minor thrill to get one of the favored tables in the enclosed sidewalk section, the waiters are cheerful, helpful and earnest, and the customers are having a good (often slightly boisterous) time. So what is there to complain about?

The food, for one: always devoid of finesse, some of the dishes are now rather tasteless as well. The selection, for another: e.g., roast suckling pig, which has been a Friday-Saturday-Sunday special for years, and though the restaurant is open until one-thirty in the morning, this dish, for which people may come considerable distances, is often out by eight-thirty. Management of the dining room, for a third: you look around for your waiter, you catch his eye, he takes a deep drag on his cigarette, puts it down and approaches to ask your pleasure, talking smoke.

By far the best items on Victor's menu are the fresh orange juice (to start) and the superb, strong coffee (to conclude). In between, quality is hard to find. The depressing list of appetizers includes sardines, assorted cold cuts, shellfish cocktails, etc., and should be avoided. The soups, once hearty, are now almost Germanic in their lumpen quality—the white-bean soup is oily and mealy, which is as it should be, but lacking the spice that can make a heavy dish palatable. The red-(chili) bean soup is also rather mild, but stronger than the white, and the starch is balanced with meat. Of the lot, chicken soup is the surprising best—not only is the broth strongly flavored of chicken and supporting vegetables but as if to prove the point, an eighth of a chicken, nicely poached, comes along in the bowl.

The fried pork is a heavy and succulent dish for which sliced raw onions are a very appropriate garnish. But if a day's supply of onions are sliced up at lunchtime, by dinner hour they have lost their point. The roast fresh ham, which is supposed to be rich, is dry; and the fried beef, with garlic and onions, once an outstanding item on this restaurant's menu, now doesn't even revive memories—it is tamed for the sightseers. The Shrimp Asopao is one of those dishes which provide odd moments of pleasure during an otherwise boring experience—Oh, an olive! Goody, a caper! Wow, a shrimp! (there are five).

The side dishes are more interesting. Fried plantains are available ripe or "green." If the ripe are fully ripe, the dish has a dark, honeylike quality; if less ripe, they are hardly worth eating; the green are an acquired taste, usually acquired during a Caribbean childhood. The corn tamales—a thick corn-meal pancake stuffed with pork—are another rather bland item, but the texture is interesting—slightly grainy—and the flavor of corn meal is strong and pleasing.

The desserts? It would be impossible for a blindfolded customer to distinguish the custard from the double-egg custard from the coconut custard from the bread pudding from putty. Malted milks are available.

The sangría is much too sweet. The Spanish wine is terrible.

Tourist Traps

One sets aside a chapter for tourist traps as an even higher service than any performed by the other sections of this book. Everyone wonders at least a little about what these well-known circuses are like, but few want to suffer through a meal to find out. Journalism to the rescue. The truth shall set you free of your curiosity.

○ ASTI

13 East 12th Street
DINNER.
Closed Mondays, and July and August.
Reservations, AL 5–9095.
Credit cards: AE, BA, CB, DC, MC.
Medium-priced.

Asti would be worth a visit about once a decade if it had at least an element of professionalism in its management. There are times when an exuberant drunken evening, in deafening surroundings, is in order, such as your college roommate's fourth bachelor party. And Asti does provide some hilarious moments, a few of them intentional.

Asti is a barnlike place in which no effort has been spared to eliminate comfort, intimacy and charm. The giant room is dominated by a bar, at which middle-aged adolescents brandish their *joie de vivre*, starting at cocktail time, only to find it transformed into *Weltschmerz* at midnight. The principal competition for the bar comes from the bandstand, where waiters, hosts and customers bellow operatic familiarities in a spectrum running roughly from Gilbert & Sullivan to Verdi, all accompanied by a chubby pixie at an electric organ. The cigarette girl throws on a shawl to sing *Carmen* in French, supported by a chorus in Italian and English. The highlight of the evening is a five-minute production of *Il Trovatore,* featuring an Anvil Chorus, in which the bartender smashes out home runs on a chime installed near the Scotch; and a "Miserere," for which the lights are dimmed, as a busboy in a hooded cloak blesses the diners, while he leads a candle-carrying procession from the kitchen, through the dining room, to the telephone.

Apparently the waiters find this amusing night after night. They become enthralled and forget about their customers, which is just as well, because the food is not good enough to actually serve.

Asti does win a prize for pictures on the walls: floor to ceiling, front to back, Beniamino Gigli and Richard Tauber mingle with Marilyn Monroe and Count Fleet. There is still room for one or two postage stamps, but no encroachment will be permitted on the sacred parcel of rear wall allotted to an oil of Caruso during his mad period.

Half the people present wander around managerially, as if they owned the place. An actual proprietor (identified as such when he called a waiter "dopey") was observed eating a plate of Fettuccine Romana, so if you get stuck here, try that, it may be palatable.

In this crowd "You gotta have respeck" is the motto. And they do have respeck. They keep hands off Mozart.

○ BENIHANA OF TOKYO

47 West 56th Street
LUNCH, MONDAY TO SATURDAY; DINNER, DAILY.
Reservations, LT 1–0930.
Credit cards: AE, BA, CB, DC, MC.
Medium-priced.

Except for an interlude in the forties, in this country the Japanese have always enjoyed a reputation for graciousness and hospitality. To erase this stigma, and to demonstrate at the same time that the Japanese can play the American game of creating an offensive restaurant gimmick to be duplicated all over the country (this country), a chain of eateries—Benihana This, Benihana That—has been strung from Puerto Rico to Honolulu. The people who frequent these establishments seem not to realize that Benihana violates or ignores many of the simple niceties of decent restaurant service.

To begin with, your protein-nourished six-foot American football star is expected to consume his lunch or dinner ensconced in (on) a chair that would be perfect in a Japanese kindergarten. These seats, in turn, are tightly assembled at the famous Benihana table—a twelve-inch wooden ledge around a gas-heated grill (which competes, victoriously, with the air conditioning in the summertime, and which supplements, and renders superfluous, the heating in wintertime), at which a trained juggler/"chef" prepares most of your dinner before (the menu points out) "your very eyes." As this system is most efficient (for the management) when a single chef cooks for a large group, the tables are designed for six or eight persons, and smaller groups are seated with perfect (or imperfect) strangers. If this is not enough to inhibit personal or confidential, not to mention intimate, conversation, the pace of the meal is determined not by your appestat, but by the availability of customers to fill out the tables, and of the chefs to put on their performances.

The complete dinner at these places consists of three set first courses, a choice of five main courses (four of which are steaks prepared in the same way), and those most traditional of Japanese desserts—ice cream or sherbet.

Waitresses serve drinks, soup and salad, one right after the other, and these items promptly overoccupy one's allotted ledge space. The soup (called "Onion au Gratin ala Japanese") is a harmless broth, cheeseless as well, in which a few scallion and mushroom slivers meander about. The "salad" is a batch of health food, with a touch of ginger in the dressing to prove it is Oriental.

Then the performing chef arrives, pushing his nurse's cart, and bangs the sauce dishes together with loud clacks to focus your attention on himself, and away from your companions. He oils the grill (still garnished with traces of the previously served meals) and proceeds to sauté the next course—shrimp (shells, and flavor, removed)—deftly, rapidly, and unnecessarily dissecting and de-tailing them in a series of rapid slices and shoves, tossing the tails, more or less accurately, into a refuse bowl deliberately placed two feet from the action, with a flick of the spatula, to oohs and aahs. He adds lemon, cooks a little further, then distributes these on the dinner plates in front of each diner, and you better eat 'em up now because already he is sautéeing the onions and zucchini which are part of the next course and—get this—flavors them with sesame seeds, yes, but how? By throwing the sesame seeds where? Right! Into the air! And where do they land? Right! *On the onions and zucchini!* Flip, flip, flip, flip, flip, flip, flip, flip, and eight people have sautéed onions and zucchini on their plates. Believe it or not, the steaks are this very moment being cut into bite-size (chopstick-size) pieces, to be cooked with the mushrooms. And how do you like your steak, sir? Rare? Bang! You got it (with raw mushrooms). Medium? Bang, bang! You got it (with medium mushrooms). Well-done? Bang, bang, bang! You got it (with tired mushrooms). A pile of bean sprouts is then prepared exactly like the shrimp, onions, zucchini, steak (or chicken) and mushrooms (with soy sauce, sesame, salt and pepper), the clown departs and you get your first moment's peace.

Your own early departure is clearly suggested when your check arrives with your ice cream. If you don't leave promptly, the table is set up for the next victims while you are still at it.

The steaks are good. Wine is out of the question. Warm sake is available, or the excellent Kirin beer from Japan. But the whole scene is an insult—to Americans, to the Japanese and to the digestion. There are other Benihanas in New York, at one of which—Benihana Palace—the hospitality is especially welcoming: in the cocktail lounge drinks are served on the floor.

Convenient for families of six or eight.

● # BO-BO

20½ **Pell Street (near Mott Street)**
LUNCH AND DINNER.
Reservations accepted for three or more, WO 2–9458.
No credit cards.
No liquor.
Inexpensive.

It is raining and it is cold and there is almost no one on the streets in Chinatown. Moreover, it's early for dinner, say, six o'clock. In most of the hundreds of restaurants down here the waiters are sitting down to eat, confident that the customers will not be arriving for at least an hour, particularly in this miserable weather. But at Bo-Bo every table is already filled, a line of waiting customers extends from the dreary counter at the front of the restaurant out the front door into the weather. This is the Toots Shor of Chinatown, where the principal commodity is contumely, dispensed in surroundings that would do an injustice to the great tradition of the railroad-car diner, and where an Oriental customer is taken for a spy. The waitresses push the $7 dinner and answer questions about what else might be available with such brevity, scorn and flaunted boredom that almost everyone caves in and has it.

"What else do you have?" a timid experimenter asks.

"We got fish, chicken, pork," she answers and stares back, blankly, grudgingly, sleepily.

"What kinds?"

"What kind you want?"

"Do you have spareribs?"

"No spareribs no chop suey no chow mein."

Actually, you can get virtually any Cantonese dish that you might want here, in decent versions, and the $7 dinner itself is not bad. It includes either a delicate Winter Melon Soup, with fresh peas, bits of chicken, barely cooked slices of zucchini, and lots of mild, translucent winter melon; or Wonton Soup, the little wontons stuffed with pork, and surrounded with spinach, black mushrooms, chicken and pork, crisp water chestnuts, and bamboo shoots. After that, there are no choices. You get a crisp spring roll, steamy inside, with bits of lobster and lots of green vegetables and onions. You get little dumplings. Then comes the Special Shrimp ("What do you call this shrimp?" "It's special shrimp"), coated with egg and bacon, and served in an insipid sweet sauce that fails to detract from the good quality of the shrimp itself. There is fried rice, of course—well made, each grain of rice separate and firm, the mound pebbled with bits of roast pork, fried egg, shrimp, raw lettuce (a very good touch) and sharp scallions. Of course the customers here must get their beef if the $7 dinner is to sell, so there it is, chunks of chuck, tough though rare, in a thickened gravy, surrounded by slices of pineapple and tomato that are adorned with red and green preserved cherries. Absurd. The dessert looks like a painted snowman: a ball of ice cream (the base), surmounted by a preserved lichee nut (the body), with a cherry or kumquat on top. The kumquats are good.

Behind the small counter at the front of the store there are coffee urns, and often as not, a member of the staff, his back to the waiting customers, reading a newspaper. The place is papered in a hideous pattern of writhing silver on an ivory ground; there are ceiling fixtures on the walls; the facilities are grungy. Bring your own beer or wine.

At lunchtime this is a dumpling house—good dumplings, but as soon as you have dispatched your last one, your check, which has been on your table for some time already, is picked up and handed to you.

○ JOE'S PIER 52

144 West 52nd Street
LUNCH AND DINNER.
Reservations, 245–6652.
Credit cards: AE, BA, CB, DC, MC.
Expensive.

Middle Americans with weighted middles and mountains of plasticized and/or metallicized hair compete boisterously ("Charlie, on you dat bib looks like a necktie") with a steel band of busboys who clear away dishes with a cacophonous vigor that must break 30 percent of them. Flat-faced waiters, arms folded, sucking their teeth, watch bored while others, frantic and inept ("Who gets scrod? Who gets crabs?"), serve a group of ten in such fashion that when the last dish is put down, the first is quite cold. Waiters and busboys fight it out on the dining-room floor. ("Hey! Water over here! More budda fer dese nice people!")

Thousands of clams and oysters must be served each day in this busy restaurant, and they are always fresh. But the distinction between littlenecks and cherrystones is honored only if inventory is in balance. An order of littlenecks may arrive with two cherrystones. ("May I exchange these two cherrystones for three littlenecks?" "Sorry,

no substitutions." "What about two for two?" "Look, dat's what dey gamey. Dat's it.")
A promotional piece on the table:

> The Original Joe's Stone Crabs . . . Presented the way they have been winning acclaim from the critics of the world for the past fifty years in Miami Beach. CONTINUOUS PERFORMANCES DAILY.

Not true: they are often not available, even in season; and though they are served hot or cold in Florida, Pier 52 serves them only cold. Their temperature is not specified on the menu, but mention of drawn butter suggests hot shellfish. (If you dip a lump of cold crabmeat into melted butter and then stare at the moist object for a moment or two, you can see the butter revert to its congealed state right before your eyes.) Waiters and captains (well, cocktail pushers) are incredulous at the suggestion that a Floridian would eat a stone crab hot.

A specialty here is red snapper stuffed with spinach. And when they say red, they mean red. Painted with paprika when it was first cooked, and repainted and stuck under the broiler before serving, this delicious Florida fish arrives mushy, and as tasteless as this restaurant's white bread. The spinach tastes like new-mown artificial lawn. The whole mess may be one of the ten worst dishes served in any restaurant in New York. It is accompanied by a potato which has been baked in an aluminum-foil shield for ten days or two weeks. The jacket is limp, and the potato is floury. Tons of salt, pepper and butter are needed to make it edible.

The apple pie consists of undercooked sour apples, a few raisins and a cup of powdered cinnamon between two strata of unleavened brick. The pecan pie is topped with a bent cylinder of toothpaste from an elephantine tube. You're OK if you just pick out the nuts.

If you must eat here, choose the food that requires no preparation (clams, oysters), or food that doesn't suffer much from early preparation (chowders and seafood stews), or food that is made to order (lobster, steak).

There is a house wine "from Pier 52 special stock" sold in quarter and half liters. It tastes like mineral oil.

The check arrives with the coffee.

• MAMMA LEONE'S

239 West 48th Street
LUNCH, MONDAY TO FRIDAY; DINNER, DAILY.
Reservations, JU 6–5151.
Credit cards: AE, BA, CB, DC, MC.
Medium-priced.

It has been a quarter of a century since Mamma was interred, but for a long time after they bought the place, Restaurant Associates omitted their tag line ("Another Restaurant Associates Great Place") from Mamma Leone advertisements, presumably to perpetuate the notion that there is a real Mamma Leone someplace who watches over this Disneyland of the restaurant world.

Mamma Leone's has been called the most underrated restaurant in New York, which tells us more about the ratings than about the restaurant. There are worse restaurants in New York, but those are the ones which cannot be described in words, the ones that can only be rendered by example or anecdote. The English language can cope, however, with Mamma's place—it is stunningly garish and ugly, the food is decent, the service automatic, the customers contented and unliberated cows with bulls and broods in tow. The place may well make more money than any other restaurant in town—the tourists come here in droves.

First of all, the restaurant is mammoth (a series of huge rooms), approximately sixty times as large as La Petite Ferme. And to fill a place like this, you need a lot of stuff, right? So you get some red plastic lobsters and stick them on the mirrors, frame the mirrors in gold tinsel and hang green fish net over the whole thing. (Sometimes you substitute a green paper anchor for the lobster.) You slice life preservers in half (the way you bisect a bagel for a sandwich) and stick them on the ceiling. Then you acquire a batch of heraldic pennants and give over the ceiling of at least one room to these. Also, you should get lots of paintings for the walls—for instance, a nice oil of a couple of voracious, poorly shaven monks salivating comically over their dinner (a good place for such an *objet* would be near the coat room, between signs that read "No Furs Checked"). Larger, more heroic canvases are also needed, for the grander rooms—such as swooning seminudes, giraffe-size; and heavenly encounters of godlike folk looking heroic.

But these are merely decorations. The place has to be filled—the space, not the walls —so we need Sculpture. Somebody in the sculpture game had Mamma's number, and as soon as he learned it, he started chiseling and selling, selling and chiseling, and she took it all. And what did this sweet little old lady like? You guessed it—good-looking girls, their clothes falling off, in pain. The stuff is all over the place. (There is so much of it that you may fail to notice the matched portraits of Eisenhower and Leone.) The statues are on pedestals, standing on the floor, in niches—all of them well-built females with troubles. The crass waiters (a pox on them) insert stray menus in these statues —under their arms, and you can imagine where else.

But the place needs still more. It needs action. So we get strolling (well, shuffling) musicians—sawyers and squeezers, the kind that wander from room to room appraising with bored, half-closed eyes each and every table, looking for the clue to the $5 tip. They throw a tune or two in that direction, snatch a couple of puffs and continue their search—cynical musical prostitutes whose mothers made them take lessons.

But this is a restaurant. So when you sit down you are brought celery, olives, tomatoes, and a block of soap the size of half a loaf of Wonder bread, and you cut off a hunk and go to the washroom to wash before dinner, and a few old hands restrain you good-naturedly and say no, no, that's cheese, for to eat, not soap. And you say no, no, it's soap, I can tell from the taste. And they say oh no you can't, because it doesn't have any taste! And everyone has a good laugh.

So you order dinner and a few cans (cans) of beer. You wanted to order wine, but the witty waiter says the Bardolino will put hair on your chest, and half the table demurs.

The menu at Mamma Leone's is a statistically perfect compendium of the most familiar dishes in New York's Italian restaurants. There is shrimp cocktail; anchovies and peppers (green ones, sautéed, not canned pimentos); an antipasto which includes those items as well as decent cabbage, beet and onion salad, insufficiently sautéed eggplant (tastes raw), melon, paper-thin prosciutto, a tube of bologna wrapped around a bread stick, a slice of good Genoa salami, and so on.

There is a soup called "Fresh" Chicken Soup, which either means fresh from the chicken or fresh from the pot. At any rate, it is listed as "pasta." The manicotti are literally fluffy, with a good strong meat sauce. The white clam sauce is too obviously thickened to retain the briny quality this sauce should have—it tastes like salty goo.

The main courses are the big comedowns. To satisfy out-of-town people, the over-cooked Italian sausage has as much taste as a drugstore hamburger—neither hot nor sweet. God forbid your roast chicken should be moist, so it is dry and stringy. And so on: bland Veal Piccata (theoretically a contradiction in terms), dismal Saltimbocca.

Pasty cheese cake with a layer of Ann Page pineapple preserves; rum cake decorated with pastel icing; a Zuppa Inglese that is much like the rum cake, but with good whipped cream instead of the toothpaste.

Mamma Leone's is such a solid tourist attraction that there are more horse-drawn cabs waiting for customers in front of Mamma's than there are on Central Park South. Lots of knee-length skirts and kiddies in crew cuts and suits with short pants. The waiters take the orders because the captains are busy snapping family group photos with the customers' own Instamatics. (As the man said at the Last Supper, everyone who wants to be in the picture better come around to this side of the table.) It has been suggested that the menu list f-stop and shutter-speed settings for standard films in various parts of the restaurant.

○ OLD HOMESTEAD

56 Ninth Avenue (near 15th Street)
LUNCH, MONDAY TO FRIDAY; DINNER, DAILY.
Reservations, CH 2-9040.
Credit cards: AE, BA, CB, DC, MC.
Expensive.

The tables are too small, the background music is too loud, the air conditioning is arctic, and the doggy-bags leak. The Old Homestead bills itself as "New York's Oldest Steak House," and it bedecks itself with hideous turn-of-the-century accoutrements, which bedazzle some of New York's visitors: "This is a *historic* place," says he, his gaze dwelling reverently, now on the brass chandeliers (Lampland), now on the art (Artland); her gaze follows his; the stuffed moose (not from Mooseland, but moldering; possibly c. 1868, when the place opened) gaze straight ahead.

Not to slight the local customers—they constitute the bulk of the clientele, and they are mostly what Manhattanites imagine their Queens neighbors to be. She, ventricose and pendulously bosomed, obscures her chair as she sits down beside the table and waits for his move; he, columnar and hard, takes his position opposite, and with the seat of his chair in his hands, by little hops, inches himself and the table toward her, forcing it between her upper and nether protuberances; she crosses right thigh over left, lifting her abdomen and establishing the family grip through meal's end. They smoke throughout, he a cool young Kent with his shrimp, a full-bodied Bering with his "Heavy Cut Boneless Sirloin Steak. For the trencherman who isn't satisfied with the average portion. About a pound and a half of our prime boneless sirloin. More than a match for the heartiest eater. Our steaks are aged for four weeks in our scientifically controlled aging boxes"; she sticking by her Pall Malls (you can light either end) from lobster cocktail through "Extra Heavy Cut Prime Ribs of Beef Au Jus." If you thought the next generation long ago turned from the crass ways of its antecedents, come to the Homestead, where up-and-coming goons court their fishwives-to-be. Martinis and beer do nothing to unbend the silent, ritual courtship dinners of these doomed robots. Only the groups of young men (full-time jobs and no obligations) seem to do any laughing.

They know their customers, the management here, and they give them even less than they deserve. You're greeted by one of a pair of confused schedulers. She assures you that there will be a wait of ten minutes, appends your name to a list and departs. Her male counterpart materializes within the minute and leads you to a table at once. (Perhaps they are competitors and she is just now learning the ropes; perhaps they are paid piecework, per seated body, and there is a whole section of the many-roomed place that she does not know about.) The food is dreadful—from the waterlogged shrimp or lobster cocktail, or the limp herring, to the mealy, tasteless roast beef and the resilient steak, accompanied by leathery cottage fries or powdery home fries, through the claylike cheese cake. Miraculously, there is a decent apple pie, made with green apples, cinnamon and a good lard crust. The waiters are almost workmanlike—sooner or later you get what you ask for.

○ THE SIGN OF THE DOVE

1110 Third Avenue (near 65th Street)
LUNCH, TUESDAY TO SUNDAY; DINNER, DAILY.
Reservations, UN 1–8080.
Credit cards: AE, BA, CB, DC, MC.
Expensive.

Potted trees, statuary, flowers; in one room a velvet ceiling; huge mirrors that are so smooth and polished that they look like open doorways; interior walls of stained glass; rosy brick pillars, walls and archways; a glass dome over what was once an interior courtyard (starry sky above); pink linen on the well-spaced tables; double-breasted navy-blue blazers and fawn-colored trousers (black silk stripes down the sides) on the mostly tall, dark and handsome, often mustached waiters. And that is just about it—because you can design a place, order it, get it and sure enough have it, but that procedure will not provide good food and decent service day in and day out. So when the host attempts to match the ceremony to the surroundings, he pirouettes to deliver his "Come with me" and glides you right up to a table that is very nice but covered with cake plates and coffee cups and lipsticked Kleenex. He solves the problem by forgetting your existence behind him, and is heading back to his post when you collar him and remind him of what he lately was about. Then there are the waiters, who seem to work in noncommunicative teams; three or four will ask for your order when you have already ordered. And then there are the busboys; your dinner plate is picked up, and then another is picked up and its contents dumped into the first so that a neat stack can be formed, and this process is continued until he has a column of perhaps a dozen dinner plates, a mound of bones, and other remains on the top one. And all this in such a pretty restaurant.

And such a pretty menu, too—a huge folder, silkscreened, with doves and berries and flowers and butterflies and things all flying around together. And then there are the listings within, so imaginative and informative. Lump crabmeat, for example, is served "on Snow," and we are told that the Roquefort cheese is "Made from Ewe's milk cured in Limestone Caves, Roquefort, France." Tell us please, where are these stuffed mushrooms from? Never mind; they are from yesterday, stuffed in a large batch, refrigerated, and heated under a broiler when they are ordered and served in an irrelevant, thickened beef stock. And is not the seafood in "A Variety of Sea Food, Gratinée Neptune" lacking in variety, since it is uniformly previously frozen and currently warmed up in a greasy sauce of oil and cheese?

But take heart, because it is possible to get palatable food here if you restrict yourself to the least pretentious dishes. You might, for example, fear that "Fresh Calf's Liver à l'Allemande (Bacon and Apple)" sounds too ambitious for so incompetent a kitchen, but in fact the ring of warm apple can be discarded as soon as it arrives, and you will find yourself with a dish of good liver and bacon. The broiled steaks and chops are good, and they must sell a lot of duck here because the "Brandied Duckling, Sign of the Dove" is apparently roasted the day you get it, and the brandied sauce, with a hint of chopped nuts, is sort of nice. The vegetables are not kept in a steam table, but in a warm bath.

At this point it may be a good idea to have salad, because the salads are good and the desserts are merely concoctions. The watercress and endive, for example, are served in two separate mounds, the endive sliced into long slivers, both items dressed in a clear vinaigrette. But if you want something sweet, and you accept a suggestion of mousse cake, you get something for which you will instantly think up several names better than mousse cake. How about brandy-candy-maraschino-chocolate-orange delight? It weighs a pound and hasn't an ounce of mousse in it. Would you like something a little simpler? OK, have an orange tart—visualize a triangle of tolerable pastry on which rests a triangle of custard of identical shape, surmounted by a few slices of the kind of orange that is not juicy enough for orange juice, not tasty enough to eat straight— now you know what they are for.

There is a bar with a pianist. Here you will learn to pity the poor gigolo; as the night wears on, wretched ladies press their attentions on their escorts, and the miserable hirelings drink and kiss, kiss and drink.

Alphabetical Index

About the Author

SEYMOUR BRITCHKY was born in Manhattan, has lived there all his life and can't imagine living anywhere else. He has been interested in restaurants and food—he is a pretty fair cook himself—since childhood, but he claims that his highly developed palate is based on nothing more than the fact that he has "eaten three meals every day of my life."